RESPONSE OF
PHYSICAL SYSTEMS

RESPONSE OF
PHYSICAL SYSTEMS

John Dezendorf Trimmer

Professor of Physics, University of Tennessee

JOHN WILEY & SONS, INC., NEW YORK

CHAPMAN & HALL, LIMITED, LONDON

50332

PRINTED IN THE UNITED STATES OF AMERICA

PREFACE

This book is directed both to students and workers in engineering and applied physics, who have an immediate interest in learning the theory applicable to physical systems, and to those who have a different or broader interest in system response and can therefore profitably survey the successful application of mathematics to physical systems. It is not implied that these two groups are mutually exclusive, but the second group is considered to be larger—including, in addition to physicists and engineers, workers in such fields as biology, sociology, economics, and philosophy.

The book is based on the conviction that both classes of readers should be led over the same path, a broad horizontal traverse of the whole domain at a modest elevation, rather than the scaling of any individual peaks of learning. This conviction has influenced the nature and scope of the work toward a maximum combination of simplicity, generality, and continuity. Some of the trials that beset the effort to achieve this combination may be mentioned.

A most vexing problem is the choice of symbols and terms. The ideal state, of having a single meaning for each symbol, and vice versa, is doubtless beyond human grasp. But it may seem to the reader, viewing the multitudinous q-symbols in the text, that I have deliberately struck out in the opposite direction. This is not so: in every case, the plain q has the same meaning, namely, the response quantity in the problem at hand; and every other q-symbol means a quantity having the same dimensions as q. (There is one exception, the symbol q^*, introduced in Section 5.4.) I feel that this notation is an important means of establishing the desired generality and continuity of viewpoint, and the reader who is at first repelled by the notation (as many doubtless will be) is asked to evaluate it in view of these goals.

To the extent consistent with these aims, an effort has been made to adopt symbols and terms already in use by established workers in various fields of system response. In this I have been particularly influenced by my association from 1937 to 1941 with

Professor C. S. Draper, Aeronautical Engineering Department, The Massachusetts Institute of Technology. Although I freely coined terms and symbols when it seemed necessary to do so, not every apparent instance of this is genuine. For example, the usage of the word "parameter," which will seem strange to those accustomed to its mathematical sense, is essentially the same as that employed by N. Minorsky over a period of some years.

In short, concerning symbols and terminology the reader is asked to view sympathetically an honest effort to deal with a distressing problem. To ease the inevitable pain, a comprehensive glossary of terms and symbols is included as Appendix 3.

A second principal problem, in an effort such as is represented by this book, is the degree of mathematical knowledge expected of the reader. The aim here has been to keep to the minimum any requirement beyond a full working knowledge of the calculus. To derive full value from the book calls for some concurrent study of the subject of differential equations, for the organization of the book is very closely built around the differential equation as a central concept.

A difficult decision regarding mathematical content was the question of whether the treatment of linear systems should be based on the Laplace transform or on the classical solution of linear differential equations with constant coefficients. The decision in favor of the latter was due not to any lack of appeal of the elegant Laplace method, but to a strong feeling that a thorough familiarity—the familiarity that is gained only by prolonged, detailed experience—with the classical method is an absolutely essential part of the foundation to be laid. It is only in the classical view of these simple linear systems that, at the present stage of the subject's development, the interplay of physics and mathematics can be followed with such instructive explicitness. To miss any of this by concentrating on a method of "working problems faster" would be a poor trade.

Of course, the Laplace transformation is more than a method of working problems rapidly. A fuller appraisal of it and a brief presentation of its working procedures are given in Appendix 1. Thus I have no quarrel with use of the Laplace method, so long as it is presented as a supplement to the classical method and not a substitute for it, and so long as the classical method also receives some of the same striving for perfection of detail which many writers have lavished on the Laplace method.

The book is based to a large extent, particularly in Chapters 2, 3, 4, and 7, on material used for lecture and laboratory sessions of the course, entitled "Instrumentation," which I have taught in the Physics Department of the University of Tennessee since 1946. At that time Dr. K. L. Hertel, Head of the Department, was looking for someone to teach an instrumentation course, and I, stationed at nearby Oak Ridge, was looking for the chance to develop such a course. The result of this coincidence, in a formal sense, is a three-quarter, three-hour course, with two hours of lecture and one two-hour laboratory per week. The course is offered to seniors and graduate students in science and engineering.

In a less formal sense, the result seems to be the emergence of a discipline which may be called "system response." What exact relation this bears to instrumentation is a question that needs further consideration. The same is true of the relation of instrumentation and system response to the newly defined field of cybernetics. (N. Wiener, *Cybernetics*, John Wiley and Sons, 1948.) I have published elsewhere (*The Scientific Monthly*, **LXIX**, 328, 1949) some discussion of these matters, under the title "Instrumentation and Cybernetics." The budding science of man and his automata rivals, in contemporary interest and importance, the other great unexplored subject, nonlinearity.

These are doors opening on new and challenging horizons. It is my hope that the present volume may encourage at least a few adventurers to sally forth and also that it may in some measure equip them for the journey.

JOHN D. TRIMMER

Knoxville, Tennessee
August, 1950

CONTENTS

A Pattern for Systems

1·1 A general pattern. Much of human thought and experience fits more or less readily into a kind of general pattern, suggested by Fig. 1·1. This figure is purposely left vague, in that the various parts are labeled only with the meaningless symbols: *a*, *b*, *c*, and *d*. Attention is directed to the *form* of the pattern. What is this form? The arrangement suggests the following: "something *a*" goes into "something *b*," from which emerges "something *c*," and this process or situation is in some manner embraced or dominated by a "something *d*."

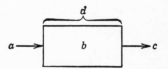

FIG. 1·1. Pattern of experience.

Now these "somethings" must indeed be given names or definitions. It is desirable, however, to select names that will reflect the extremely general nature of the pattern. A procedure which at the same time illustrates the generality of the pattern and leads toward selection of suitable names is to tabulate some possible or typical names for *a*, *b*, *c*, and *d*—that is, names in common usage in situations to which the pattern of Fig. 1·1 is supposed to apply. Such a list is shown in Table 1·1, with the names arranged in alphabetical order so as to give equal emphasis to all. (The reader is invited to play the game by thinking of more words to add to the lists.)

Notice that every word included in these lists is already a word which has at least one commonly accepted general meaning—it would have been pointless to include any words having only specialized meanings. Now in trying to pick a single word of sufficiently general meaning so that it may include all the other general

1

TABLE 1·1

a	b	c	d
agent	apparatus	achievement	agreement
aspiration	body	action	code
cause	cell	answer	covenant
compulsion	circuit	effect	custom
demand	device	expression	equation
desire	group	feeling	habit
drive	individual	mood	law
excitation	mind	output	principle
force	network	reaction	rule
impetus	organization	replica	theory
impulse	organism	response	tradition
incentive	society	result	
inducement	structure	sensation	
influence	system	thought	
input	unit		
motive			
need			
question			
reference			
signal			
source			
spur			
standard			
stimulus			
urge			

terms in a column of the table, one may invent or derive a new word, or one may choose (perforce, rather arbitrarily) an existing word and if necessary give it a new, more general definition.

The title of this book reveals the choices to be made here from columns *b* and *c*—namely, "system" and "response." The word "system," taken in the straight dictionary sense of "an arrangement or combination, as of parts or elements, in a whole," seems admirably suited to this purpose; it applies with equal readiness to a cell, a human being, a society—an atom, a planet, a galaxy. The choice of "response" is more arbitrary, since this word does not have in any conventional usage a sufficient scope. It is here given a new, broader definition, inclusive of all the concepts that might be listed in column *c*.

One may now ask: to what does a system respond? Agent, cause, force, influence, motive, stimulus, urge? The word "force" has much to recommend it; but there is a serious objection, namely, the great importance of its specialized meaning in physics. In the hope of retaining the advantages and overcoming the objection, the participial noun "forcing" is proposed. It is worth noting that the element of compulsion, implicit in force and forcing as ordinarily used, must be minimized in the broader definition needed to cover all the concepts of column *a*.

Finally, if the word "law" is chosen for the "something *d*," one is ready to label Fig. 1·1, as shown in Fig. 1·2. The pattern of this figure is supposed to apply to any situation or process in which a system subjected to forcing gives a response according to a law. But what is meant by "is supposed to apply" and "according to a law"? The next two sections may help to answer this question.

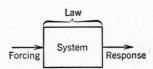

Fig. 1·2. Labeled pattern.

1·2 Difficulty of isolation. The significance and applicability of the pattern of Fig. 1·2 are subject to a pair of qualifying conditions which may be called **isolation of the system** and **isolation of the event.** Complete isolation would mean that a single system, all by itself, gives a certain response to a single forcing, operating all by itself.

An illustrative example may help here. Suppose the system is a typical human family, say the Jones family. Let the forcing to which the family is subjected be the change of residence from one section of the country to another. Let the response be the change in speech habits of the Jones family. In other words, the problem is to study the speech habits of the Jones family, as affected by a change of residence. Although this problem fits the pattern of Fig. 1·2, one has the feeling that the actual problem would not be so simple as the figure implies. Questions arise as to whether the family will remain as a fixed, easily defined unit, and as to whether the changes in speech can all be ascribed to the one forcing, the change of residence.

Suppose, for instance, that soon after the move one of the Jones boys accepts employment that requires him to travel far and often. Is he still to be counted as part of the family for this problem? Or suppose one of the Jones girls marries and she and her husband live with her parents. How does the husband fit into the definition of the family? In short, it appears that the family, instead of being a fixed, clearly defined system, changes and inter-acts with other systems in a way that calls for constant reappraisal of its boundaries. That is, the system is not isolated.

Similarly, the event of moving is not an isolated event. Other more or less simultaneous events will affect the speech of the Jones family. The children may start listening to a new radio program (which they could have heard as well in their former location). How can the response to this forcing be distinguished from the response to the moving?

Since it appears that actual experience does not consist of iso-lated events with isolated systems, as implied in Fig. 1·2, one may question the validity of the pattern of this figure. The point is that the pattern is valuable, not as a means of *describing* experi-ence, but as a means of *thinking about* experience. That is, whether or not isolated events with isolated systems do in fact occur, one can always imagine them and consider the various aspects of this imagined pattern. This approximation to reality is, indeed, a kind of make-believe, but it is nonetheless useful in promoting understanding.

1·3 Criterion of ideal response. According to what law does the response of the Jones family occur? Though the full law in this situation is unknown, one would at least expect that the Jones' speech habits would gradually change in the direction of conformity with the average of the new community, and that this change would be more rapid with the younger members of the family. If this law were violated—that is, if the Jones' speech became more and more different from the community average, or if the younger children continued their former speech habits while their parents promptly took up local idioms—the situation, al-though not morally or legally wrong, would still be colloquially described by saying, "There's something wrong here."

Just as for this particular example, so in every case to which the pattern applies there is a right response and a wrong response, or, at least, a degree of rightness can be associated with any given response. Other word pairs which may be used, according to the particular instance, in place of right and wrong, are: normal and abnormal, healthy and diseased, sane and insane, precise and erratic, usual and unusual, good and bad.

The implication is that response according to the law is right, and response in violation of the law is wrong. This is indeed the meaning to be attached to the general concept (something d) here named law, provided the word "right" is understood in the sense of typical, usual, normal. The law is a generalization of experience and observation; it states what *does* happen (on the average or in a typical event). The question as to what *should* happen, or what one would like to have happen, brings in another concept —the criterion of ideal response.

Consider, for instance, a system whose response is a replica of a standard or reference, and which may therefore be called a **duplicator**. Many important technical devices can be so described. To name a single example, a telephone receiver produces in the ear of the listener a replica of the sounds uttered by the speaker. The criterion of response of a duplicator is degree of equality or identity; an ideal response is one which is an exact replica of the forcing reference. Thus the value of a telephone receiver is measured by how nearly ideal its response is, but this actual response is governed by a law based on the principles of physics, which are quite independent of any value concepts in the minds of the designer or of the user of the telephone.

It appears, then, that the fourth element of the pattern, the law, is something that exists because of the pattern, since it is merely the generalized statement about the response to be expected from the system subject to a certain forcing. The value or usefulness of the system must be expressed in terms of a fifth factor, the criterion of ideal response.

1·4 Types of problems. Given the complete pattern of forcing, system, response, and law, together with a criterion, it becomes possible to enumerate the kinds of problems that might arise. Before proceeding with this, however, it is convenient to introduce one more concept, namely, the **properties of the system.** This term (or briefly, properties) will be used to denote those attributes of a system which are pertinent to the relationship between forcing and response.

Now one can list five distinct types of problems, as follows:

1. The direct problem. For given forcing, system, and law, what is the response?

2. The converse problem. For given response, system, and law, what is the forcing?

3. The inverse problem. For given forcing, response, and law, what are the properties of the system?

4. *The inductive problem.* For given forcing, system, and response, what is the law?

5. *The design problem.* How does one design a system to meet a given criterion?

It will be noticed that the first four types have this in common, that in each type three of the four elements of the pattern are known and the problem is to determine the fourth element. By contrast the design problem stands alone. This emphasizes the fact that the criterion is not a part of the pattern itself but is something which exists, in conjunction with the pattern, in the mind of the designer, user, or observer of the system. Hence in the design problem all four elements enter on an equal basis, since all must be considered. The problem may be expressed this way: in view of known laws, how can one achieve a system which, when subject to certain forcings, will give the desired responses?

To illustrate the five types of problem, let the system under consideration be an airplane. Let the forcing be the pilot's manipulation of control levers. The direct problem would be, for a given airplane with known properties, to predict how it would respond to specified control manipulations. The converse problem would be to deduce from observed maneuvers of the airplane what must have been the control manipulations which caused the airplane to execute these maneuvers. The inverse problem would be to deduce information about the airplane's properties (engine horsepower, wing surface area, etc.) from the observed response to a known control change. The inductive problem consists of attempting to establish laws governing the response of airplanes by generalizing from observed responses of known airplanes to specified control manipulations. Finally, the design problem is to design an airplane which will execute specified maneuvers in response to specified control manipulations.

1·5 Physical systems. The discussion up to this point has been on a very general basis, such as might apply to any kind of system. This extremely general approach has two advantages: first, it stimulates thinking in analogies and comparisons, which is a fruitful mode of thought in any field; second, it makes necessary a clear definition of any special field of interest, setting it off from the others. Saying it another way, this general approach makes the specialist think about fields related to his, and it makes him think about that essential nature of his own field which distinguishes it.

The special field with which this book deals is physics. The systems to be studied are physical systems. So it is necessary to state what it is that distinguishes physical systems from other systems to which the pattern of Fig. 1·2 might apply.

One of the conditions which must be met in a physical system is that the properties of the system, the forcing, and the response must all be numerically measurable. But this condition alone would not set off physics from other fields such as economics, which also involve numerically measured magnitudes. The comparison with economics is, in fact, interesting because of the analogy between money in economics and energy in physics. "Energy is the currency of physics."

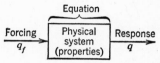

FIG. 1·3.   Physical system.

So for physical systems the forcing and the response are forms of energy. Usually these forms of energy are expressed, because of convenience in measurement or in utilization, in terms of some quantity other than energy. For example, in an electrical circuit, rate of energy flow may be thought of as the product of voltage and current, whereas the ratio of voltage to current is a constant property of the circuit. Therefore, forcing energy may be specified as forcing voltage (or current), since the relation of this quantity to the forcing energy is a fixed property of the system. (See Section 5·4.)

If the symbol q is adopted for physical quantity,[1] the pattern of Fig. 1·2 may be restricted to physical systems by further labeling, as in Fig. 1·3. The forcing quantity is given the symbol q_f, and the plain q is used for the response. The law is replaced by the equation, since for most cases the law of a physical system may be expressed in a mathematical equation.

In this pattern the process of physical measurement is of great importance, since it is the means and the only means by which one can "know" the forcing, the response, and the system's properties. Conversely, measuring instruments are physical systems to which the type of analysis associated with the pattern may profitably be applied. For these two reasons the subject of instru-

[1] The q-notation used here is also suggested by the generalized coordinates of Lagrange.

ments plays an important role in response of physical systems, a role discussed more fully in Chapter 7.

1·6 Why study physical systems? The answer to this question is obvious to those who have a direct interest in physics and therefore in physical systems. To scientists less directly interested in physics, any reasons may seem far-fetched. For those in both groups, however, who are interested in cementing together separate fields of scientific thought, the following paragraphs are intended.

Physical systems are by far the simplest systems available for study. The most direct evidence of this is the highly successful application of mathematics to physical systems. Study of such systems, therefore, can serve as an intellectual muscle-builder for the more complicated study of other systems. One can start from the simplest cases and proceed gradually toward more difficult ones, becoming thoroughly practiced in that repetitious manipulation of a problem which alone brings revelation of all its aspects.

The individual reader may judge for himself how far into detail the analogy between physical systems and other systems should be carried. But certainly the neat way in which physical systems and other systems fit into the same pattern of Fig. 1·2 suggests that there is a rich mine of analogy to be exploited.

Returning to the example of the Jones family and their moving from one city to another, one might on reflecting expect to see in their response a transient component and a long-range component; that is, one component determined by their state at the time of moving and by the nature of the moving, and a second component determined by the continuing characteristics of the new community and their response to these characteristics. Now, as is shown in succeeding chapters, this analysis of response into transient and forced components is a standard feature of the response of physical systems. Indeed, it is an inescapable feature, since the mathematical analysis forcibly directs attention to it. This is one example (and almost every succeeding page of this book could furnish another) of a point of view inherent in the treatment of physical systems which may be of value in studying some nonphysical system.

Physical Systems

2·1 Example of a physical system. As an example of a physical system consider the familiar mercury-in-glass thermometer. The properties of this system are made up of the properties of the glass, of the mercury, and of any film, such as dirt, which might be on the outside of the glass or on the inside of the glass, between it and the mercury. ⌊To go further, one must identify the physical quantities to be considered as forcing and as response. This is a matter in which there is usually a certain freedom of choice. In the present instance it may be assumed that the forcing would be considered the external temperature, that is, the temperature of the air or other medium in which the thermometer bulb is immersed. As response, however, one might choose the internal temperature (of the mercury inside the glass bulb), or the position of the end of the mercury column, or the observed or indicated temperature which one might read from the scale printed along the mercury column. To each of these choices there would correspond a slightly different list of the system's properties. Thus, if internal temperature is the response, the properties (e.g., accuracy of bore) of the glass capillary tube in which the mercury column rises are of slight importance, and the scale markings on the outside of the glass tube are of no importance. But, if the position of the column end is taken as response, the capillary tube is very important; and for the indicated temperature all the properties of the thermometer, including the scale marks on the glass tube, must be taken into account.

Thus, depending on the particular interest in the problem, one may make different choices of forcing and response for any given physical system. For this reason (and for other reasons which will be illustrated later) in speaking of the properties of a system one does not mean all the physical data that might be gathered pertaining to the system, but only that fraction of such data which is significantly useful for the purposes at hand.

Suppose now that the thermometer is immersed in a medium of changing temperature—a kettle of water being heated on a stove, or the air in a room disturbed by the opening and closing of a door into a warmer room. Under such circumstances the changing external temperature would result in changes of the internal temperature. For any one thermometer the details of this time relationship between forcing and response will depend on the kind of time function q_f happens to be; and for any given q_f these details will differ for different thermometers because of differences in the physical properties of one thermometer compared to those of another.

If there are two kettles of water, for example, one might be at (constant) room temperature and the other at some fixed higher temperature. Suppose also that there are two thermometers—one a "fast" thermometer with relatively thin glass walls and small volume of mercury, the other a "slow" thermometer with relatively thick walls and large mercury volume. Let both thermometers be in equilibrium in the room-temperature vessel, and then suppose they are both very rapidly transferred, simultaneously and in identical fashion, to the hotter vessel. Upon immersion in the hot water, internal temperatures of both thermometers will rise, but that of the fast thermometer will rise more rapidly. Similarly, if the two thermometers are suspended in a room in which the air temperature varies in sinusoidal fashion (owing perhaps to the starting and stopping of an automatic heater), the response of the fast thermometer will stay more closely in step with the external temperature.

2·2 Simple systems. Solution of the problems of physical systems calls for the use of various mathematical methods and tools. The most important of these is the differential equation. It is important because it may be directly useful in obtaining many desired solutions. In addition, it has great value as a basis for classifying physical systems and for organizing the subject of response of physical systems. The present treatment of this subject is, to a large extent, organized and presented according to the various types of differential equations applicable to various physical systems. Two other types of equations, integral equations and difference equations, are also important tools for investigating response of physical systems. Such equations are closely related to differential equations and may more readily be understood by one versed in the use of differential equations.

It is an important and often difficult procedure to write down the equations pertaining to a given system. Generally speaking, the differential equations are the mathematical expressions of the physical laws which, according to the problem at hand, may be drawn from any of the branches of the science of physics. The inductive problem—establishing a law on the basis of observed response to known forcing—is not treated in this book. The laws of physics are assumed to be known. Moreover, in general the reader is assumed to be capable of selecting the laws pertinent to a given system and of putting them in the form of differential equations; at the same time there are included some illustrative examples and suggestions as to technique in taking these steps.

As a first step in developing the relations between physical systems and their differential equations, a certain class of physical systems will be called **simple systems.** By way of definition, any physical system is a simple system if its differential equation is a first-order or second-order linear ordinary differential equation with constant coefficients. This definition, it should be noted, involves four qualifications of the differential equation: its order; its linearity; the fact that it is ordinary (as opposed to partial); and the fact that its coefficients are constant. Each of these mathematical restrictions has an important physical meaning. These relationships are discussed in later sections of this chapter. Systems failing in any way to meet all these restrictions may be called **complex systems.**

The aforementioned mercury-in-glass thermometer is an example of a simple system. For, as will now be shown, it satisfies a first-order linear ordinary differential equation with constant coefficients. Taking the temperature of the air or other medium in which the thermometer is immersed as the input temperature T_i, and the temperature of the mercury inside the bulb as the output temperature T_o, the differential equation relating them is of the kind mentioned. Heat flows into the mercury at a rate proportional to $(T_i - T_o)$; that is, the rate of heat flow is $K(T_i - T_o)$, where K is a heat transfer constant. (K is a constant, of course, only for a given thermometer and a given medium; that is, its value depends on such things as the total area of bulb surface, the thickness and thermal conductivity of the glass, and the properties of the medium whose temperature is being measured.) The rate of change of T_o is given by this heat flow, divided by the mass M of mercury and its specific heat S. Thus $(dT_o/dt) = (K/MS)$ $(T_i - T_o)$, or, multiplying through by (MS/K),

$$\left(\frac{MS}{K}\right)\frac{dT_0}{dt} + T_o = T_i \qquad (2\cdot 1)$$

It is seen that this differential equation is of the first order, since it involves only first-order derivatives. The equation involves only first-degree terms in the independent variable T_o and its derivative and is therefore a linear differential equation. The derivative is not partial but ordinary, and all coefficients are constant (i.e., not functions of the dependent variable T_o or of the independent variable t). Thus the thermometer is seen to satisfy the four mathematical conditions specified in the definition of simple systems.

The next two chapters are devoted to a thorough treatment of simple systems. It is most important to master this material in complete detail, for the following three reasons: first, a large number of important problems can be solved directly in terms of simple systems; second, the mathematics of simple systems is in principle the same as that of higher-order linear systems, so that study of simple systems is an indispensable introduction to the higher-order systems; and third, the most useful approach in many cases involving complex systems, where an exact analysis would be more or less out of the question, is to replace the actual system by an approximate equivalent of one or more simple systems.

2·3 Properties and parameters. In the thermometer equation 2·1 the quantity (MS/K) might well be replaced by a single symbol. For the equation to be dimensionally homogeneous (i.e., for all its terms to be of the same dimensions), it is clear that the ratio MS/K must have the dimension of time. It may therefore be called a **time constant** and referred to by the symbol τ. Suppose further that T_o and T_i are replaced by the more general symbols q and q_f. Then (using the more convenient dot notation for differentiation with respect to time) Eq. 2·1 becomes

$$\tau\dot{q} + q = q_f \qquad (2\cdot 2)$$

This is the **standard form** of the first-order differential equation, which means merely that by introducing appropriate definitions the differential equation of any simple first-order system can be reduced to the form of Eq. 2·2, and that in the interests of generality it will be convenient to reduce all such equations to this form. In the next section more will be said about the definition of q_f. Here the emphasis is on the effect of replacing the ratio MS/K by the single symbol τ.

An obvious remark is that it is easier to write one symbol than to write three. This is certainly an advantage, though a rather minor one. The important point is that all systems (not just all thermometers) having the same time constant have the same response. Hence, by talking about τ rather than about M, S, and K, one has a basis for comparing the response of a given thermometer, not only with the response of any other thermometer, but with the response of any other first-order system, whatever its nature. This great gain in generality is the principal advantage given by dealing with the parameter τ rather than with the properties, M, S, and K. (Throughout this book there appear a certain number of remarks to the effect that this or that mathematical result, derived in connection with a certain example, is not limited in usefulness to that particular example. These are merely gratuitous repetitions, for emphasis, of one of the main themes of the book: that many problems have the same mathematical structure and that, therefore, when one is solved, all have been solved.)

Speaking generally, **properties** are those physical quantities which directly describe the physical attributes of the system; **parameters** are those combinations of the properties which suffice to determine the response of the system. Properties can have all sorts of dimensions, depending upon the system being considered; parameters are dimensionless, or have the dimension of time or its reciprocal. "Reducing the differential equation to standard form" means writing it in terms of q, q_f, and the parameters.

In practically all problems the differential equation as written down, expressing the physical laws governing the system, involves the properties (or simple combinations of properties) as coefficients of q and its derivatives. If the differential equation is of the nth order, there are $n + 1$ coefficients which may be replaced by n parameters. (There is more discussion of this in Section 2·8.) First-order systems have one parameter and may therefore be called single-parameter systems. So replacing the properties by the parameter does not permit much choosing, since one must use either τ or its reciprocal. In higher-order systems, however, there is considerable freedom in choosing particular combinations of properties to serve as parameters. Even with second-order systems the choice of parameters is a question of some importance, as discussed in Chapter 4.

The parameters of a system cannot, of course, be a complete substitute for the properties, since two systems with the same parameters might have completely different properties. This is another way of saying that it is sometimes necessary to know more about a physical system than its response to various forcings. For example, many problems, particularly those involving the connecting of systems to each other, call for much use of the concept of **impedance.** It is not convenient at this point to go into a full discussion of impedance (see Chapter 5) other than to note that here is a useful concept which must be defined directly in terms of physical properties, so that knowledge of a system's parameters does not suffice to specify its impedance.

The inverse problem consists of deducing the system's parameters from its response to some forcing function. The fact that only the parameters can be determined in this way means that, to convert the n parameter values into the $n + 1$ actual coefficients, one needs one additional item of information beyond that furnished by response characteristics. Usually one of the coefficients can be measured rather easily or is available from manufacturer's specifications.

In summary, then, it may be said that full description of a physical system can be given only by listing its properties. For problems concerning response of systems, however, great advantages of generality and simplicity are gained by combining the properties into the minimum requisite number of parameters.

2·4 Response criterion. In addition to replacing MS/K by τ, the rewriting of Eq. 2·1 in the form of Eq. 2·2 involved two other changes. One of these was to replace T_o by q. This step, the definition of q for a particular problem, is usually straightforward, guided by the idea that q should be the quantity in which one is most directly interested in the problem at hand. It is worth noting that sometimes the differential equation, as written down to express the pertinent physical law, will have as dependent variable some quantity other than the one which might most conveniently be defined as q. In such equations a simple substitution will usually suffice to convert the dependent variable to the desired quantity q. For example, if the equation for an electric circuit happens to come out in terms of current and for convenience one would prefer to define q as a voltage, one can pick from the circuit a resistance R and let $q = E = IR$. In other situations, of course, the substitution might not be so simple, but the motivation would be the same.

The third difference in notation between Eqs. 2·1 and 2·2 is the substitution of q_f for T_i. Although it is straightforward in the example of the thermometer, this step of defining q_f in a particular problem may sometimes lead to difficulty and confusion. The guiding motive here is the effort to adopt as standard form of the differential equation that form which is most intelligible in regard to the performance expected of the physical system. In many cases ideal response can be represented by the equality of two quantities. One might therefore be inclined to define q and q_f as the two quantities which the criterion of ideal response demands should be equal to each other, and whenever possible to write the differential equation relating them in the form:

(Terms involving system parameters

$$\text{and derivatives of } q) + q = q_f \quad (2\cdot3)$$

If one defines as **error** the instantaneous difference between q and the quantity it is supposed to duplicate, the above criterion of response can be called the **criterion of minimum error.** If q_f is the quantity to be duplicated, the form of Eq. 2·3 makes it clear that, when the terms in parentheses are small, the system will approach ideal performance. There are, however, systems (of which the electrical circuit discussed at the end of this section is an example) for which the differential equation is not in the form of Eq. 2·3, even though the criterion of minimum error applies. Hence it is desirable to have a different symbol, q_d, for the quantity which q should duplicate, and to reserve q_f for the quantity appearing on the right-hand side of Eq. 2·3. Frequently, of course, q_f and q_d will refer to the same quantity, but in all cases the criterion of minimum error means that $q = q_d$ is perfect response, and error is defined as $q - q_d$. q_d will be called the **reference quantity.**

"Equality" between q and q_d should be interpreted in the broad sense of including proportionality as well as strict equality, since any magnification or amplification is covered by a constant factor which can be absorbed in the definition of q_d. With this understanding one can say that the criterion of minimum error applies to: **instruments,** where the indicated value (q) should at all times equal the true value (q_d) of the quantity being measured; **servomechanisms,** where the "slave" signal (q) should at all times follow (i.e., be equal to) the "master" signal (q_d); and **automatic controls** where the controlled quantity (q) should at all times be equal to the reference value (q_d). These devices all come under the class called duplicators in Chapter 1.

The devices known as **amplifiers** are interesting in that some are built for minimum error, whereas in other instances the **criterion of minimum distortion** applies. The difference between error and distortion is that zero error means zero instantaneous difference, whereas zero distortion means zero difference in the waveforms of q and q_d, though the waveform of q may be delayed relative to that of q_d. Zero error is thus equivalent to zero distortion plus zero delay. (See Chapter 5.) For other systems still other criteria are used. Thus the criterion of minimum error is by no means universal. It is, however, so much more nearly universal than any other that it seems proper to give it a central role in the response of physical systems and to choose as standard form of the differential equations a form which makes this central role evident.

If one is fully convinced of the wisdom of getting the differential equation in the form of Eq. 2·2, or more generally 2·3, the proper definition of q_f gives little difficulty. One simply arranges q and the terms in its derivatives on the left-hand side of the equation, with any necessary factor divided out so as to make q stand by itself; then one defines as q_f whatever is left on the right-hand side, thus automatically throwing the equation into the form of Eq. 2·3. Note that this procedure also insures that q and q_f shall have the same dimensions.

As an example, the electrical circuit of Fig. 2·1 satisfies the differential equation,

$$R(C_1 + C_2)\dot{E}_o + E_o = C_1 R \dot{E}_i \qquad (2\cdot4)$$

To put this in the form of Eq. 2·2 one defines $q = E_o$ and $\tau = R(C_1 + C_2)$. Now the next question concerns the function of the circuit—its response criterion. If E_o is to duplicate E_i, one puts $q_d = E_i$ and $q_f = C_1 R \dot{E}_i$—that is, q_d and q_f are different. But, if the circuit is a differentiating circuit, its function is to have E_o duplicate $\dot{E}_i$; so that both q_d and q_f would be $C_1 R \dot{E}_i$. For either criterion the fact that the time derivative of E_i rather than E_i itself figures in the definition of q_f puts no limitation at all on the usefulness of the differential equation. If one knows the time dependence of E_i, one can differentiate the expression and put it in the definition of q_f, thus giving a known function to use for q_f in working with the differential equation.

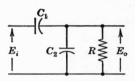

Fig. 2·1. Circuit illustrating definition of q_f.

2·5 Distributed systems. One of the conditions to be met by any physical system for it to be called a simple system, according to the definition given in Section 2·2, is that its response should be given by ordinary, rather than partial, differential equations. The condition is actually never met exactly, and it is therefore important to understand the approximation involved and to recognize the need in some problems of using partial differential equations.

Physical systems exist in time and space. Mathematical treatment of such systems would therefore be expected in general to lead to equations involving at least two independent variables— one to represent time, and one or more to represent space coordinates. If the equations in question are differential equations, they would belong to the class called partial differential equations, which includes all those involving functions of more than one independent variable. Mathematical physics might thus be expected to deal directly only with partial differential equations, whereas ordinary differential equations—those involving functions of a single independent variable—would enter only in a purely mathematical role into the problems of dealing with the partial equations.

This picture of the application of mathematics to physics is, in fact, basically right. It is true that many physical systems are treated directly in terms of ordinary differential equations, but such treatment is always more or less of an approximation in the physics, no matter how rigorous the mathematics may be.

In the field of mechanics, for instance, much use is made of the concept of a "particle," especially in celestial mechanics. Now to treat an object such as the moon as a particle is, rather obviously, an approximation. The moon does have mass—the essential particle property—but it also has many non-particle properties, such as size, shape, and the possibility of other motions besides simple translation of its center of mass. Thus to treat the moon as a particle is to ignore, for reasons of convenience in a given problem, a certain number of the moon's physical properties. So long as its limitations are borne in mind, this procedure is useful and therefore justifiable. Mathematically the motion of a particle is studied by considering its three space coordinates to be dependent variables, depending on the one independent variable, time, so that the problem is one in ordinary differential equations.

When an extended object, such as the moon, is treated as a particle, one can say that a certain property, namely, mass, which in reality is distributed over a sizable portion of space, is thought of as being concentrated or "lumped" at a single point. This lumping of the properties of physical systems is of use in other aspects of mechanics besides particle dynamics, but it is above all in the field of electrical engineering that the method has had its most widespread application. The concepts of lumped resistance, capacitance, and inductance have become most commonplace, and the theory of circuits made up of combinations of such elements has furnished subject matter for countless pages of books and journals.

The technique of treating lumped electrical circuits has been highly developed, with well-standardized symbols for the various circuit elements and with definite mathematical ways of specifying their physical properties. Thus the physical situation represented by the diagram of Fig. 2·1, for example, is easy to grasp. Electrical situations are particularly easy to visualize because resistors and capacitors exist as discrete physical objects and because one can perform the direct act of connecting them to each other and to a voltage supply or measuring instruments by means of connectors specifically designed for the purpose. How much of an advantage this is in sensing the lumped character of the elements may be appreciated by thinking again of the mercury-in-glass thermometer.

Although the thermometer cannot be taken apart into two pieces, one representing a resistance and one a capacitance, the physical nature of the thermometer can be represented by the diagram of Fig. 2·2, to the same degree of approximation as would apply to an electrical circuit made up of a resistor and a capacitor connected together as shown. Moreover, both the thermal and the electrical systems would be equally well governed by the differential Eq. 2·2. For the thermometer the resistance is $R = (1/K)$ and the capacitance is $C = MS$; and for both systems the time constant is $\tau = CR$.

The terms "lumped system" and "distributed system" may be used as abbreviations for "system with lumped properties" and "system with distributed properties." Now both the thermometer and the analogous electrical circuit are, in strict physical reality, distributed systems. The fact that the electrical system can more

readily be taken apart into discrete elements does not necessarily mean that it is any less a distributed system than the thermometer. In fact these two systems are equally subject to the general rule which applies to all systems and according to which

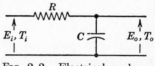

Fig. 2·2. Electrical analogue of thermometer.

the individual circumstances of a particular problem must determine whether a system should be treated as lumped or as distributed.

It is hard to put the rule in quantitative form, but its general nature can be made clear. That which has been called "response of a physical system" is not something which appears simultaneously at all points of the system; energy is propagated at finite velocity through the system. Knowing the nature of a given system (i.e., whether it is electrical, mechanical, thermal, etc.), one has some knowledge of what this velocity of propagation is. Then one can estimate the propagation time across any one element of the system, and it is a good approximation to consider this element lumped if the propagation time is negligibly small. The term "negligibly small" is of course a relative one, implying an approximation which should be freshly appraised in each new problem.

Taking an electrical circuit as an example, the propagation velocity may be a substantial fraction, say one-half, of the free-space velocity of light. Now suppose that one of the circuit elements is a resistor 2 inches long. The propagation time across this resistor is about 3×10^{-10} second. The fact that this is a small number does not necessarily mean that it is negligibly small. That depends on the way in which the circuit is being used—the maximum rate of change of q_f and the information that is sought about the response to q_f. If neither of these factors requires consideration of any time interval smaller than a millisecond, it is clear that the propagation time, 3×10^{-7} millisecond, is indeed negligibly small. On the other hand, if q_f is a sinusoidal voltage of 1500-megacycle frequency, the propagation time is a half-period, so that the potentials at the two ends of the resistor differ by 180 degrees of phase. To this forcing the resistor is not responding as a unit, and treating it as a lumped element would obviously be a poor approximation.

It is important to realize that the validity of the lumping approximation does not depend alone on the nature of q_f. For instance, the circuit might be suddenly connected to a battery by the closing of a switch. Here the question of lumping must be answered according to the information sought in the response q, rather than according to the nature of q_f. If the problem concerns the behavior of the circuit in the first thousandth of a microsecond after closing of the switch, the distributed nature of the circuit must be taken into account. For study on a coarser time scale, on which anything happening in less than a millisecond cannot be discerned, the circuit may be considered lumped.

The problem of deciding on the validity of lumping is sometimes far from simple. But a good rule of thumb is this: if the response is instantaneously the same throughout an element, the element may be treated as lumped; if the response shows instantaneous differences along the element, it should be treated as distributed. The key word "instantaneously" is used in the sense set forth in the preceding paragraphs. An interesting example of the transition from lumped to distributed behavior is discussed in Chapter 10, which deals more fully with the response of distributed systems.

2·6 Parametric forcing. Since the introduction of the forcing q_f in connection with Fig. 2·1, the discussion has implied that q_f acts on the system in a way which can be treated mathematically by placing q_f on the right-hand side of the differential equation of the system, as in Eq. 2·3. Problems that can be handled in this way may be spoken of as involving **direct forcing.** There are, however, other cases where the system is forced in a different way, by the changing of one or more of the system's properties. The response called forth in this way may be said to be due to **parametric forcing.**

Physical examples of direct and parametric forcing are furnished by two common types of microphone. In the electromagnetic microphone the sound waves move a diaphragm carrying a small coil of wire. The coil moves in the gap of a magnet, so that a voltage appears at the coil terminals. In this process the properties of the microphone remain constant, the forcing acts directly on the system, and the forcing is therefore direct. In the condenser microphone, however, the sound waves move a diaphragm which is one plate of a capacitor. The resulting change of capacitance gives rise to the output signal. Here it is clearly a property of the system, its capacitance, which is acted upon by the forcing, giving parametric forcing.

From a mathematical standpoint, parametric forcing may be identified with **variable coefficients,** since one or more of the coefficients of the differential equation are time dependent. This violates one of the conditions put on simple systems in Section 2·2, so that systems subject to parametric forcing are not simple systems. The differential equations met with in parametric forcing are more difficult to handle than the corresponding ones for direct forcing. This is true for linear and for nonlinear equations. However, because of the great difficulty of dealing with any nonlinear equations, the relative difference between constant and variable coefficients is less significant for nonlinear than for linear equations. Linear equations with constant coefficients can be treated in closed, compact fashion; although not completely free of difficulties, this treatment is inherently far simpler and more finished than anything that can be done with linear equations with variable coefficients.

The subject of parametric forcing is treated further in Chapter 9.

2·7 Nonlinear systems. In writing physical laws in mathematical form, there is one approximation which is almost always made implicitly but is seldom mentioned explicitly. This concerns the range of values of the variables over which the equation remains true. The mathematical equation is a reasonably accurate representation of physical reality only over a finite range of the variables, becoming less and less accurate as one or more of the variables pass beyond this range.

This limitation applies particularly to linear differential equations. Such equations are usually only a first approximation to a full description of the physical situation, and a better approximation could be had by making the equation nonlinear. For many purposes, of course, the first approximation furnishes ample accuracy; at other times a more or less substantial loss of accuracy may be accepted as the price paid for the great gain in simplicity achieved by making the equation linear. For the difficulty of working with nonlinear equations is so great that comparatively little is known about the analysis of nonlinear systems.

Better understanding of nonlinear systems is a most needed development in the subject of response of physical systems. It is needed not only to give a finished form to the academic and theoretical aspects of the subject but also to promote a fuller realization of the practical possibilities inherent in physical systems. An introduction to the study of nonlinear systems is given in Chapter 11.

2·8 Higher-order systems. In establishing the concept of simple systems it is hard to know where to draw the line on the order of the differential equation. Indeed, it is something of a temptation not to draw the line at all. This is because the mathematical treatment of linear differential equations with constant coefficients is, in form at least, practically independent of the order of the equation. This is, however, a mathematical circumstance which, in terms of physical reality, is not deeply significant. It seems wise, therefore, to restrict simple systems to those governed by equations of the first or second order, and to classify as **higher-order systems** those whose equations satisfy the other conditions for simple systems but are of higher than second order. (This definition is to be understood as applying to the unmodified term "higher-order system," and as therefore leaving open the possibility of using the terms "higher-order distributed system," "higher-order system with parametric forcing," and "higher-order nonlinear system.")

The typical differential equation of a higher-order system may be taken as the nth-order equation,

$$A_n \frac{d^n q}{dt^n} + A_{n-1} \frac{d^{n-1} q}{dt^{n-1}} + \cdots + A_1 \frac{dq}{dt} + A_0 q = F(t) \quad (2\cdot5)$$

The A's in this equation are constants involving the properties of the physical system. This form of the equation does not imply any special limitation on the dimensions of any of the symbols; the product $A_0 q$ can be of any dimensions, and the separating of the quantity q is guided by considerations of convenience, as mentioned above at the beginning of Section 2·4.

Suppose Eq. 2·5 is divided through by A_0. Then define B_j $= (A_j/A_0)$, where j is an index running from 1 to n; also define $q_f = (F/A_0)$. Then the equation is

$$B_n \frac{d^n q}{dt^n} + \cdots + B_1 \frac{dq}{dt} + q = q_f \qquad (2·6)$$

This is seen to be in the form of Eq. 2·3. The $n + 1$ A's of Eq. 2·5 are replaced by n B's, each of which has the dimension of a power of time—that is, dimensionally $B_j = t^j$. The B's may be used as parameters, as was done above for first-order systems, where B_1 was called τ; or the B's may be replaced by any other n parameters defined in terms of the A's.

Equation 2·6 as it stands would be called **unhomogeneous** because of the function of time, q_f, appearing on the right-hand side of the equation. If q_f were identically equal to zero (that is, if zero appeared in place of q_f in the equation), the equation would be **homogeneous**. Thus, even though the equation of the physical system is in general unhomogeneous, one can speak of the corresponding homogeneous equation, obtained from the actual equation by putting zero in place of q_f. Now the problem of finding the solution of the unhomogeneous Eq. 2·6 can be divided into two parts: first, finding the **complementary function,** which is the general solution of the corresponding homogeneous equation; and second, finding the **particular integral,** which is a solution of the unhomogeneous equation. The complete solution of the unhomogeneous equation is then given as the sum of the complementary function and the particular integral.

In order to emphasize the physical ideas involved the complementary function will be called the **transient response** and given the symbol q_t; and the particular integral will be called the **forced response** and given the symbol q_r. The **complete response** q is then

$$q = q_t + q_r \qquad (2·7)$$

There is a general expression for the transient response—namely,

$$q_t = C_1 e^{r_1 t} + C_2 e^{r_2 t} + \cdots + C_n e^{r_n t} \qquad (2·8)$$

In this equation the r's in the exponents are the n roots of the algebraic equation, derived from Eq. 2·6,

$$B_n r^n + B_{n-1} r^{n-1} + \cdots + B_1 r + 1 = 0 \qquad (2·9)$$

This algebraic equation is called the **auxiliary equation**.

The C's in Eq. 2·8 are constants whose values must be fixed in terms of **initial conditions**. Since there are n of these constants, a problem, to be determinate, must include specification of n initial conditions—that is, specified values of q or its derivatives at specified times. One can always express the C's in terms of the initial conditions. This process is simple enough to be worthwhile for first- and second-order systems, and it is employed in the next two chapters. (Note that the C's are evaluated in terms of q, not of q_t. Therefore, according to Eq. 2·7, q_r is involved, and the full process of expressing the C's in terms of initial conditions cannot be carried out until q_r is known.)

The conditions that determine the C's have been called initial conditions, implying that they refer to some particular instant of time, the initial instant. This is, in fact, the usual situation in practical problems of response of physical systems. From a more general point of view, however, this problem, of specifying q in terms of n conditions on q and its derivatives at a single instant, is one extreme of a range of possibilities. The other extreme is the problem in which n different instants of time are involved, for each of which a value of q is specified. These two extremes have been called, respectively, the Cauchy integration problem and the Lagrange integration problem. Between these extremes there are, of course, all sorts of combinations. As mentioned above, the Cauchy problem is the one of primary interest here and, unless otherwise noted, is to be understood as the one being considered.

Equation 2·8 must be modified in the case of **multiple roots** —that is, when two or more roots of Eq. 2·9 are the same. Suppose, for example, that r_1 and r_2 are the same. Then the first two terms of Eq. 2·8 would be replaced by $(C_1 + C_2 t)e^{r_1 t}$, so that the complete expression for q_t would still involve n of the C's. In general, for every root r of multiplicity m, one replaces m terms of the expression 2·8 by $P_{m-1} e^{rt}$, where P_{m-1} is a polynomial of degree $m - 1$, involving m of the C's.

So much for the general process of determining q_t. It is quite straightforward, with the one exception of finding the roots of

Eq. 2·9 for higher-order systems; even this can be carried out by numerical calculation. The general process of determining q_r is another matter. Indeed, it is in questionable taste to speak of a general method, since the best method will vary according to the nature of the equation, and particularly according to the nature of the forcing q_f. The problems arising in this book, however, may profitably be dealt with as follows: Since q_r is *any* function satisfying Eq. 2·6, one is tempted to try guessing. Moreover, since q_r is called forced response because it is largely influenced by the forcing q_f, a logical guess is that q_r would be the same kind of function as q_f. As developments of later chapters show, this guess brings results. (This method is called, in texts on differential equations, the method of "undetermined coefficients.")

The foregoing paragraphs present, in a schematic way, the solution of the direct problem for simple and higher-order systems. This material is needed as a basic reference for much of the work throughout the book.

Before leaving this section it should be said that many problems, though they may be transformed into the terms of Eq. 2·5, nevertheless do not naturally occur in that form. In particular, direct formulation of a problem frequently leads to a simultaneous system of differential equations, each of the first or second order. Such a problem may be handled either by dealing directly with the simultaneous equations, in which case the analysis still has much in common with that outlined above, or by transforming the simultaneous equations into an equivalent single equation in the form of Eq. 2·5. For the present, it will be assumed that the second alternative will usually be chosen. If in some problems it is convenient to use also the first, appropriate attention will be given to the necessary analysis.

Heaviside's operational calculus has been widely used for treating linear systems. The modern, rigorous version of this technique is the Laplace transformation. To maintain the desired generality and unity of viewpoint throughout this book, Laplace transform methods are not included as an integral part of the text. A concise summary of the subject is given in Appendix 1.

CHAPTER
3

First - Order Systems

3·1 The direct problem. A first-order system is, by definition, one whose response is given by the first-order differential equation,

$$\tau\dot{q} + q = q_f \tag{3·1}$$

already given in Eq. 2·2 as the standard form of the first-order equation. As outlined in the final section of Chapter 2, the response will consist of the sum of a transient response q_t and a forced response q_r; and the equation for q_t will be $q_t = Ce^{-t/\tau}$. The arbitrary constant C is to be determined from an initial condition, which may be specified as $q = Q_1$ when $t = T_1$. (Usually, $T_1 = 0$.)

Then the complete expression for q, evaluated at time T_1, is

$$Q_1 = q_r(T_1) + Ce^{-T_1/\tau}$$

so that

$$C = [Q_1 - q_r(T_1)]e^{T_1/\tau} \tag{3·2}$$

The quantity in brackets is the initial value of the transient response; it will be given the symbol Q_i. Equation 3·2 then becomes

$$C = Q_i e^{T_1/\tau} \tag{3·3}$$

Substitution of this value for C in the expression for q_t then gives the **standard form of the solution**

$$q = q_r + Q_i e^{-(t-T_1)/\tau} \tag{3·4}$$

This equation solves the direct problem, provided of course the forced response q_r is known. Table 3·1 gives q_r for common types of forcing q_f. In order to keep the entries dimensionless, each one

26

TABLE 3·1

FORCED RESPONSE OF FIRST-ORDER SYSTEM TO VARIOUS FORCINGS
(Q_2 is a constant having the same dimensions as q_f)

	q_f/Q_2	q_r/Q_2
1	1	1
2	$\dfrac{t}{\tau} + A$	$\dfrac{t}{\tau} + A - 1$
3	$\left(\dfrac{t}{\tau}\right)^2 + A\dfrac{t}{\tau} + B$	$\left(\dfrac{t}{\tau}\right)^2 + (A - 2)\left(\dfrac{t}{\tau}\right) + B - A + 2$
4	$\left(\dfrac{t}{\tau}\right)^3 + A\left(\dfrac{t}{\tau}\right)^2 + B\dfrac{t}{\tau} + C$	$\left(\dfrac{t}{\tau}\right)^3 + (A - 3)\left(\dfrac{t}{\tau}\right)^2$ $+ (B - 2A + 6)\left(\dfrac{t}{\tau}\right) + C - B + 2A - 6$
5	$\left(\dfrac{t}{\tau}\right)^4 + A\left(\dfrac{t}{\tau}\right)^3 + B\left(\dfrac{t}{\tau}\right)^2$ $+ C\left(\dfrac{t}{\tau}\right) + D$	$\left(\dfrac{t}{\tau}\right)^4 + (A - 4)\left(\dfrac{t}{\tau}\right)^3$ $+ (B - 3A + 12)\left(\dfrac{t}{\tau}\right)^2$ $+ (C - 2B + 6A - 24)\left(\dfrac{t}{\tau}\right)$ $+ D - C + 2B - 6A + 24$
6	$A_n\left(\dfrac{t}{\tau}\right)^n + A_{n-1}\left(\dfrac{t}{\tau}\right)^{n-1}$ $+ \cdots + A_1\dfrac{t}{\tau} + A_0$	$\displaystyle\sum_{k=0}^{n}\left(\dfrac{t}{\tau}\right)^k \sum_{j=k}^{n}(-1)^{j-k}\left(\dfrac{j!}{k!}\right)A_j$
7	$e^{\rho_f t}$	$\dfrac{e^{\rho_f t}}{1 + \rho_f \tau}$
8	$e^{j\omega_f t}$	$\dfrac{e^{j\omega_f t}}{1 + j\omega_f \tau} = \dfrac{e^{j(\omega_f t - \tan^{-1}\omega_f \tau)}}{\sqrt{1 + (\omega_f \tau)^2}}$
9	$e^{\sigma_f t} = e^{(\rho_f + j\omega_f)t}$	$\dfrac{e^{\sigma_f t}}{1 + \sigma_f \tau} = \dfrac{e^{\sigma_f t - j\tan^{-1}\frac{\omega_f \tau}{1 + \rho_f \tau}}}{\sqrt{(1 + \rho_f \tau)^2 + (\omega_f \tau)^2}}$
10	$\left(\dfrac{t}{\tau}\right)e^{\sigma_f t}$	$\left[\dfrac{1}{1 + \sigma_f \tau}\left(\dfrac{t}{\tau}\right) - \dfrac{1}{(1 + \sigma_f \tau)^2}\right]e^{\sigma_f t}$

has a constant Q_2 divided out, so that columns are headed q_f/Q_2 and q_r/Q_2. This table was derived by the "guessing" technique mentioned in Section 2·8. It will be noticed that in each instance q_r is the same kind of function as q_f.

The customary complex exponential notation for sinusoids is used in items 8, 9, and 10. That is, $e^{j\omega_f t}$ is written for $\cos \omega_f t$.

Equation 3·4 and Table 3·1 give the solution of the direct problem. Some examples will now be considered. Suppose $Q_1 = 0$, and $q_f = Q_2$. This case is commonly described by saying that q_f is a step function, meaning that q_f is zero for all negative time and at zero "steps" to some value Q_2. This is somewhat misleading, however, since in reality it makes no difference to a first-order system what q_f was for all negative time, so far as response after $t = 0$ is concerned. The only thing that matters is that q should be equal to Q_1 at $t = 0$. For this reason it is preferable to call this case "response to a constant" rather than "response to a step function," and to drop the restriction that Q_1 must be zero and let it be any constant, positive or negative.

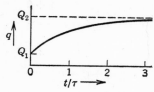

FIG. 3·1. First-order response to constant.

Then $q_f = Q_2$, and item 1 of Table 3·1 states that $q_r = Q_2$. So $Q_i = Q_1 - Q_2$, and

$$q = Q_2 + (Q_1 - Q_2)e^{-t/\tau} \qquad (3\cdot5)$$

The graph of this response for Q_1 and Q_2 both positive and Q_2 greater than Q_1 is shown in Fig. 3·1. It is clear from Eq. 3·5 that, of the total change to be made from Q_1 to Q_2, e^{-1} or 36.8 per cent remains to be made when $t = \tau$; e^{-2} or 13.5 per cent remains when $t = 2\tau$; e^{-3} or 4.98 per cent when $t = 3\tau$; and so on. This may be made more obvious by rearranging Eq. 3·5 in the form

$$\frac{Q_2 - q}{Q_2 - Q_1} = e^{-t/\tau} \qquad (3\cdot6)$$

for then the left-hand side is "the fraction of the change remaining to be made."

Taking natural logarithms of both sides of Eq. 3·6,

$$\ln \frac{Q_2 - q}{Q_2 - Q_1} = -\frac{t}{\tau} \qquad (3\cdot7)$$

This means, of course, that a plot of Eq. 3·6 on semilogarithmic paper is a straight line. This is true, regardless of the signs and relative magnitude of Q_1 and Q_2. This is a good way to plot experimental data on response to a constant since, besides making it easy to see what τ is (the inverse problem, see next section), the straightness of the line provides an easy check on the scattering of the data.

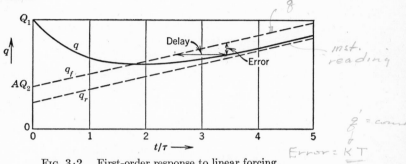

FIG. 3·2.   First-order response to linear forcing.

As a second example of the direct problem let $q_f = Q_2[(t/\tau) + A]$, which is a straight line of slope Q_2/τ and intercept AQ_2. Then, using item 2 of Table 3·1,

$$q_r = Q_2 \left(\frac{t}{\tau} + A - 1 \right)$$

so that $q_r(0) = Q_2(A - 1)$ and $Q_i = Q_1 - AQ_2 + Q_2$. Then Eq. 3·4 is

$$q = Q_2 \left(\frac{t}{\tau} + A - 1 \right) + (Q_1 - AQ_2 + Q_2)e^{-t/\tau} \qquad (3\cdot8)$$

This response is drawn in Fig. 3·2 for a particular case in which A and Q_2 are positive and Q_1 is greater than AQ_2. Besides illustrating response to linear forcing, this figure serves to illustrate two important definitions: **delay** and **error**. Delay is the time interval from the instant q_f takes on a certain value until q takes on that same value. Error is the instantaneous difference, $q - q_f$ (or $q - q_d$, in general; cf. Section 2·4). It can be seen from Eq. 3·8 and Fig. 3·2 that, after the transient has died out and $q = q_r$, the delay is τ and the error is $-Q_2$.

A third example is sinusoidal forcing, $q_f = Q_2 \cos \omega_f t$. Item 8 of Table 3·1 gives

$$q_r = \frac{Q_2}{1 + j\omega_f\tau} e^{j\omega_f t} \sim \frac{Q_2}{\sqrt{1 + \omega_f{}^2\tau^2}} \cos(\omega_f t + \phi)$$

where $\phi = -\tan^{-1} \omega_f\tau$. Then $q_r(0) = Q_2 \cos \phi/\sqrt{1 + \omega_f{}^2\tau^2}$, and $Q_i = Q_1 - Q_2 \cos \phi/\sqrt{1 + \omega_f{}^2\tau^2}$. Equation 3·4 then becomes

$$q = \frac{Q_2}{\sqrt{1 + \omega_f{}^2\tau^2}} \cos(\omega_f t + \phi) + \left(Q_1 - \frac{Q_2 \cos \phi}{\sqrt{1 + \omega_f{}^2\tau^2}}\right) e^{-t/\tau} \quad (3·9)$$

This derivation was not for the general sinusoidal function, however, since q_f was assumed to be a cosine function. The general

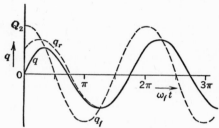

FIG. 3·3.   First-order response to sinusoidal forcing.

assumption is $q_f = Q_2 \cos(\omega_f t + \theta)$, where θ is an arbitrary phase angle. If one introduces a complex $\mathbf{Q}_2$, defined as $Q_2 e^{j\theta}$, $q_f = \mathbf{Q}_2 e^{j\omega_f t}$, and the derivation proceeds as before, yielding

$$q = \frac{Q_2}{\sqrt{1 + \omega_f{}^2\tau^2}} \cos(\omega_f t + \theta + \phi) + \left[Q_1 - \frac{Q_2 \cos(\theta + \phi)}{\sqrt{1 + \omega_f{}^2\tau^2}}\right] e^{-t/\tau}$$

$$(3·10)$$

Figure 3·3 shows the response to a cosine function for the particular case $Q_1 = 0$, and assuming Q_2 positive. In this case, even after q_t has died out and $q = q_r$, the delay and the error both vary throughout the cycle, so that the relation between q_f and q_r is better specified by other means. Since both are sinusoids, there will be only two differences between them—a difference of amplitude and a difference of phase. But these are precisely the two factors easily deduced from item 8 of Table 3·1. In fact, the sense of this item may be expressed thus: if q_f is a sinusoid, q_r is also a sinusoid, but with amplitude $1/\sqrt{1 + \omega_f{}^2\tau^2}$ as large and lagging in phase by $\tan^{-1}\omega_f\tau$. This kind of statement can be made not only about first-order systems but about second-order and higher-order systems as well, as study of later chapters will show.

For a variety of mathematical and technical reasons the relation of forcing and forced sinusoids is very important. Hence it is natural and convenient to speak of a **gain ratio** G, which includes

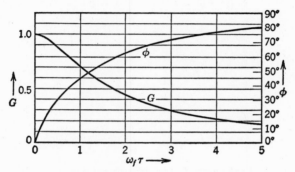

FIG. 3·4.   Gain and phase characteristics of first-order systems.

the amplitude and phase differences.   In the complex notation this is easy; for if q_{fa} and q_{ra} are the complex amplitudes of the forcing and forced sinusoids (so that $q_f = q_{fa}e^{j\omega_f t}$ and $q_r = q_{ra}e^{j\omega_f t}$), the complex number **G**, defined as $\mathbf{G} = q_{ra}/q_{fa}$, is the desired quantity. Writing $\mathbf{G} = Ge^{j\phi}$, one can call G the **gain,** or, considered as a function of ω_f, the **gain characteristic**; and ϕ, the **phase,** or the **phase characteristic.**   For a first-order system

$$G = \frac{1}{\sqrt{1 + \omega_f{}^2\tau^2}} \tag{3·11}$$

and

$$\phi = -\tan^{-1}\omega_f\tau \tag{3·12}$$

These gain and phase characteristics are plotted in Fig. 3·4.

One consequence of using the complex notation for sinusoids is that items 7, 8, and 9 of Table 3·1 are actually all covered by item 9. Thus one can replace the formulas of 3·11 and 3·12 by the more general ones,

$$G = \frac{1}{\sqrt{(1 + \rho_f\tau)^2 + {\omega_f}^2\tau^2}} \qquad (3\cdot13)$$

and

$$\phi = -\tan^{-1}\frac{\omega_f\tau}{1 + \rho_f\tau} \qquad (3\cdot14)$$

These more general gain and phase characteristics, relating to exponentially damped sinusoids, are plotted in Figs. 3·5 and 3·6.

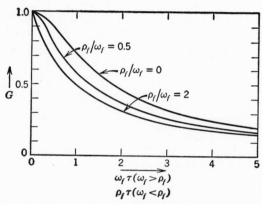

FIG. 3·5.   More general gain characteristics.

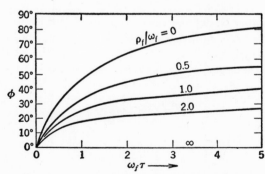

FIG. 3·6.   More general phase characteristics.

Notice that the curves of Fig. 3·4 are included here as the extreme case, when $\rho_f = 0$. The other extreme, $\omega_f = 0$, refers to the simple exponential of item 7. (Since it would be embarrassing to try to explain what is meant by the phase of an exponential, it is lucky for the author that for this value the phase becomes identically zero!) In order to be able to show both these extremes on a single plot, it was necessary to adopt the convention, for the abscissa scales, that the numbers refer to $\omega_f \tau$ for $\omega_f > \rho_f$, and to $\rho_f \tau$ when $\omega_f < \rho_f$.

The special case in which $\rho_f \tau = -1$ involves the apparent difficulty that item 7 of the table gives an infinite value of q_r. The difficulty can be resolved by considering the complete Eq. 3·4, which involves the indeterminate form $Q_2(e^{\rho_f t} - e^{-t/\tau})/(1 + \rho_f \tau)$. Evaluation by L'Hospital's rule gives this the value $Q_2(t/\tau)e^{-t/\tau}$. This problem is worth considering rather closely, as it suggests that the mathematical separation of q into q_r and q_t is more or less artificial and that one should not always expect

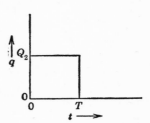

FIG. 3·7.   Pulse forcing.

to see clearly the dividing line between these "parts" of the response (cf. also Eqs. 3·30 and 3·31).

As a final example of direct problems, response to the forcing shown in Fig. 3·7 may be studied. The forcing is a constant for a limited time, from 0 to T, and then drops to zero. Besides being interesting on its own account, this example illustrates the process, which must be used in many problems, of calculating the response in two or more stages, corresponding to changes in the forcing. Thus in the present example one must first calculate the response over the time interval from 0 to T, and then, using as initial value the response $q(T)$, calculate the response for time after T.

For $0 < t < T$, $q_f = Q_2$, $q_r = Q_2$, $Q_i = Q_1 - Q_2$, and

$$q = Q_2 + (Q_1 - Q_2)e^{-t/\tau} \tag{3·15}$$

which is, of course, the same as Eq. 3·5. For $t > T$, $q_f = 0$, $q_r = 0$, and

$$Q_i = q(T) - 0 = Q_1 e^{-T/\tau} + Q_2(1 - e^{-T/\tau}) \tag{3·16}$$

so that

$$q = q(T)e^{-(t-T)/\tau}$$

or

$$q = Q_1 e^{-t/\tau} + Q_2(1 - e^{-T/\tau})e^{-(t-T)/\tau} \tag{3·17}$$

This formula may be used to plot q for any values of Q_1, Q_2, and T. An interesting question concerns the ultimate form of the response as T is made smaller and smaller. If T is made small without any corresponding increase of Q_2, the limit is zero. But suppose Q_2 is increased just enough to keep the product Q_2T constant. Then the expression $3 \cdot 16$ for Q_i takes the limiting form

$$Q_i = Q_1 + \frac{I}{\tau} \qquad (3 \cdot 18)$$

where the symbol I has been introduced for the **impulse**, Q_2T. Thus, for length of pulse T short compared to τ, the net effect of

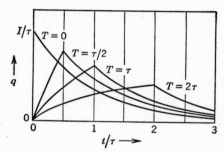

FIG. 3·8.   First-order response to pulse forcing.

the impulse is to add the constant I/τ to the effective value of Q_1. In Fig. 3·8 the response is shown for several values of T, including the limiting case of zero, all for the same values of Q_1 and I. (Q_1 is taken as zero.)

Before leaving the subject of the direct problem it should be understood that, if the forcing consists of the sum of two functions, the forced response consists of the sum of the individual forced responses. For instance, if the forcing consists of the sum of a straight line and a sinusoid, one would write

$$q_f = Q_2 \left(\frac{t}{\tau} + A \right) + Q_2' e^{j\omega_f t}$$

Then, by items 2 and 8 of Table 3·1,

$$q_r = Q_2 \left(\frac{t}{\tau} + A - 1 \right) + \mathbf{G}Q_2' e^{j\omega_f t}$$

3·2 The inverse problem. The inverse problem, finding τ from the known response to a known forcing, takes on a different form for each different kind of forcing. It will therefore be discussed separately for each of the common kinds of forcing.

Determination of τ from the response to a constant is seen from Eq. 3·6 to be possible by estimation of the time at which 36.8 per cent of the change remains to be made, or at which 63.2 per cent of the change has been made. This is true, whether or not the point from which one defines "change to be made" is at the initial instant or at some later time; in other words, starting at *any* point of the response and defining "change to be made" as the difference between the response at that time and Q_2, 63.2 per cent of that change will have been made just τ units of time later. This generality is important because in some experiments it is not easy to get a good record of the very beginning of the response. Thus response to a constant furnishes a very easy and convenient way of determining τ.

In connection with Fig. 3·2 it was shown that the delay of the forced response to a linear forcing is τ. Hence the inverse problem is solved very easily from linear forcing, provided the record of the response is long enough to indicate clearly what the forced response is.

The forced response to sinusoidal forcing may furnish τ, either from amplitude measurement or from phase measurement. Knowing either G or ϕ, $\omega_f \tau$ may be derived either from Fig. 3·4 or from Eqs. 3·11 or 3·12. Knowing ω_f then gives τ.

Finally, the response to pulse forcing also furnishes a solution to the inverse problem. Referring to Eq. 3·17 and Fig. 3·8 it is seen that the response reaches a maximum at time T and that this maximum is $Q_2 + (Q_1 - Q_2)e^{-T/\tau}$. Hence

$$\tau = \frac{T}{\ln \dfrac{Q_2 - Q_1}{Q_2 - q_{\max}}} \tag{3·19}$$

where $q_{\max}$ is the peak value of the response.

Although the inverse problem may be solved from response to other forcings, the above examples include the most common ones and should moreover amply point the way toward the solution of the problem on the basis of any forcing.

3·3 The converse problem. This problem appears trivial in the mathematical sense, since the standard form of the differential equation, $\tau\dot{q} + q = q_f$, shows that if q and τ are known q_f may readily be found. The only question would be as to how $\dot{q}$ should be determined from q. If q is known in analytical form (by empirical curve fitting, for example), $\dot{q}$ can be obtained by analytical differentiation. Otherwise, graphical or numerical differentiation could be carried out. The same sort of remarks apply to the converse problem for second-order systems, so that this problem need not be explicitly treated in Chapter 4.

The fact that there is little to be said about the converse problem from the mathematical side must not obscure its physical importance. It plays a significant part in the subject of response of systems, as will appear in later chapters (cf. in particular the end of Section 7·10).

3·4 Stability. It has been implicit in the discussion thus far that τ is a positive quantity. So long as the time constant is positive, the sense of Eq. 3·4 is that the transient response is something that more or less gradually decreases in magnitude and eventually disappears. If τ is negative, the transient response is seen to be a growing quantity which would sooner or later pass any given bound—that is, it becomes infinite. Such a runaway condition in a physical system is commonly described by saying that the system is unstable. Therefore, the **stability condition** for first-order systems is that τ be positive; or, in terms of the original coefficients, that the coefficients of q and $\dot{q}$ have the same sign.

3·5 Thermal models. The remainder of this chapter is devoted to the discussion, as examples, of several first-order physical systems. Most of these examples are suitable for laboratory experiments or demonstrations.

The first example to be discussed is the one already mentioned in Chapter 2, the common mercury-in-glass thermometer. It was shown there that this familiar instrument is a typical first-order system, with time constant $\tau = MS/K$. M and S are mass and specific heat of the enclosed mercury, and K is the thermal conductance of the glass envelope. As a laboratory exercise it is interesting to attempt the inverse problem from response to a constant, using beakers of water at different fixed temperatures, and relying on visual observation and stop-watch timing. Since the time constant for typical laboratory thermometers is of the order of a second, the data thus obtained provide an instructive exercise in use of the semilogarithmic plot of Eq. 3·7. Attempts to transfer the thermometer "instantaneously" from one beaker

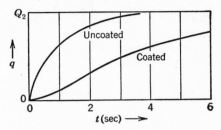

FIG. 3·9.   Thermometer responses.

to another point up the difference between the theoretical concept of a step function and the forcing one is actually able to accomplish.

An additional exercise with the thermometer is to coat the bulb with a thin layer of some poor thermal conductor, such as modeling clay. Response to a constant now shows two differences from the response of the uncoated bulb. First, the time constant is much longer, perhaps four or five times as long; and second, the first part of the response is noticeably different, unlike that of a first-order system. The difference is illustrated in Fig. 3·9. The fact that the response of the coated thermometer starts out with zero slope indicates that it is acting as a higher-order system, probably second-order.

This is understandable from consideration of the circuit diagram of the coated thermometer (cf. Fig. 2·2 for uncoated thermometer). Taking into account both the thermal capacitance and the thermal resistance of the coating, the diagram would be as shown in Fig. 3·10(a). This is a second-order system. However, one might try as an approximation the first-order circuit of Fig. 3·10(b), or even, neglecting the coating's capacitance,

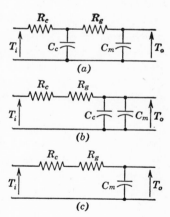

FIG. 3·10.   Circuits of coated thermometer.

that of Fig. 3·10(c). In each of these diagrams, R_c and R_g are
the resistances of the coating and of the glass; C_c and C_m are the
capacitances of the coating and of the mercury.

Now the question arises as to which is the "correct" diagram for
the coated thermometer. The answer, of course, is that there is
no correct circuit for a given system, but only a circuit more or
less well adapted to the purposes of a particular problem involving
the system. The fact that the response of the uncoated thermometer looks like that of a first-order system is due solely to the
crudity of the method of observation. Assuming the forcing to
be instantaneously applied, high-speed observation of the response
would show it starting out with
zero slope, just as the response of
the coated thermometer shows on
a coarser time scale. Thus, assigning a certain order to a physical
system involves an arbitrary approximation and hence a limitation
on the accuracy of any results

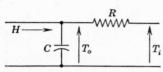

FIG. 3·11.   Circuit of thermal
model.

derived on the basis of this approximation. As an exercise
in dealing with such approximations one can attempt to calculate
the thermal conductivity of the material used as coating, assuming
the following to be known: response to constant of bare thermometer; response to constant of same thermometer coated; dimensions
of coating (thickness, area covered) and of glass bulb; thermal
conductivity of glass.

Another thermal example, closely related to the thermometer, is
the system whose circuit diagram is shown in Fig. 3·11. The
difference between this and the thermometer is that here some
heat is introduced directly into the capacitance C, whereas in the
thermometer it all had to be transferred to C through R. The
present circuit would apply, for instance, to the temperature T_o
of a room of thermal capacitance C, in which a certain rate H of
heat production is in effect and which loses heat to the outside
(temperature T_i) through the resistance R of the walls and
windows.

The system was set up on a laboratory scale by representing C
in the form of an aluminum cylinder 3 inches long and 2 inches in
diameter. A small hole was drilled along the axis of the cylinder
to accommodate a thermocouple; other holes drilled near the center

took electric heating elements. The cylinder was wrapped with
¹⁄₁₆-inch asbestos paper and then jacketed in a thin brass shell
and immersed in an ice-water bath. By measuring the electrical
power going into the heaters, a known source of heat was available, as represented by the symbol H in Fig. 3·11. If, up to time
zero, the value of H had been zero long enough for the aluminum
to be at the temperature of the ice bath, and then, at time zero, a
constant value of H was applied, the response of the aluminum
temperature was that of a first-order system with a τ of about
6 minutes. Thus the system is dynamically similar to the thermometer system. But there is a difference, as consideration of the
differential equation will show.

The equation may be written on the basis of what becomes of
the heat flow H. Part goes to raise the temperature T_o of the
aluminum, and part flows through the resistance R. Thus

$$H = C \frac{dT_o}{dt} + \frac{T_o - T_i}{R} \tag{3·20}$$

where T_i is the temperature of the ice bath. Then, letting $\tau = CR$,
$q = T_o$, and $q_f = RH + T_i$, this becomes a standard first-order
equation. Thus this problem includes the thermometer problem,
which is the special case of $H = 0$.

3·6 Hydraulic models. Consider the flow of water from one
cylindrical container to another through a rather small tube. In
Fig. 3·12 it is the supply vessel from which water flows into the

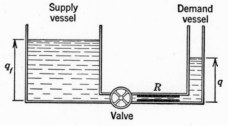

Fig. 3·12.   Hydraulic model.

demand vessel through the tube denoted by R. Let q and q_f be
the height of the level in the demand and supply vessels, and A_d
and A_s the cross-section areas.

The general relation between q and q_f is

$$gD(q_f - q) = R\frac{d(A_d q)}{dt} \qquad (3 \cdot 21)$$

where g is the gravitational constant and D the density of water. Thus the left-hand side of Eq. $3 \cdot 21$ is the pressure difference across the connecting tube. This must equal the right-hand side according to the definition of R, namely, pressure per unit volume velocity. Equation $3 \cdot 21$ can be put in standard form by letting $\tau = A_d R/gD$.

Neglecting any water in the tube, the total volume of water in the whole system is $A_d q + A_s q_f$. If this is a constant, say V_0, then by eliminating q_f Eq. $3 \cdot 21$ may be written

$$\frac{A_d R}{gD[1 + (A_d/A_s)]}\dot{q} + q = \frac{V_0}{A_s[1 + (A_d/A_s)]} \qquad (3 \cdot 22)$$

If A_d is negligibly small compared to A_s, the forcing constant and the time constant of this equation obviously simplify.

The resistance R is given by the expression $128\eta L/\pi d^4$, where η is the coefficient of viscosity, L the length of the resistance tube, and d its diameter. For example, a 10-centimeter length of 1-millimeter capillary tube, with A_d of 6 square centimeters, gives τ of about 240 seconds, depending on the value of η (and therefore on the temperature of the water).

It should be understood that Eq. $3 \cdot 22$ applies only to the response to a constant obtainable with a fixed volume of water, whereas Eq. $3 \cdot 21$ gives q in response to any change whatever of q_f. Of course, the model of Fig. $3 \cdot 12$ could give nothing but constant volume, since no method is shown for increasing or decreasing the total amount of water. An arrangement for giving q_f a more complex time dependence is shown in Fig. $3 \cdot 13$.

Here, in addition to the supply and demand vessels, there is an overflow vessel which serves to maintain a fixed level. It is convenient then to measure q and q_f from this overflow level. Now, if the overflow valve is opened, q_f will decrease to zero, and q will respond, if the supply valve is open, by also decreasing to zero according to Eq. $3 \cdot 21$. Assuming that A_d is negligibly small compared to A_s, the drop in q_f will have the time dependence of a first-order system's response to a constant—that is, it will be exponential. Then q will be the response to an exponential forcing.

The foregoing assumption that these hydraulic models would behave as simple first-order systems is subject to a condition which must be mentioned now. This is the condition that the fluid flow in the resistance tube be laminar rather than turbulent. The criterion for this is the Reynolds number, SDd/η, where D, d, and η have the same meaning as above, and S is the linear speed of fluid flow. At low speeds the flow is laminar, but as the speed

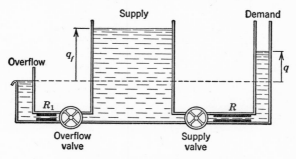

FIG. 3·13.   Second hydraulic model.

increases the flow changes from laminar to turbulent, usually at a Reynolds number of about 2000. Only for laminar flow is the pressure drop across a tube proportional to the velocity, as assumed in writing Eq. 3·21; for turbulent flow it varies with a power, roughly the square, of the velocity. Thus, when the flow is turbulent, the differential equation becomes nonlinear and the system can no longer be called simple.

So with the model of Fig. 3·13 q_f will have an exponential time dependence only if R_1 is large enough to insure laminar flows. If R_1 consists of a short, wide tube, q_f will be a parabolic (square-law) function of time. Discussion of this time dependence of q_f is a nonlinear problem and as such is treated in Chapter 11. If the supply-demand vessel system is linear, however, the response to this square-law forcing can be calculated here (item 3 of Table 3·1).

Figure 3·14 illustrates the transition from turbulent to laminar flow in the system of Fig. 3·12. The effects of turbulence (increased friction) are apparent over the first 10 or 12 seconds. This response was taken with R in the form of a 20-centimeter length of tubing of 3.5-millimeter internal diameter (area of 0.0963 square centimeter). A_d was 6.16 square centimeters, and water temperature was 15.8° C, corresponding to η of about 0.011 poise. The magnitude of $Q_2 - Q_1$ was 11 centimeters. The response was observed to change 1 centimeter in the first second, giving a speed S of $(6.16/0.0963) = 64.0$ centimeters per second and a Reynolds number of $(64 \times 0.35 \times 1)/0.011 = 2035$. Thus the flow starts in the turbulent form and gradually changes to fully laminar flow.

As shown in Fig. 3·14 the observed τ for the laminar portion of the response is 9 seconds. Calculation with the data given above

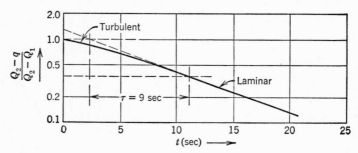

Fig. 3·14.   Flow transition.

yields 3.75 seconds. This poor agreement is due to inaccurate estimation of the internal diameter of the tube and to extra resistances in the connections. The average diameters of several lengths of tubing were measured by weighing the amount of mercury held in the length; results varied by 10 to 15 per cent. This accounts for a large effect, since the diameter enters to the fourth power in the expression for resistance. By simplifying the apparatus to avoid resistance in valves, bends, and connections, and by carefully measuring the average diameter of the particular tube, much better agreement can be obtained. The limiting factor then becomes the *uniformity* of the tube diameter.

3·7   Hydrophone pressure equalizer.   In the design of hydrophones (that is, underwater microphones) a rather serious problem may be presented by the large hydrostatic pressure of the water. In round numbers, 30 feet of water give 15 pounds per square inch hydrostatic pressure; so the rule of thumb is ½ pound per square inch per foot of water. Thus the hydrostatic pressure at only a few feet is very large compared to ordinary sound pressures. If the hydrophone is designed to operate by the action of the sound pressure on a more or less sensitive diaphragm, this diaphragm would be crushed in by hydrostatic pressure unless some safeguard is provided. A method of continuously equalizing the pressures on the two sides of the diaphragm will now be discussed as a practical application of the principles illustrated by the hydraulic models.

Suppose that on the back side of the diaphragm (i.e., the side away from the acoustic medium being measured) there is an enclosed space of fixed volume V. Suppose further that this volume is connected to the acoustic medium through a more or less fine capillary tube of length L and internal diameter d. Let the external pressure in the water or other acoustic medium be denoted by p_1, and the pressure inside the volume by p_2. If these pressures at any instant are unequal, a flow of fluid through the capillary will result such that, if the volume of fluid per unit time is denoted by $\dot{V}$, the flow into the enclosed space will be

$$\dot{V} = \frac{\pi d^4 (p_1 - p_2)}{128 \eta L} \tag{3·23}$$

in which η is the coefficient of viscosity of the fluid medium.

Now the time rate of change of the inside pressure is $\dot{p}_2 = \dot{V}/KV$, where K is the compressibility of the fluid. Combining this with Eq. 3·23 gives an equation in p_2,

$$\tau \dot{p}_2 + p_2 = p_1 \tag{3·24}$$

with

$$\tau = \frac{128 \eta L K V}{\pi d^4} \tag{3·25}$$

Thus the hydraulic system is analogous to an electric circuit combining a series resistor $R = 128 \eta L / \pi d^4$ and a shunt capacity $C = KV$.

Since the quantity which actuates the microphone is the difference between inside and outside pressures, it is convenient to take $q = p_2 - p_1$. Introducing the value of q in Eq. 3·24 gives an equation of the standard form, with $q_f = -\tau \dot{p}_1$, in analogy with the electrical circuit of Fig. 2·1.

Now suppose one of the design conditions to be that the equalizer introduce a relative loss, on sinusoidal forcing, of 30 per cent at 1 cycle per second. If p_{1a} is the amplitude of the forcing pressure, this means that q_{ra}/p_{1a} should be 0.7 at 1 cycle per second. Since

$q_f = -\tau \dot{p}_1$, $q_{fa} = -j\omega_f\tau p_{1a}$ and $q_{ra}/p_{1a} = \omega_f\tau G$, where G is given by Eq. 3·11. This function, $\omega_f\tau G$, may be called the gain characteristic of the equalizer; it is plotted in Fig. 3·15. (Note that, as plotted on a logarithmic scale for $\omega_f\tau$, this function is the same as G with the frequency scale reversed. For instance, $G(10) = 0.1G(0.1)$; or, in general, $G(1/\omega_f\tau) = \omega_f\tau G(\omega_f\tau)$. Hence Fig. 3·15 is useful both for G and $\omega_f\tau G$.) For instance, the effect

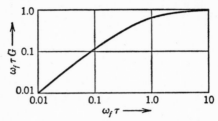

FIG. 3·15.   Equalizer gain characteristic.

of waves, considered as sinusoids of 4 cycles per minute, on the system with time constant of 0.156 second, is given by Fig. 3·15, for $\omega_f\tau = (2\pi \times 0.156)/15 = 0.0654$, as 0.065. That is, the diaphragm would be actuated by only 6.5 per cent of the pressure actually caused by the waves.

The design condition mentioned at the start of the preceding paragraph is seen from Fig. 3·15 to mean that $\omega_f\tau$ should be about

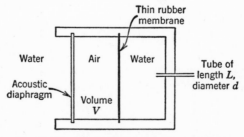

FIG. 3·16.   Hydrophone pressure equalizer.

0.98 at 1 cycle per second. This corresponds to τ of $0.98/2\pi$ or 0.156 second. Now a τ of 0.156 could be achieved using the compressibility of water, though not without encountering some extreme dimensions. A more practical design is obtained by including a volume of air inside the enclosed space, as indicated in Fig. 3·16. If this is done, the viscosity in Eq. 3·25 is that of water, but the compressibility is that of air. The following numerical values will then give the desired value of τ:

$$L = 8.6 \text{ centimeters}$$
$$d = 0.63 \text{ centimeter}$$
$$V = 100 \text{ cubic centimeters}$$
$$K = 7 \cdot 10^{-5} \text{ square centimeter per dyne}$$
$$\eta = 0.01 \text{ poise}$$

It is important to take into account the dependence of the effective capacitance, $C = KV$, on depth. If the air obeys the adiabatic law, $pV^\gamma = \text{constant}$, the compressibility is $1/\gamma p$. Hence $C = \text{constant}/\gamma p^{(\gamma+1)/\gamma}$; since γ is a constant close to 1, the value of C and therefore of τ will decrease approximately as the square of the pressure. At any given depth this would mean that the time constant was determined by that depth, but the system would still be a simple first-order system. However, if the depth were changing continuously, as in steady lowering of the microphone, the nonlinearity would become important.

3·8   Automatic speed control. As a further example a simple automatic control will now be considered. Suppose the quantity to be controlled is the rotational speed of a shaft. Suppose further that the shaft is loaded with inertia (its own inertia and load inertia) and nothing else—i.e., no friction or stiffness. Let the total moment of inertia be denoted by I and the angular velocity by q. Then if a disturbing torque u acts on the shaft the result, in the absence of a control mechanism, would be angular acceleration according to the relation, $I\dot{q} = u$. But, if a control device is connected in the system, such that an instantaneous controlling torque is applied proportional to the deviation of the speed q from its desired value q_d, the system's equation becomes $I\dot{q} + S(q - q_d) = u$, where S is the control sensitivity, i.e., the corrective torque applied per unit angular velocity difference. This equation may be rewritten

$$\frac{I}{S}\dot{q} + q = q_d + \frac{u}{S} \tag{3·26}$$

which is put in standard form by letting $\tau = I/S$ and $q_f = q_d + (u/S)$. (Notice this additional illustration of the possible differences between q_d and q_f.)

The stability condition, that τ be positive, has the simple physical meaning that S must be positive, which means that the control torque must act to reduce the error, $q - q_d$.

Equation $3 \cdot 26$ makes it clear that so long as there is a disturbing torque there will be error. The best that can be done is to make this error (u/S) small by making S large. Another consequence of making S large is the reduction of the time constant. This is an advantage in that it reduces the error due to the term $\tau \dot{q}$.

3·9 Production of radioisotopes. One way of obtaining radioactive isotopes is to subject neutral atoms of a properly chosen element to the flux of neutrons in a nuclear chain reactor. The neutrons have a certain probability of colliding with these neutral atomic nuclei, transforming them more or less directly into radioactive nuclei. The number of these radioisotope atoms will change with time, in the manner of a first-order system.

Let q be the number of the radioactive atoms and n the number of neutral (target) atoms. Then, if τ is the decay period of the active element, q satisfies the differential equation

$$\dot{q} = -\frac{q}{\tau} + F\sigma n \qquad (3\cdot27)$$

or

$$\tau \dot{q} + q = F\sigma n \tau \qquad (3\cdot28)$$

where F is the neutron flux (neutrons per area per time) and σ is the cross section for capture of the neutrons by the original inactive nuclei (it has the dimensions of area and measures the probability of the collisions).[1] Thus the first term on the right of Eq. $3\cdot27$ measures the rate at which q is falling owing to its own radioactive decay, and the second term measures the rate at which q is increasing owing to formation of new radioactive atoms by neutron capture.

Here the forcing is $q_f = \sigma F \tau n$, of which σ and τ are constants, properties of the atoms involved. In general, the neutron flux F might be a function of time, but for the present it is assumed that the reactor is operating at a fixed level and that F is therefore

---

[1] The concept of cross section may be explained, in terms of "projectiles" shot at "targets," as the ratio, hits per target per unit time divided by projectiles per unit area per unit time. The flux F in these terms is projectiles per unit area per unit time, and n is the number of targets. Therefore σF is hits per target per unit time, and $\sigma F n$ is hits per unit time.

constant. So the time-dependent quantity in q_f is n, the number of target atoms. What sort of time dependence does n have? This by itself is a first-order problem. Assuming that at $t = 0$ a certain number n_0, the initial charge, of atoms of the target material was put into the reactor, this number can only decrease, and that for only one reason—the atoms being hit by neutrons. It

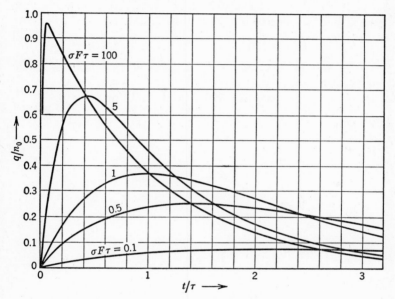

FIG. 3·17.   Growth of radioisotope concentration.

follows that $\dot{n} = -\sigma F n$. This is a first-order equation with zero forcing, and the complete response for initial value n_0 is $n = n_0 e^{-\sigma F t}$.

Returning now to the main problem, the determination of q, the equation is

$$\tau \dot{q} + q = \sigma F \tau n_0 e^{-\sigma F t} \tag{3·29}$$

This equation is to be solved for $Q_1 = 0$. Use of Eq. 3·4 and item 7 of Table 3·1 gives

$$\frac{q}{n_0} = \frac{\sigma F \tau}{1 - \sigma F \tau} \left(e^{-\sigma F t} - e^{-t/\tau} \right) \tag{3·30}$$

In the special case of $\sigma F \tau = 1$ this becomes

$$\frac{q}{n_0} = \frac{t}{\tau} e^{-t/\tau} \tag{3.31}$$

The plot of q/n_0 versus t/τ according to these equations is given in Fig. 3·17 for several values of $\sigma F \tau$. The peaks of these curves indicate the time to leave the target material exposed to the neutron flux in order to obtain the maximum value of q/n_0, i.e., the maximum yield of radioactive nuclei per atom of original charge.

Besides the application to production of radioisotopes, Eqs. 3·30 and 3·31 and Fig. 3·17 apply to any first-order system forced by a decreasing exponential, with initial condition $Q_1 = 0$.

Second-Order Systems

4·1 Choice of parameters. Following the general scheme of notation presented in Eqs. 2·5 and 2·6, the second-order differential equation would be written

$$A_2\ddot{q} + A_1\dot{q} + A_0q = A_0q_f \qquad (4\cdot1)$$

or

$$B_2\ddot{q} + B_1\dot{q} + q = q_f \qquad (4\cdot2)$$

Now B_2 and B_1 may be used as parameters, or they may be replaced by any other two parameters properly defined in terms of B's (or A's). Of the various ways in which this choice may be made, one would expect those to be seriously considered which have particular mathematical significance in the differential equation and its various solutions. It is quite surprising, considering that only two parameters are to be chosen, how many different choices do have such significance.

It would be burdensome and confusing to present here a list of the various choices. A better plan seems to be to start using a chosen pair of parameters. Then as knowledge of second-order systems is accumulated the significance of the chosen parameters will become clear; and sooner or later some of the alternative choices will be introduced naturally, according to their particular convenience or advantage.

The parameters to be chosen are ζ and ω_n, defined as

$$\omega_n = \frac{1}{\sqrt{B_2}} = \sqrt{\frac{A_0}{A_2}} \qquad (4\cdot3)$$

and

$$\zeta = \frac{B_1}{2\sqrt{B_2}} = \frac{A_1}{2\sqrt{A_0 A_2}} \qquad (4\cdot4)$$

In terms of them the differential equation is

$$\frac{\ddot{q}}{\omega_n{}^2} + \frac{2\zeta}{\omega_n} \dot{q} + q = q_f \qquad (4\cdot5)$$

In general, it will suffice to regard Eq. $4\cdot5$ as the **standard form** of the second-order differential equation.

As mentioned in connection with Eq. $2\cdot6$, B_1 has the dimensions of time, and B_2 of time squared. So ζ is dimensionless, and ω_n has the dimensions of frequency (reciprocal time). For reasons that will become apparent, ζ is called **damping ratio,** and ω_n is called **natural angular frequency.** The quantity $f_n = \omega_n/2\pi$ is called **natural frequency.**

It is clear that any dimensionless parameter other than ζ, arrived at by any simple combination of the A's or B's, would be very directly related to ζ. Examples of dimensionless parameters in more or less common usage are sharpness of resonance, usually given the symbol Q in electrical engineering, which is simply $\frac{1}{2}\zeta$; and logarithmic decrement, which is $2\pi\zeta/\sqrt{1 - \zeta^2}$.

From Eqs. $4\cdot3$ and $4\cdot4$ it is seen that so long as A_0 and A_2 have the same sign ζ and ω_n are real, but that they are imaginary if A_0 and A_2 are of opposite signs. This is mentioned here simply as one indication that ζ and ω_n might sometimes be awkard or inconvenient. Nevertheless, they serve excellently for beginning the study of second-order systems.

4·2 The direct problem. Applying the general discussion of Section $2\cdot8$ to the particular conditions of second-order systems, it is seen that the response of a second-order system involves two arbitrary constants in q_t and therefore requires two initial conditions to specify the value of the constants. The Cauchy integration problem is based on the two initial conditions, $q(T_1) = Q_1$, and $\dot{q}(T_1) = \dot{Q}_1$.

The auxiliary equation is

$$\left(\frac{r}{\omega_n}\right)^2 + 2\zeta \frac{r}{\omega_n} + 1 = 0 \qquad (4\cdot6)$$

of which the roots are given by $r/\omega_n = -\zeta \pm \sqrt{\zeta^2 - 1}$, or

$$\begin{aligned} r_1 &= -\zeta\omega_n + \omega_n\sqrt{\zeta^2 - 1} \\ r_2 &= -\zeta\omega_n - \omega_n\sqrt{\zeta^2 - 1} \end{aligned} \qquad (4\cdot7)$$

It is convenient to introduce the symbol ω, defined by

$$\omega = \omega_n \sqrt{|\, 1 - \zeta^2 \,|} \qquad (4\cdot8)$$

where the vertical bars denote the absolute magnitude of the quantity between them. Thus ω, by definition, is real whether ζ is larger or smaller than 1. Then $r_{1,2} = -\zeta\omega_n \pm \omega$ for $\zeta > 1$; and $r_{1,2} = -\zeta\omega_n \pm j\omega$ for $\zeta < 1$; and consequently for $\zeta > 1$

$$q_t = e^{-\zeta\omega_n t}(C_1 e^{\omega t} + C_2 e^{-\omega t}) \qquad (4\cdot9)$$

and, for $\zeta < 1$,

$$q_t = e^{-\zeta\omega_n t}(C_1 e^{j\omega t} + C_2 e^{-j\omega t}) \qquad (4\cdot10)$$

To proceed in this direction would be awkward, because of the complex numbers when ζ is less than 1. Expressions for q_t which involve only real numbers may be had by replacing C_1 and C_2 by A and B, such that

$$A = C_1 + C_2$$
$$B = (C_1 - C_2)\sqrt{\zeta^2 - 1} \qquad (4\cdot11)$$

Then the equations for q_t are, for $\zeta < 1$,

$$q_t = e^{-\zeta\omega_n t}\left(A \cos \omega t + \frac{B}{\sqrt{1 - \zeta^2}} \sin \omega t\right) \qquad (4\cdot12)$$

and, for $\zeta > 1$,

$$q_t = e^{-\zeta\omega_n t}\left(A \cosh \omega t + \frac{B}{\sqrt{\zeta^2 - 1}} \sinh \omega t\right) \qquad (4\cdot13)$$

Also, as ζ approaches 1, Eq. 4·12, with the second term written $B\omega_n t[(\sin \omega t)/\omega t]$, is seen to approach the limit

$$q_t = e^{-\omega_n t}(A + B\omega_n t) \qquad (4\cdot14)$$

which is thus the transient response for $\zeta = 1$.

The three Eqs. 4·12, 4·13, and 4·14 express q_t for all real values of ζ, and the constants A and B have the same meaning in all three equations.

Differentiation of Eq. 4·12 gives

$$\dot{q}_t = e^{-\zeta\omega_n t}\left[(-\zeta\omega_n A + \omega_n B) \cos \omega t - \left(\omega A + \frac{\zeta\omega_n B}{\sqrt{1 - \zeta^2}}\right) \sin \omega t\right]$$
$$(4.15)$$

Taking the initial time T_1 to be zero, Eqs. 4·12 and 4·15 give

$$Q_i = q_t(0) = A$$
$$\dot{Q}_i = \dot{q}_t(0) = -\zeta\omega_n A + \omega_n B \tag{4·16}$$

or, solving for A and B,

$$A = Q_i$$
$$B = \frac{\zeta\omega_n Q_i + \dot{Q}_i}{\omega_n} \tag{4·17}$$

Now the initial conditions are

$$Q_1 = q_r(0) + Q_i$$
$$\dot{Q}_1 = \dot{q}_r(0) + \dot{Q}_i$$

so that

$$Q_i = Q_1 - q_r(0) \tag{4·18}$$

and

$$\dot{Q}_i = \dot{Q}_1 - \dot{q}_r(0) \tag{4·19}$$

Putting the values of A and B from Eqs. 4·17 into Eqs. 4·12, 4·13, and 4·14, the final standard forms of the complete response are:

$$\text{For } \zeta < 1: q = q_r + e^{-\zeta\omega_n t}\left(Q_i \cos \omega t + \frac{\zeta\omega_n Q_i + \dot{Q}_i}{\omega} \sin \omega t \right)$$
$$\tag{4·20}$$

$$\text{For } \zeta = 1: q = q_r + e^{-\omega_n t}[Q_i + (\omega_n Q_i + \dot{Q}_i)t] \tag{4·21}$$

$$\text{For } \zeta > 1: q = q_r + e^{-\zeta\omega_n t}\left(Q_i \cosh \omega t + \frac{\zeta\omega_n Q_i + \dot{Q}_i}{\omega} \sinh \omega t \right)$$
$$\tag{4·22}$$

Since these equations may be considered simply as three forms of a single equation, it is not necessary to work with all three in order to express a result valid for all ζ-values. So, unless there is a special reason for considering $\zeta = 1$ or $\zeta > 1$, the usual practice in what follows is to consider $\zeta < 1$ and use Eq. 4·20.

These equations, together with a table for q_r for various q_f's, solve the direct problem. Table 4·1 gives q_r for a certain number of forms of q_f. For convenience in evaluating $\dot{Q}_i$ in Eq. 4·19, $\dot{q}_r$ is also listed. It will be noted that items corresponding to items

TABLE 4·1

Forced Response of Second-Order System to Various Forcings

	q_f/Q_2	q_r/Q_2	$\dot{q}_r/\omega_n Q_2$
1	1	1	0
2	$\omega_n t + A$	$\omega_n t + A - 2\zeta$	1
3	$(\omega_n t)^2 +$ $A\omega_n t + B$	$(\omega_n t)^2 + (A - 4\zeta)\omega_n t$ $+ B - 2\zeta A + 8\zeta^2 - 2$	$2\omega_n t + A - 4\zeta$
4	$e^{\rho_f t}$	$Ge^{\rho_f t}$	$\alpha G e^{\rho_f t}$
5	$e^{j\omega_f t}$	$Ge^{j(\omega_f t + \phi)}$	$\beta G e^{j[\omega_f t + \phi + (\pi/2)]}$
6	$e^{\sigma_f t}$ $= e^{\rho_f t + j\omega_f t}$	$Ge^{\rho_f t + j(\omega_f t + \phi)}$	$G\sqrt{\alpha^2 + \beta^2}\, e^{\rho_f t + j[\omega_f t + \phi + \tan^{-1}(\beta/\alpha)]}$
7	$\omega_n t e^{\rho_f t}$	$G[\omega_n t - 2(\zeta + \alpha)G]e^{\rho_f t}$	$G[\alpha\omega_n t + (1 - \alpha^2)G]e^{\rho_f t}$

4, 5, and 6 of Table 3·1 are omitted here. If needed, these responses can be found by the same "guessing" technique which furnished all the items in Tables 3·1 and 4·1. Items 4, 5, 6, and 7 are all expressed in terms of quantities α, β, and $\mathbf{G} = Ge^{j\phi}$, defined by

$$\alpha = \frac{\rho_f}{\omega_n}$$

$$\beta = \frac{\omega_f}{\omega_n}$$

$$G = \frac{1}{\sqrt{(1 + 2\zeta\alpha + \alpha^2 - \beta^2)^2 + 4\beta^2(\zeta + \alpha)^2}} \qquad (4\cdot23)$$

$$\phi = -\tan^{-1}\frac{2\beta(\zeta + \alpha)}{1 + 2\zeta\alpha + \alpha^2 - \beta^2}$$

With due regard as to whether ρ_f or ω_f (and hence α or β) happens to be zero, the single equation $q_r = Q_2 \mathbf{G} e^{\sigma_f t}$ is adequate for cases 4, 5, and 6.

Detailed attention will be given in the following sections to the direct problems of response to a constant, response to sinusoidal forcing, and response to pulse forcing.

4·3   Response to a constant.   If $q_f = Q_2$, then $q_r = Q_2$, and $Q_i = Q_1 - Q_2$. Assuming $\dot{Q}_1 = 0$, it follows that $\dot{Q}_i = 0$, and Eq. 4·20 becomes

$$q = Q_2 + (Q_1 - Q_2)e^{-\zeta\omega_n t}\left(\cos\omega t + \frac{\zeta}{\sqrt{1-\zeta^2}}\sin\omega t\right)$$

or

$$\frac{Q_2 - q}{Q_2 - Q_1} = e^{-\zeta\omega_n t}\left(\cos\omega t + \frac{\zeta}{\sqrt{1-\zeta^2}}\sin\omega t\right) \qquad (4\cdot24)$$

which may be compared with Eq. 3·6 for the corresponding first-order response. The left-hand side here is again the "fraction of the change remaining to be made."

It is useful to have Eq. 4·24 in the form

$$\frac{Q_2 - q}{Q_2 - Q_1} = \frac{e^{-\zeta\omega_n t}}{\sqrt{1-\zeta^2}}\sin(\omega t + \cos^{-1}\zeta) \qquad (4\cdot25)$$

The corresponding form for $\zeta > 1$ is

$$\frac{Q_2 - q}{Q_2 - Q_1} = \frac{e^{-\zeta\omega_n t}}{\sqrt{\zeta^2-1}}\sinh(\omega t + \cosh^{-1}\zeta) \qquad (4\cdot26)$$

and, for $\zeta = 1$,

$$\frac{Q_2 - q}{Q_2 - Q_1} = e^{-\omega_n t}(1 + \omega_n t) \qquad (4\cdot27)$$

Equations 4·25, 4·26, and 4·27 may be used to plot the response to a constant, for any value of ζ. This response is plotted in Fig. 4·1 for several values of ζ.

Consideration of this figure and the equation on which it is based contributes to understanding of ζ and ω_n. With zero damping ($\zeta = 0$) the response is seen to consist of a continuing sinusoid of angular frequency ω_n. An appreciable amount of damping ($\zeta = 0.2$) modifies the response in two ways: the peak amplitudes are successively reduced, and the frequency of oscillation is smaller than in the undamped response. This second difference, that ω is smaller than ω_n for $\zeta < 1$, is evidenced also in Fig. 4·2. This is a plot of ω/ω_n versus ζ, which is convenient for the many necessary transformations back and forth among these quantities.

Since the case of $\zeta = 1$ represents the transition from Eq. 4·25 to 4·26, this situation of **critical damping** gives the minimum amount of damping which still suffices to prevent the response from crossing the zero line—i.e., from oscillating. Figure 4·1 does

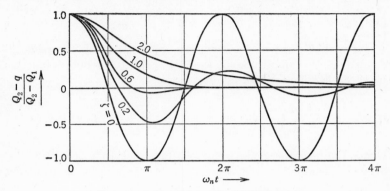

Fig. 4·1. Second-order response to constant.

not show this clearly and would still not show it clearly if many additional ζ-values near 1 were illustrated. As a matter of fact, from a practical standpoint the "critical" value is more nearly 0.6 than 1.0, as the following discussion shows.

The significance of ζ and ω_n may be further explored by attempting to apply the criterion of minimum error; that is, by considering the question: for any change from Q_1 to Q_2, what choice of ζ and ω_n will yield a system capable of making such changes rapidly and accurately? It is instructive first to think back to first-

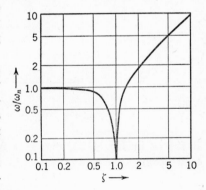

Fig. 4·2. Effect of damping on frequency.

order systems and to realize that there was only one thing to do to minimize error—namely, to reduce τ. With second-order systems the problem is more complicated. For reduction of ζ helps by minimizing the time for the response to reach Q_2, but, on the other hand, too small a ζ means that the response will oscillate a great deal before settling **down**.

In Fig. 4·1 the "time to first zero" may be denoted by T_2 and found from Eq. 4·25 to be given by

$$\omega_n T_2 = \frac{(\pi/2) + \sin^{-1}\zeta}{\sqrt{1 - \zeta^2}} \qquad (4\cdot 28)$$

Along with T_2 one wishes to know the amount of "overshoot," defined as the amplitude of the first peak. To determine this Eq. 4·25 is differentiated, giving

$$\frac{d}{dt}\left(\frac{Q_2 - q}{Q_2 - Q_1}\right) = -\frac{\omega_n e^{-\zeta\omega_n t}}{\sqrt{1 - \zeta^2}} \sin \omega t \qquad (4\cdot 29)$$

Hence the response peaks occur at times such that $\omega t = 0$, π, 2π, 3π, $\cdots$. Taking the first value after zero, namely, π, and putting

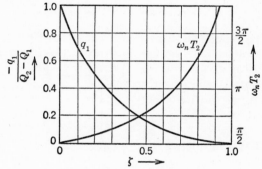

FIG. 4·3.   Effect of damping on error.

it for ωt in Eq. 4·25, one gets for q_1, the peak overshoot, the expression

$$\frac{q_1}{Q_2 - Q_1} = -e^{-\zeta\pi/\sqrt{1-\zeta^2}} \qquad (4\cdot 30)$$

in which, for present purposes, the minus sign in front of the exponential may be ignored.

Now Eqs. 4·28 and 4·30 may be used to make quantitative plots of the two error factors, time to zero and overshoot. Figure 4·3 gives such plots. This figure shows that there is no clearly defined optimum value of ζ, since too large a value means large T_2 and too small a value means large q_1. The circumstances of a particular problem must establish the relative weights of the two factors and so fix a compromise optimum ζ.

In most cases the best choice of ζ would be about 0.6 or 0.7. Since for $\zeta = 0.7$ the overshoot is less than 5 per cent, the probability of choosing an optimum ζ greater than this is rather small. This is the basis of the statement made above that the critical value of ζ, for practical purposes, is nearer to 0.6 than to 1. It is common practice to speak of critical damping ($\zeta = 1$) as the optimum. It is clear that critical damping may differ from optimum damping by an appreciable margin.

Response to a constant is generally not the only criterion. Response to sinusoidal forcing is usually at least equally important. However, in the next section it will appear that optimum choice of ζ is also 0.6 or 0.7. Since this nearly always applies in fact, regardless of the nature of q_f, it is convenient to specify the degree of damping in three ranges: oscillatory systems, for which ζ is less than about 0.6; near-critical systems, for which ζ is between 0.6 and 2; and overdamped systems, for which ζ is greater than 2. Emphasis here is not on the exact values of the limits, but on the concept of the three ranges.

The discussion thus far has been based on the implication that ω_n was fixed and that an optimum ζ was to be determined. In terms of the coefficients of Eq. 4·1, this would mean, given a fixed ratio of A_0/A_2, to find an optimum value of A_1. In general, however, the values of all three coefficients may be adjusted for optimum design. Now, considering ω_n as well as ζ adjustable, there is the additional inference to be drawn from Fig. 4·3, that for given ζ the response will be faster (T_2 will be smaller) the larger ω_n is made. When changing ω_n as well as ζ, however, the thing to remember is that ζ depends on all three coefficients; if any two are held fixed, then (but only then) ζ may be considered simply a measure of the third.

For example, suppose, instead of ζ and ω_n, ζ and τ had been chosen as parameters, where τ as for first-order systems is defined as A_1/A_0. With this pair of parameters,

$$\tau = \frac{A_1}{A_0}$$

$$\zeta = \frac{A_1}{2\sqrt{A_0 A_2}}$$

$$(4·31)$$

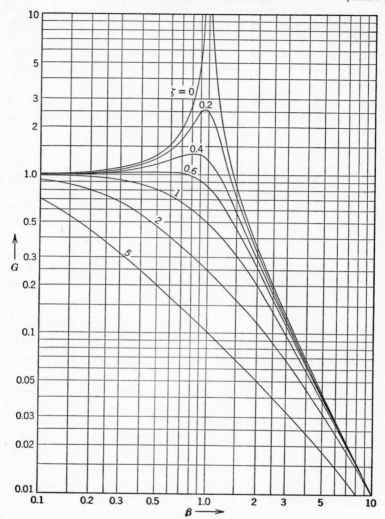

Fig. 4·4. Second-order gain characteristics.

it would be reasonable to call ζ a mass ratio, or an inductance ratio, since if A_1 and A_0 (not merely their ratio!) are both fixed, ζ becomes a measure of A_2—mass in a mechanical system, inductance in an electrical system.

4·4   Sinusoidal forcing.   In Chapter 3 the complete response of a first-order system to sinusoidal forcing was worked out in Eq. 3·10 and illustrated in Fig. 3·3.   As mentioned there the complete response to sinusoids is relatively seldom of interest, the important thing being the forced sinusoidal response.   For this reason the complete response for second-order systems will not be discussed here.   An illustration is given in connection with the liquid level control discussed in Section 4·9.

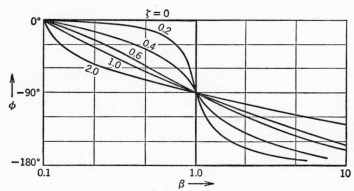

Fig. 4·5.   Second-order phase characteristics.

Turning to the forced response, use will be made of the quantity $\mathbf{G} = Ge^{j\phi}$, with G and ϕ as given in Eq. 4·23, considering $\alpha = 0$; that is,

$$G = \frac{1}{\sqrt{(1 - \beta^2)^2 + (2\zeta\beta)^2}} \qquad (4·32)$$

and

$$\phi = -\tan^{-1}\frac{2\zeta\beta}{1 - \beta^2} \qquad (4·33)$$

The meaning of $\mathbf{G}$ is as given in Chapter 3; that is, if q_{fa} is the complex amplitude of the forcing sinusoid, then $\mathbf{G}q_{fa}$ is the complex amplitude, q_{ra}, of the sinusoid constituting the forced response.

Equations 4·32 and 4·33 may be used to plot the gain and phase characteristics of Figs. 4·4 and 4·5.   A few key properties of these important curves will be stated.

The gain characteristics have maxima, or resonance peaks, for values of ζ less than $1/\sqrt{2}$. This can be shown by differentiating Eq. 4·32, giving

$$\frac{dG}{d\beta} = \frac{2\beta(1 - \beta^2) - 4\zeta^2\beta}{[(1 - \beta^2)^2 + (2\zeta\beta)^2]^{3/2}} \tag{4·34}$$

Setting the numerator equal to zero shows that the peaks of the curves come at $\beta^2 = 1 - 2\zeta^2$. Hence the peak comes at $\beta = 0$ for $\zeta = 1/\sqrt{2}$. Putting $\beta^2 = 1 - 2\zeta^2$ into Eq. 4·32 yields the values of maximum gain,

$$G_{\max} = \frac{1}{2\zeta\sqrt{1 - \zeta^2}} \tag{4·35}$$

This may be compared with the gain at $\beta = 1$, which is $\frac{1}{2}\zeta$.

The phase characteristics have two features especially worth noting. One is the fact that the phase shift is 90 degrees at $\beta = 1$, for all ζ-values. The other is the fact that the slope of the phase characteristic $d\phi/d\beta$ is equal, at $\beta = 1$, to $1/\zeta$.

A combined picture of G and ϕ is given by the curves of Fig. 4·6. The parabolas are the loci of the reciprocal of the **G**-vector, for fixed ζ, as β varies; that is, the abscissa is $1 - \beta^2$ and the ordinate is $2\zeta\beta$. The circles are labeled with the values of G, and the radii with the values of $-\phi$.

Not only does this figure give the entire story of second-order sinusoidal forcing in terms of ζ and ω_n, but it also gives the story in terms of ζ and τ. The ordinate $2\zeta\beta$ is the same as $\omega_f\tau$. ($2\zeta\beta = 2A_1\omega_f/2\sqrt{A_0A_2}\sqrt{A_0/A_2} = A_1\omega_f/A_0 = \omega_f\tau$.) Hence one can ignore the abscissa scale laid out in terms of β and measure frequency along the ordinate axis. Then, as discussed in connection with Eqs. 4·31, ζ may be thought of as measuring A_2, the coefficient that makes the system second-order. Zero value of A_2, or infinite ζ, would correspond to a first-order system. This is represented by the ordinate axis itself; the intersections of this axis with the ϕ-radii and the G-circles give the same information as the characteristics of Fig. 3·4. This is one example of the general proposition: any result obtained for second-order systems in terms of ζ and τ will transform, in the limit as ζ becomes infinite, into the corresponding result for first-order systems.

If the forcing consists of several sinusoids added together, the forced response will in general show error due to both gain and phase characteristics: **gain error,** because G is not the same for all the sinusoids; and **phase error,** because ϕ is not the same for all the sinusoids.   Consideration of the characteristics shows that

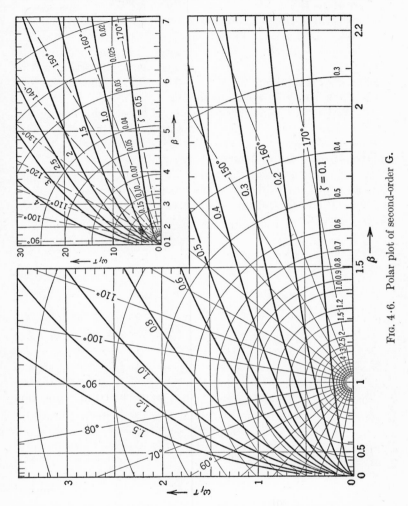

FIG. 4·6.   Polar plot of second-order G.

gain error will be small over a maximum range of β if ζ is 0.6 or 0.7, but that small phase error will be obtained over a comparable β-range only if ζ is near zero.   Thus the criterion of minimum error, applied to forced sinusoidal response, does not clearly indicate an optimum ζ. Instead of this criterion, however, consider the criterion of minimum distortion (mentioned in Section 2·4 and discussed further in Chapter 5). **Gain distortion** is small, like gain error, to the extent that G is the same for sinusoids of all frequencies; but **phase distortion** is small to the extent that the **delay,** ϕ/ω_f, is the same for all sinusoids—that is, to the extent that the phase characteristic is a straight line. Inspection of the characteristics shows that both gain and phase distortion will be small over a maximum β-range if ζ is 0.6 or 0.7. Hence optimum ζ here is the same as for constant forcing.

4·5 Pulse forcing. The response of a second-order system will be calculated for the pulse forcing shown in Fig. 3·7. This consists of a constant Q_2, which lasts from time zero to time T and then drops "instantaneously" to zero.

Although in most practical problems the value of $\dot{Q}_1$, and perhaps also of Q_1, would be zero, the more general case of arbitrary values of Q_1 and $\dot{Q}_1$ will be solved here. For $0 < t < T$, $q_r = Q_2$, and so Eq. 4·20 is

$$q = Q_2 + e^{-\zeta\omega_n t}\left[(Q_1 - Q_2)\cos \omega t + \frac{\zeta\omega_n(Q_1 - Q_2) + \dot{Q}_1}{\omega}\sin \omega t\right]$$

$$(4\cdot36)$$

This is more general than Eq. 4·24, which was derived for $\dot{Q}_1 = 0$. Similarly more general than Eq. 4·29 is the derivative,

$$\dot{q} = e^{-\zeta\omega_n t}\left[\dot{Q}_1 \cos \omega t - \frac{\omega_n{}^2(Q_1 - Q_2) + \zeta\omega_n\dot{Q}_1}{\omega}\sin \omega t\right] \quad (4\cdot37)$$

These results for q and $\dot{q}$ are valid for any value of time after zero. For the present problem of pulse forcing, however, they are used only up to a time T, after which the forcing is zero. For this second stage of the problem, the response after T, the initial values are $Q_1 = q(T)$ and $\dot{Q}_1 = \dot{q}(T)$, where $q(T)$ and $\dot{q}(T)$ are obtained by putting $t = T$ in Eqs. 4·36 and 4·37. These values of Q_1 and $\dot{Q}_1$ are then put in

$$q = e^{-\zeta\omega_n(t-T)}\left[Q_1 \cos \omega(t - T) + \frac{\zeta\omega_n Q_1 + \dot{Q}_1}{\omega}\sin \omega(t - T)\right]$$

$$(4\cdot38)$$

to give the response for $t > T$.

Making use again of the impulse, $I = Q_2 T$, the limiting form of the response, as T approaches zero with I held constant, may be deduced. The expression for $q(T)$ and $\dot{q}(T)$ as given by Eqs. 4·36 and 4·37 approaches the limits, as T approaches zero,

$$q(T) = Q_1$$
$$\dot{q}(T) = \dot{Q}_1 + \omega_n{}^2 I \qquad (4·39)$$

Thus the limiting effect for very short T and large Q_2 is to change the effective $\dot{Q}_1$ by the term $\omega_n{}^2 I$. This may be compared with the effect on first-order systems given in Eq. 3·18. (See also Eq. 4·79 and discussion, Section 4·9.)

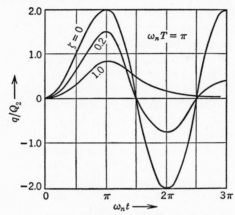

Fig. 4·7.   Response to pulse forcing for various ζ-values.

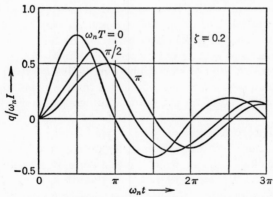

Fig. 4·8.   Response to pulses of various widths.

Equations 4·36 and 4·38 may be used to plot the response for any values of Q_2 and T and for any values of the parameters ζ, ω_n. Examples of the range of possibilities are the curves of Fig. 4·7, which show the responses to a single pulse width (i.e., fixed $\omega_n T$) for various ζ-values; and the curves of Fig. 4·8, which show the responses to various pulse widths, for a single ζ. Both figures are based on a fixed value of $\omega_n I$, and on Q_1 and $\dot{Q}_1$ equal to zero.

4·6 The inverse problem. With second-order systems, as with first-order systems, the inverse problem may be solved from the response to a wide variety of forcings. With second-order systems, however, there is the additional complication that there are two parameters to be found, so that, theoretically at least, there is the possibility of finding one parameter from one forcing and the second parameter from another forcing. It is obviously impossible in limited space to go into all the possibilities and combinations. What will be attempted here is to cover rather thoroughly the important practical problems of constant forcing and of sinusoidal forcing.

The usual practice will be to attempt to find ζ and ω_n, though in some situations it is convenient to find first other parameter pairs. In any case it is a simple matter to transform from any given parameter pair to any other pair.

Consider first response to a constant, as given in Eqs. 4·25, 4·26, and 4·27, and illustrated in Fig. 4·1. It will be necessary to consider the problem separately for oscillatory, near-critical, and overdamped systems. Since the ability to distinguish these is based on knowledge of ζ, it may look as though the problem is to be solved by making use of the answer. The fact is that oscillatory response can easily be recognized at a glance, and to this extent the problem of determining ζ and ω_n can be solved at a glance. The method to be given below for oscillatory response is simply a means of getting more accurate values. As to the other two cases, which are not so obviously recognizable, the procedure must be to choose one or the other and to apply the appropriate method, for the outcome will show whether the choice was good or bad.

For oscillatory response, Eqs. 4·29 and 4·30 provide the solution. Equation 4·30 was obtained by putting into Eq. 4·29 the first time-value after zero which gives a peak overshoot. Instead of the first, take the nth, and designate the nth peak by q_n. Equation 4·30 then becomes (leaving out a possible minus sign)

$$\frac{q_n}{Q_2 - Q_1} = e^{-n\pi\zeta/\sqrt{1-\zeta^2}}$$

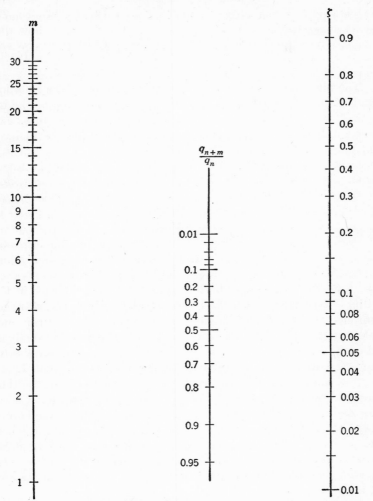

FIG. 4·9. Nomogram for inverse problem using oscillatory response to constant.

Similarly, for the $(n + m)$th peak,

$$\frac{q_{n+m}}{Q_2 - Q_1} = e^{-(n+m)\pi\zeta/\sqrt{1-\zeta^2}}$$

Hence the ratio of the amplitude of the $(n + m)$th peak to that of the nth peak, taken without regard as to whether peaks are positive or negative, is

$$\frac{q_{n+m}}{q_n} = e^{-m\pi\zeta/\sqrt{1-\zeta^2}} \qquad (4 \cdot 40)$$

The nomogram of Fig. 4·9 solves this equation. The equation and the chart are useful for the direct problem as well as the inverse, since for known ζ they give the successive peak values. (In using the chart and equation, only integral values of m have significance.)

Once ζ has been found from the peak values, ω_n may be found from time intervals. The time from one peak to the next, and also from one zero to the next, is π/ω. Usually, the zero points are more readily and accurately fixed. Then, knowing ζ and ω, $\omega_n = \omega/\sqrt{1 - \zeta^2}$, and the inverse problem is solved.

For near-critical damping, the solution is based on the critically damped response, Eq. 4·27. As $\omega_n t$ takes on the successive values 1, 2, 3, $\cdots$, the expression on the right of Eq. 4·27 takes on values $2e^{-1}$, $3e^{-2}$, $4e^{-3}$, $\cdots$, or 0.736, 0.406, 0.199, $\cdots$. Hence in the drop toward the first zero, if the change remaining to be made goes through the values of 73.6 per cent, 40.6 per cent, 19.9 per cent, etc., at exactly equal time intervals, the value of ζ is exactly 1. As can be seen in Fig. 4·1, these intervals are successively shorter for ζ less than 1, and successively longer for ζ greater than 1. So curves can be drawn as in Fig. 4·10, giving the ratio of the time intervals as a function of ζ. The curves labeled $\omega_n t_1$ and $\omega_n t_2$ are for finding ω_n after ζ is known. That is, starting with the knowledge of t_1, t_2, t_3, $\cdots$, the first step is to find ζ; then the value of $\omega_n t_1$ or $\omega_n t_2$, which gives ω_n. The ratio $(t_3 - t_2)/(t_2 - t_1)$ is included more particularly for those cases in which the experimental record does not furnish a clear indication of the initial instant, $t = 0$.

The response of an overdamped system to constant forcing is best treated by employing the parameters τ_1 and τ_2 defined, with reference to Eqs. 4·7, as

$$\tau_1 = -\frac{1}{r_1}$$

$$\tau_2 = -\frac{1}{r_2}$$

In terms of τ_1 and τ_2 the differential equation is

$$\tau_1 \tau_2 \ddot{q} + (\tau_1 + \tau_2)\dot{q} + q = q_f \tag{4·41}$$

And the response to a constant, written like Eq. 4·24, is

$$\frac{Q_2 - q}{Q_2 - Q_1} = \frac{\tau_1}{\tau_1 - \tau_2} e^{-t/\tau_1} - \frac{\tau_2}{\tau_1 - \tau_2} e^{-t/\tau_2} \tag{4·42}$$

From the definition of τ_1 and τ_2 (Eqs. 4·7) it can be seen that, when ζ is near 1, τ_1 and τ_2 are nearly equal; and that, as ζ be-

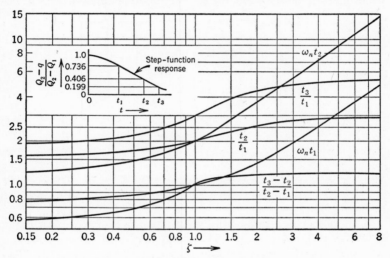

FIG. 4·10.   Inverse problem for near-critical systems.

comes larger, τ_1 becomes larger than τ_2. The exact ratio τ_1/τ_2 is $(\zeta + \sqrt{\zeta^2 - 1})/(\zeta - \sqrt{\zeta^2 - 1})$; for large ζ this is approximately equal to $4\zeta^2$ (within 1 per cent for $\zeta = 5$, and more accurately for larger ζ). Thus for $\zeta = 5$, τ_1 is about 100 times as large as τ_2. With this in mind, a glance at Eq. 4·42 shows that then the exponential in τ_2 plays a very small part in the response because it soon dies out and also because its amplitude is small to begin with. So, except for this small initial difference, the semilogarithmic plot of $(Q_2 - q)/(Q_2 - Q_1)$ should look like that of a first-order system of time constant τ_1; and τ_1 may be found from such a plot in exactly the same way as for a first-order system (Section 3·2). It is worth noting, too, that as ζ increases τ_1 does in fact approach equality with τ, the difference being approximately $\frac{1}{4}\zeta^{2}$; for instance, for $\zeta = 5$, τ_1 differs from τ by about 1 per cent.

Figure 4·11 gives the plot on semilogarithmic scales of the initial part of the response for a system of $\zeta = 5$. The straight line corresponding to e^{-t/τ_1} is extended back, as shown dotted, and its intersection with the ordinate axis is indicated in terms of q_{ext}. Notice the highly magnified scales. Assume, for example, that τ_1 were 1 second; then the initial difference of only 1 per cent, between the actual response and the related first-order response, has been more than halved at the end of the first hundredth of a sec-

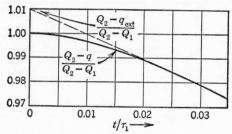

FIG. 4·11. Overdamped response to constant.

ond. Clearly, any usefulness of q_{ext} in solving the inverse problem depends directly on the accuracy with which the very first instants of the response are recorded.

Assuming that a reasonably good indication of q_{ext} is available from the response record and that τ_1 has been determined, the remainder of the inverse problem is solved by Fig. 4·12. The value of q_{ext} fixes a value of ζ, which in turn fixes a value of $\omega_n \tau_1$. With τ_1 known, this determines ω_n.

Turning to the inverse problem with the forced sinusoidal response, many possibilities are available. Perhaps the neatest solution is in terms of accurate phase measurements. If the frequency is found for which ϕ is exactly 90 degrees, this gives ω_n, regardless of ζ. Then by making further measurements near this frequency, the slope of the phase characteristic at $\beta = 1$ is found, and this is $1/\zeta$.

Another neat solution is possible if G and ϕ are both known at some one frequency. On Fig. 4·6 the two values serve as polar coordinates to locate a point. The parabola passing through the point fixes ζ, and reference of the point to the β-scale determines β (and therefore, since ω_f is known, ω_n).

Solutions by formula are possible based on any pair of values of G, of ϕ, or of ϕ and G. The combination just mentioned, G and ϕ known at the same frequency, is solved by the formulas,

$$\beta = \sqrt{1 - \frac{\cos \phi}{G}} \qquad (4\cdot43)$$

and

$$\zeta = \frac{-\sin \phi}{2G\sqrt{1 - (\cos \phi/G)}} = \frac{-\sin \phi}{2\beta G} \qquad (4\cdot44)$$

If ϕ is known at ω_{f1} and G at ω_{f2}, the formulas are somewhat more complicated. To express the result in compact form, it is helpful

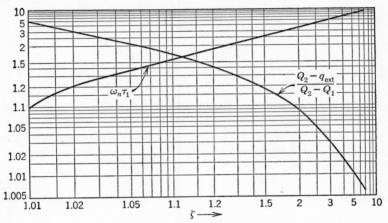

FIG. 4·12.   Inverse problem for overdamped systems.

to introduce a symbol σ for the ratio ω_{f1}/ω_{f2} of the two known frequencies. ω_n is given by

$$\beta_2{}^2 = \left(\frac{\omega_{f2}}{\omega_n}\right)^2$$

$$= \frac{1 + \tan^2 \phi - \sqrt{\left(2 - \sigma^2 - \frac{1}{\sigma^2}\right)\tan^2 \phi + \frac{1}{G^2}\left(1 + \sigma^2 \tan^2 \phi\right)}}{1 + \sigma^2 \tan^2 \phi}$$

$$(4\cdot45)$$

and ζ by

$$\zeta = -\frac{\tan \phi}{2\sigma\beta_2}\left(1 - \sigma^2\beta_2{}^2\right) \qquad (4\cdot46)$$

These are seen to reduce to Eqs. 4·43 and 4·44 if $\sigma = 1$.

Instead of knowing one value of ϕ and one of G, suppose ϕ is known at two frequencies; that is, ϕ_1 at ω_{f1}, and ϕ_2 at ω_{f2}. The formulas giving β_2 and ζ are

$$\beta_2{}^2 = \frac{(1/\sigma) \tan \phi_1 - \tan \phi_2}{\sigma \tan \phi_1 - \tan \phi_2} \qquad (4\cdot47)$$

$$\zeta = \frac{1}{2}\left(\frac{1}{\beta_2} - \beta_2\right) \tan \phi_2 \qquad (4\cdot48)$$

In case G is known to be G_1 at ω_{f1} and G_2 at ω_{f2}, the results are

$$\beta_2{}^4 = \frac{1}{\sigma^2} + \frac{(1/G_2{}^2) - (1/\sigma^2 G_1{}^2)}{1 - \sigma^2} \qquad (4\cdot49)$$

and

$$\zeta = \frac{1}{2\beta_2} \sqrt{\frac{1}{G_2{}^2} - (1 - \beta_2{}^2)^2} \qquad (4\cdot50)$$

Of the Eqs. 4·43 to 4·50 only the first two are easily and directly solved graphically by Fig. 4·6. All the others, however, can also be solved by this figure. The procedure is a "cut-and-try" attempt to pick out a parabola passing through the given values of ϕ or G at points having β-values or $\omega_f \tau$ values corresponding to the ratio of the two given frequencies, ω_{f1}/ω_{f2}.

4·7 Stability. From the definitions of ζ and ω_n given in Eqs. 4·3 and 4·4, the condition for real values of these parameters is that A_0 and A_2 should have the same sign. If this condition is satisfied, the stability of the system still depends on the sign of A_1. In fact, to obtain a complete and sure understanding of stability of second-order systems, it is desirable to go back to the coefficients, A_2, A_1, and A_0, and to write the auxiliary equation, instead of Eq. 4·6, as

$$A_2 r^2 + A_1 r + A_0 = 0 \qquad (4\cdot51)$$

The two roots are

$$r_1 = \frac{-A_1 + \sqrt{A_1{}^2 - 4A_0 A_2}}{2A_2}$$

$$\qquad (4\cdot52)$$

$$r_2 = \frac{-A_1 - \sqrt{A_1{}^2 - 4A_0 A_2}}{2A_2}$$

There is no loss of generality by assuming that A_2 is positive (i.e., that it has been made positive, if necessary, by multiplying through the equation by minus 1). In Table 4·2 the natures of the roots are indicated for the various possibilities of signs of A_1 and A_0, assuming positive A_2.

TABLE 4·2

Case	A_1	A_0	r_1	r_2
1	Positive	Positive	Real or complex (stable)	Real or complex (stable)
2	Positive	Negative	Positive real (unstable)	Negative real (stable)
3	Negative	Positive	Real or complex (unstable)	Real or complex (unstable)
4	Negative	Negative	Positive real (unstable)	Negative real (stable)

The words "stable" or "unstable" in parentheses denote whether the root contributes a stable or an unstable component to the transient response. The criterion for this, if the roots are real, is just the sign of the root, exactly as mentioned for first-order systems in Section 3·4; if the roots are complex, it is the sign of the real part of the root that matters, positive real part denoting instability. The borderline situation of zero real part, or pure imaginary roots, corresponds to unending oscillation, of amplitude fixed by initial conditions. This is illustrated by the case of $\zeta = 0$ in Fig. 4·1.

In this table cases 1 and 3, in which A_0 is positive like A_2, correspond to the real value of ω_n; case 1, with A_1 and therefore ζ being positive, gives completely stable transients, whereas case 3 has both components unstable. Cases 2 and 4 correspond to imaginary ω_n and ζ; so here the parameters τ_1 and τ_2 (cf. Eq. 4·41) are better. Cases 2 and 4 are illustrated by the neutron chain reactor discussed in Section 4·10.

Since case 1 is the only stable one, and since it corresponds to A_0, A_1, and A_2 all having the same sign, it follows that a *necessary and sufficient condition for stability of a second-order system is that all the coefficients have the same sign.* For higher-order systems this is necessary but not a sufficient condition.

The above discussion of the relation between the roots of the algebraic Eq. 4·51 and its coefficients could be carried out readily because of the explicit relations of Eqs. 4·52. In higher-order systems such explicit relations are either hopelessly complicated or

entirely unavailable.   Certain general rules, however, can still
be used on the coefficients to determine properties of the roots,
particularly the property which is crucial for stability, namely,
the sign of the real part.   To the study of the stability problem for
higher-order systems, a thorough understanding of the second-
order case is an indispensable prerequisite; for this case, though
simple enough to be solved explicitly, still illustrates the various
possibilities that go with complex roots of the auxiliary equation.

4·8   Electrical models.   Turning to the selection of a few
examples of second-order systems, the variety and number of

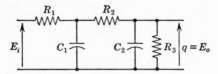

Fig. 4·13.   R-C electrical model.

available choices is very great.   Even within the limited domain
of electrical systems, there is a large variety.

The first electrical system to be discussed is similar to the double
resistance-capacitance circuit suggested in Fig. 3·10(a) as the
thermal circuit of the coated thermometer.   (Incidentally, the R-C
electrical circuits to be discussed here may profitably be thought
of with regard to hydraulic, as well as thermal, analogues.)   The
circuit is shown in Fig. 4·13.   Slight additional generality over the
circuit of Fig. 3·10(a) is obtained by including the final resistance,
R_3.   If q is taken as the output voltage E_0, the system satisfies a
standard equation, Eq. 4·5, with the following definitions:

$$q_f = \frac{E_i}{1 + \dfrac{R_1 + R_2}{R_3}} \tag{4.53}$$

$$\omega_n = \sqrt{\frac{1 + \dfrac{R_1 + R_2}{R_3}}{C_1 R_1 C_2 R_2}} \tag{4.54}$$

$$\zeta = \frac{C_1 R_1 \left(1 + \dfrac{R_2}{R_3}\right) + C_2 R_2 + C_2 R_1}{2\sqrt{C_1 R_1 C_2 R_2 \left(1 + \dfrac{R_1 + R_2}{R_3}\right)}} \tag{4.55}$$

In these formulas the effects of R_3 are evident, and in particular it is clear what happens to the expressions for ζ, ω_n, and q_f if the final resistance R_3 becomes infinite.

A somewhat more complicated resistance-capacitance circuit is that of one stage of the usual design of resistance-coupled amplifier. This is shown, with the electronic tube replaced by its equivalent of a generator and a series resistance R_p, in Fig. 4·14. The capacitance C_p is the effective plate-to-ground capacitance, including plate-to-cathode capacitance inside the tube; similarly, C_g represents grid-to-ground capacitance in the input circuit of the following tube, including grid-to-cathode capacitance inside that tube.

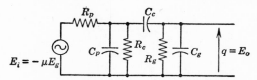

FIG. 4·14.   Equivalent circuit of amplifier.

R_c is the coupling resistance, often called plate load resistance. C_c is the coupling capacitance, and R_g is the grid resistance. The generator voltage E_i is $-\mu E_g$, where μ is the amplification factor of the tube and E_g is the voltage applied between its cathode and grid.

The differential equation of this circuit may be put in the standard form by defining

$$q_f = \frac{C_c R_g R_c}{R_p + R_c} \dot{E}_i \qquad (4 \cdot 56)$$

$$\omega_n = \frac{1}{\sqrt{\dfrac{C_c C_g R_g R_p R_c}{R_p + R_c}\left(1 + \dfrac{C_p}{C_c} + \dfrac{C_p}{C_g}\right)}} \qquad (4 \cdot 57)$$

$$\zeta = \frac{(C_c + C_g)R_g + (C_c + C_p)\dfrac{R_p R_c}{R_p + R_c}}{2\sqrt{\dfrac{C_c C_g R_g R_p R_c}{R_p + R_c}\left(1 + \dfrac{C_p}{C_c} + \dfrac{C_p}{C_g}\right)}} \qquad (4 \cdot 58)$$

A rather remarkable simplification may be achieved by introducing two resistances R_H and R_L, defined by

$$R_L = \left(1 + \frac{C_g}{C_c}\right) R_g + \left(1 + \frac{C_p}{C_c}\right) \frac{R_p R_c}{R_p + R_c} \qquad (4\cdot59)$$

$$R_H = \frac{\left(1 + \frac{C_p}{C_c} + \frac{C_p}{C_g}\right) \dfrac{R_g R_p R_c}{R_p + R_c}}{\left(1 + \dfrac{C_g}{C_c}\right) R_g + \left(1 + \dfrac{C_p}{C_c}\right) \dfrac{R_p R_c}{R_p + R_c}} \qquad (4\cdot60)$$

In terms of these the differential equation is

$$C_c C_g R_L R_H \ddot{q} + C_c R_L \dot{q} + q = q_f \qquad (4\cdot61)$$

and consequently

$$\omega_n = \frac{1}{\sqrt{C_c C_g R_L R_H}} \qquad (4\cdot62)$$

and

$$\zeta = \frac{1}{2} \sqrt{\frac{C_c R_L}{C_g R_H}} \qquad (4\cdot63)$$

Here everything is expressed in terms of two time constants, $C_c R_L$ and $C_g R_H$. Since $C_c R_L$ is the coefficient of $\dot{q}$ in Eq. 4·61, it may be called τ. For $C_g R_H$ the symbol τ_H is adopted. Thus this example leads to a new pair of parameters:

$$\tau = \frac{A_1}{A_0}$$
$$\tau_H = \frac{A_2}{A_1} \qquad (4\cdot64)$$

In passing it may be noted that the exponential $e^{-\zeta \omega_n t}$ appearing first in Eq. 4·9 is $e^{-t/2\tau_H}$. Principal interest here, however, is in the forced sinusoidal response. In the usual practical application of the amplifier, E_i may be considered to be proportional to the quantity to be duplicated, q_d. So $\mathbf{G}$ will be specified in terms of q and E_i. The ratio $q_a/q_{fa} = 1/(1 - \omega_f^2 \tau \tau_H + j\omega_f \tau)$; and since $q_{fa} = [C_c R_g R_c/(R_p + R_c)](j\omega_f E_{ia})$, the gain $\mathbf{G} = q_a/E_{ia}$ may be written

$$\mathbf{G} = G_1 \frac{j\omega_f \tau}{1 - \omega_f^2 \tau \tau_H + j\omega_f \tau} = \frac{G_1}{1 + j\left(\omega_f \tau_H - \dfrac{1}{\omega_f \tau}\right)} \qquad (4\cdot65)$$

where

$$G_1 = \frac{C_c R_g R_c}{\tau(R_p + R_c)} = \frac{R_g R_c}{R_L(R_p + R_c)} \tag{4.66}$$

is the gain at mid-frequency; that is, at the frequency for which $\omega_f \tau_H = 1/\omega_f \tau$, which in terms of ω_n corresponds to $\beta = 1$. Put in terms of ζ and ω_n, Eq. 4·65 is

$$G = \frac{G_1}{1 + j\dfrac{\beta - (1/\beta)}{2\zeta}} \tag{4.67}$$

The gain and phase characteristics are given by

$$G = \frac{G_1}{\sqrt{1 + \left(\omega_f \tau_H - \dfrac{1}{\omega_f \tau}\right)^2}} = \frac{G_1}{\sqrt{1 + \left[\dfrac{\beta - (1/\beta)}{2\zeta}\right]^2}} \tag{4.68}$$

$$\phi = -\tan^{-1}\left(\omega_f \tau_H - \frac{1}{\omega_f \tau}\right) = -\tan^{-1}\left[\frac{\beta - (1/\beta)}{2\zeta}\right] \tag{4.69}$$

The significance of the subscripts H and L on R_H and R_L and on τ_H may now be seen from Eq. 4·65. At high frequencies only τ_H will have an appreciable effect; and at low frequencies only τ. Thus τ_H might be called the high-frequency time constant, and τ the low-frequency time constant.

In practice, the band width of the amplifier and its gain at mid-frequency, G_1, are the important considerations. Band width is usually defined as the frequency range from $G = 1/\sqrt{2}$ at low frequencies to $G = 1/\sqrt{2}$ at high frequencies. From Eq. 4·68 these two β-values, β_L and β_H, are seen to be $-\zeta + \sqrt{\zeta^2 + 1}$ and $\zeta + \sqrt{\zeta^2 + 1}$; so their ratio, which is the band width, is

$$\frac{\beta_H}{\beta_L} = \frac{\zeta + \sqrt{\zeta^2 + 1}}{-\zeta + \sqrt{\zeta^2 + 1}} \tag{4.70}$$

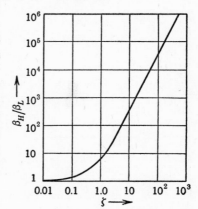

Fig. 4·15.　Effect of damping on band width.

Figure 4·15 gives a plot of this relation, which for $\zeta > 5$ is approximately $\beta_H/\beta_L = 4\zeta^2$.

For example, an audio amplifier having a band width from 40 to 10,000 cycles per second would have $\beta_H/\beta_L = 250$ and $\zeta = 7.9$. In Fig. 4·16 G is plotted against β for several values of ζ. The values of ζ less than 1 in these two figures (4·15 and 4·16) do not,

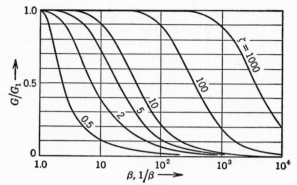

Fig. 4·16.   Gain characteristics of amplifier and analogues.

of course, refer to the amplifier circuit of Fig. 4·14, because ζ cannot be less than 1 for this circuit.

An analogous circuit, for which ζ can have any value from zero to infinity, is shown in Fig. 4·17. $G = q_a/E_{ia}$ for this circuit is

$$G = \frac{j\omega_f CR}{1 - \omega_f^2 LC + j\omega_f CR} = \frac{1}{1 + j\left(\omega_f \dfrac{L}{R} - \dfrac{1}{\omega_f CR}\right)} \qquad (4\cdot71)$$

Comparing this with Eq. 4·68, it is seen that $\tau_H = L/R$, $\tau = CR$, $\omega_n = 1/\sqrt{LC}$, and $\zeta = R/2\sqrt{L/C}$.

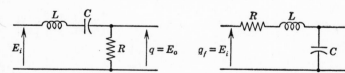
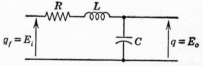

Fig. 4·17.   Analogue of amplifier.   Fig. 4·18. R-L-C electrical model.

These same definitions for ζ and ω_n apply to the circuit of Fig. 4·18, but in this case the input voltage itself, rather than its derivative, is taken as q_f. This circuit is thus a direct analogue of the circuit of Fig. 4·13.

As a final example of an electrical second-order system, a control circuit for a lifting electromagnet, Fig. 4·19, will be considered. R_0 and L_0 refer to the magnet itself; the other elements make up the control circuit. This is an example illustrating the definition of q to suit the practical interest in the problem. The quantity of interest is the current i in the magnet, for it determines the holding power of the magnet. So, even though the resistance R_0 is not accessible separately from the inductance L_0, one can still deal with $q = R_0 i = E_o$ as a measure of i and as a convenient quantity in the analysis.

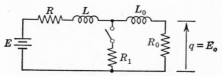

FIG. 4·19.   Magnet control circuit.

When the magnet is holding a load, the switch is open and a maximum current flows in the magnet. When the switch is closed, the current through the magnet decreases, causing the magnet to release its hold.

With the switch closed, the circuit satisfies the standard form of equation, with the following definitions:

$$q_f = \frac{R_1 R_0}{R_1 R + R_0 R + R_1 R_0} E \tag{4·72}$$

$$\omega_n = \sqrt{\frac{R_1 R + R_0 R + R_1 R_0}{L L_0}} \tag{4·73}$$

$$\zeta = \frac{R_1 L_0 + R_0 L + R_1 L + R L_0}{2 \sqrt{L L_0 (R_1 R + R_0 R + R_1 R_0)}} \tag{4·74}$$

In Eq. 4·72 the voltage E can depend in any fashion on time, although for the present problem it is shown as a constant battery voltage in Fig. 4·19; for this constant value of q_f the symbol will, as usual, be Q_2. With the further definitions, $\sigma = (R_1 R + R_0 R + R_1 R_0)/(R_1 R + R_1 R_0)$ and $\omega_0 = R_0/L_0$, it can be shown that the act of closing the switch, with the steady current $E/(R + R_0)$ flowing in the magnet, places on the system the following initial conditions:

$$Q_1 = \sigma Q_2$$
$$\dot{Q}_1 = -\omega_0 \sigma Q_2 \tag{4.75}$$

Under these conditions the response is given by

$$\frac{q}{Q_2} = 1 + e^{-\zeta\omega_n t}\left[(\sigma - 1)\cosh \omega t + \frac{\zeta\omega_n(\sigma - 1) - \omega_0\sigma}{\omega}\sinh \omega t\right] \tag{4.76}$$

The act of closing the switch, which introduces into the circuit the additional resistance R_1, is really an act of parametric forcing. Since the circuit is undisturbed after $t = 0$, however, it may be treated as a system having constant coefficients. The effect of closing the switch shows in the initial value of the slope, which changes abruptly at $t = 0$ from zero to the value given in Eq. 4.75. The physical basis for this change of slope is the inability of the current through L and L_0 to change instantaneously when the switch is closed. Hence, just after $t = 0$, there is zero current in R_1 and zero voltage across it. Therefore $L_0(di/dt) = (L_0/R_0)\dot{Q}_1$ must be equal and opposite to Q_1.

4.9 Liquid level control. The automatic control of fluid level, in a system such as is shown in Fig. 4.20, will be considered as a further example of a second-order system. The depth q of the

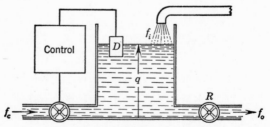

FIG. 4.20. Liquid level control.

liquid in a tank is to be held at a specified value Q_2 in spite of fluctuations in the input flow f_i. There is an output flow f_o through a fixed resistance R, so that $f_o = q/R$. The dimensions of f_o and f_i are volume per unit time. The fluid level is sensed by the device

D, which actuates the control. Regulation is accomplished by having the control operate a valve, establishing a control flow f_c. The values of q and f_c may be related in various ways, generally speaking, but the particular type of control to be considered here is the one known as integrating control, in which f_c is proportional to the time integral of the error, $q - Q_2$. That is, assuming f_c is positive when it represents flow into the tank,

$$f_c = -\int V(q - Q_2)\, dt \qquad (4\cdot77)$$

where V is a constant, representing the valve sensitivity.

If A represents the cross-sectional area of the tank, equating change of liquid volume in the tank to sum of input and output flow gives

$$A\dot{q} = f_c + f_i - f_o$$

Differentiating this equation, and putting $\dot{q}/R$ for f_o and $-V(q - Q_2)$ for f_c, one obtains a second-order differential equation which may be put in the standard form by defining $q_f = Q_2 + \dot{f}_i/V$, $\omega_n = \sqrt{V/A}$, and $\zeta = 1/(2R\sqrt{VA})$.

It is interesting to note from the definition of ζ that damping of the system is the result of having a finite value of R; that is, if R were made infinite so as to shut off completely the flow f_o, the system would have no damping and would oscillate indefinitely.

The response of the system to any given forcing function may now be calculated in the standard fashion. Suppose, for instance, that the system is in equilibrium with $q = Q_2$ under a steady flow, $f_i = 2F$, up to time zero; and that the flow is then cut off in sinusoidal fashion—that is, $f_i = F(1 + \cos \omega_f t)$ from $t = 0$ to $t = \pi/\omega_f$, after which $f_i = 0$. Then $q_f = Q_2 + (-F\omega_f/V) \sin \omega_f t$, $q_r = Q_2 + (-GF\omega_f/V) \sin (\omega_f t + \phi)$, $Q_i = (GF\omega_f/V) \sin \phi$, and $\dot{Q}_i = (GF\omega_f^2/V) \cos \phi$; and the response for $0 < t < \pi/\omega_f$ is

$$\frac{q - Q_2}{GF\omega_f/V} = e^{-\zeta\omega_n t}$$

$$\times \left[\sin \phi \cos \omega t + \frac{\omega_f \cos \phi + \zeta\omega_n \sin \phi}{\omega} \sin \omega t \right] - \sin (\omega_f t + \phi)$$

$$(4\cdot78)$$

The response for $t > \pi/\omega_f$ would be derived by putting $q_f = q_r = Q_2$ and using in Eq. 4·20 for Q_1 and $\dot{Q}_1$ the values obtained from

Eq. 4·78 by setting $t = \pi/\omega_f$. These initial values, as ω_f becomes larger and larger, corresponding to faster and faster shutting off of the flow, approach the limiting values, $Q_1 = Q_2$ and $\dot{Q}_1 = -(2F/V)\omega_n^2$. So in this limiting case the response is

$$\frac{q - Q_2}{2F\omega_n/V} = -\frac{e^{-\zeta\omega_n t}}{\sqrt{1 - \zeta^2}} \sin \omega t \qquad (4\cdot79)$$

The value of $\dot{Q}_1 = -(2F/V)\omega_n^2$, compared with Eq. 4·39, shows that the system is subject to an impulse forcing, of impulse $I = -2F/V$. The fact that the shape of $\dot{f}_i$ is sinusoidal, and not square pulse, makes no difference in the limit. If f_i changed from $2F$ to 0 on a straight line, then $\dot{f}_i$ would be a square pulse. But in the limit of infinitely rapid change of f_i, the sinusoidal change and the straight-line change have the same effect—that of an impulse.

4·10 Nuclear chain reactor. The chain reactor, widely known simply as a "pile," is a very interesting physical system. Considered in strict detail, it is so complex as to demand some of the most advanced mathematical analysis. On the other hand, many of its features can be understood on the basis of simplifying assumptions. The purpose here is to treat it as a lumped second-order system. The assumptions required to reduce it to a simple system involve some rather crude physical approximations, but this treatment nevertheless will reveal essential aspects of reactor response. The reactor is discussed further in Sections 6·6 and 9·4.

For present purposes, then, the reactor is considered to be an arrangement of materials in which neutrons are released by the fission of uranium or plutonium nuclei. The neutrons move about in the materials until they again encounter a uranium or plutonium nucleus and cause it to undergo fission, which results in the further release of neutrons. This cycle of events repeats itself indefinitely, establishing a chain of fission reactions which gives the device its name.

The quantity of most interest in this process is the density of neutrons—i.e., the number of neutrons per unit of reactor volume. This quantity is therefore chosen as q. If the density of fissionable nuclei is assumed to remain constant, the number of fissions per second is evidently proportional to q. Of course the density of fissionable nuclei does not remain strictly constant, but the rate at which these nuclei are used up is relatively so slow that it is a useful approximation to consider their number as fixed. If the fission rate is proportional to q, and if further the number of neutrons released per fission is a constant, then clearly $\dot{q}$ is proportional to q, and the reactor is a first-order system. But it is just this question of number of neutrons per fission that causes the complication, although it is more a question of "when?" than of "how many?"

Considering fission of a nucleus as a tiny explosion, one can speak of fission fragments. Now the great majority of fissions result in the release of neutrons coincident with the explosion—that is, neutrons are detected as soon as any other fragments. In a small fraction of the fissions, however, fragments are formed which emit neutrons after appreciable time has passed. Thus there are **prompt neutrons** and a small number of **delayed neutrons.** These few delayed neutrons, because their delay is a relatively long time, have a great effect on response.

Let $\rho_p q$ be the rate at which the neutrons would increase if all the neutrons were prompt. The true rate of increase, so far as the term directly proportional to q is concerned, will be less than this —it will be $(\rho_p - \rho_d)q$, where $\rho_d q$ represents the rate of formation of fragments which emit delayed neutrons. Let f represent the density of such fragments, and let $\rho_e f$ be the rate of emission of delayed neutrons from these fragments. (This is equivalent to assuming the emitting fragments to behave as a single radioactive material of decay rate ρ_e. This is an approximation, since actually there are some half-dozen different kinds of emitting fragments, each with its own decay rate.) The two quantities q and f then satisfy the pair of equations

$$\dot{q} = (\rho_p - \rho_d)q + \rho_e f + s \qquad (4 \cdot 80)$$

$$\dot{f} = -\rho_e f + \rho_d q \qquad (4 \cdot 81)$$

In Eq. 4·80 s represents a source of neutrons, other than the fission process. This might be an artificial source, such as a radium-beryllium source; or it might represent neutrons released by cosmic rays or by spontaneous fission—in short, any source of neutrons not dependent on q, the neutron density itself. s has the dimensions of neutrons per unit volume per unit time.

Here in Eqs. 4·80 and 4·81 is an example of the situation, mentioned in a final paragraph of Chapter 2, in which consideration of an nth-order system leads to n first-order equations instead of a single nth-order equation. Generally speaking, it is profitable to deal with the n equations if one is interested in more than one quantity. Here, for instance, if one wanted to investigate the time dependence of f as well as of q, the advantage would lie in dealing with the two Eqs. 4·80 and 4·81. Since at present q alone is to be discussed, the two equations will be combined to a single second-order equation.

This can be done as follows: Equation 4·80 may be considered an equation giving f in terms of q and $\dot{q}$. Differentiation of Eq. 4·80 yields an equation giving $\dot{f}$ in terms of $\dot{q}$ and $\ddot{q}$. Substituting these two expressions for f and for $\dot{f}$ into Eq. 4·80 gives the desired second-order equation,

$$ -\frac{\ddot{q}}{\rho_p \rho_e} - \frac{\rho_e + \rho_d - \rho_p}{\rho_p \rho_e} \dot{q} + q = -\frac{s}{\rho_p} - \frac{\dot{s}}{\rho_p \rho_e} \qquad (4\cdot82) $$

In this equation the direct forcing consists of the terms in s and $\dot{s}$. However, this system, like the magnet control circuit of Fig. 4·19, is actually subject also to parametric forcing by the changing of ρ_p. ρ_e and ρ_d can be treated always as positive constants, but ρ_p is a variable which can take on positive and negative values. ρ_p is a function of many factors, but for purposes of controlling the reactor the common practice is to vary ρ_p by varying the amount of some neutron-absorbing material in the reactor.

The derivation of Eq. 4·82 was on the basis that $\rho_p = $ constant. Considering that ρ_p varies, the more general equation is

$$ -\frac{\ddot{q}}{\rho_p \rho_e} - \frac{\rho_e + \rho_d - \rho_p}{\rho_p \rho_e} \dot{q} + \left(1 + \frac{\dot{\rho}_p}{\rho_p \rho_e}\right) q = -\frac{s}{\rho_p} - \frac{\dot{s}}{\rho_p \rho_e} \qquad (4\cdot83) $$

The case of parametric forcing for a sudden change in ρ_p can be treated, as for the magnet control circuit, by assuming fixed parameters after $t = 0$. It is then a simple second-order problem, though care must be taken in determining the initial conditions. An example is given below.

As for the stability implication of Eq. 4·82, the signs of the coefficients will be the same if ρ_p is negative, but they will differ if ρ_p is positive. Hence the response is unstable for positive ρ_p. This is a problem, therefore, in which it is convenient to use τ_1 and τ_2

as parameters. Comparing Eq. 4·41 with Eq. 4·82, it follows that

$$\frac{2}{\tau_1} = (\rho_e + \rho_d - \rho_p) - \sqrt{(\rho_e + \rho_d - \rho_p)^2 + 4\rho_p\rho_e}$$

$$\frac{2}{\tau_2} = (\rho_e + \rho_d - \rho_p) + \sqrt{(\rho_e + \rho_d - \rho_p)^2 + 4\rho_p\rho_e} \qquad (4·84)$$

For the differential equation in the form of Eq. 4·41, the formula for the complete response, corresponding to Eq. 4·22 in terms of ζ and ω_n, is

$$q = \frac{(\tau_1 Q_i + \tau_1\tau_2\dot{Q}_i)e^{-t/\tau_1} - (\tau_2 Q_i + \tau_1\tau_2\dot{Q}_i)e^{-t/\tau_2}}{\tau_1 - \tau_2} + q_r \quad (4·85)$$

This formula is convenient in stable or unstable equations, so long as the roots of the auxiliary equation are real. This condition is satisfied for the reactor, as inspection of Eq. 4·84 will show.

Equation 4·82 shows that under equilibrium conditions q will have the constant value $-s/\rho_p$. This means, since s is positive, that such an equilibrium value of q would be positive (and so physically significant) only if ρ_p were negative—that is, only in a stable system.

Consider now the problem of calculating the response to a change in ρ_p from some negative value, say $-\rho_{p1}$, to some positive value, ρ_{p2}, assuming s equal to a constant, S_0.

To determine the initial conditions it is necessary to consider the two Eqs. 4·80 and 4·81 rather than the single Eq. 4·82. Up until $t = 0$, $\dot{q}$ and $\dot{f}$ are zero; and $q = Q_1 = S_0/\rho_{p1}$, and $f = F_1 = (\rho_d/\rho_e)Q_1$. The instantaneous change of ρ_p from $-\rho_{p1}$ to ρ_{p2}, put into Eq. 4·80, gives

$$\dot{Q}_1 = (\rho_{p2} - \rho_d)Q_1 + \rho_d Q_1 + S_0 = \rho_{p2}Q_1 + S_0$$

Thus the initial conditions are

$$Q_1 = \frac{S_0}{\rho_{p1}}$$

$$\dot{Q}_1 = (\rho_{p2} + \rho_{p1})Q_1 = \left(1 + \frac{\rho_{p2}}{\rho_{p1}}\right)S_0 \qquad (4·86)$$

The problem of determining these initial conditions should be carefully compared with the same problem in regard to the magnet control circuit of Fig. 4·19. In both instances the effect of the parameter change is to dictate initial conditions, which cannot be deduced from the second-order differential equation itself but which must be deduced from a more detailed physical picture of the system, such as is given by the two Eqs. 4·80 and 4·81 for the

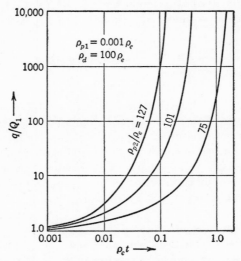

Fig. 4·21.   Reactor response to change in prompt multiplication.

reactor, and for the magnet control circuit, by considering the current in R_1 as well as in R_0.

The response is given by Eq. 4·85, with $q_r = -(S_0/\rho_{p2})$, $Q_i = (S_0/\rho_{p1}) + (S_0/\rho_{p2})$ and $\dot{Q}_i = \dot{Q}_1$. τ_1 and τ_2 are given by Eq. 4·84, with $\rho_p = \rho_{p2}$. τ_1 is negative, and therefore e^{-t/τ_1} is a rising exponential, representing the instability of the system. The shape of the response is shown in Fig. 4·21, for three different values of ρ_{p2}.

4·11 Current galvanometer. The ordinary current galvanometer of the wall-mounting type furnishes a good laboratory example of a second-order system. The suspension is a torsion pendulum to which known torques may be applied by establishing known currents in the coil; then the standard Eq. 4·5 applies, with q measuring the angular deflection of the coil and q_f the current i in the coil. Thus $q_f = (k/S)i$, where S is torsional stiffness (torque u per unit angle q) and k is torque u per unit current i; and the equation is

$$\frac{I}{S}\ddot{q} + \frac{R_m}{S}\dot{q} + q = \frac{k}{S}i \qquad (4\cdot87)$$

So ω_n is $\sqrt{S/I}$, and ζ is $R_m/2\sqrt{SI}$, where I is the moment of inertia of the coil and R_m is the torsional damping or resistance.

Step functions are easily applied, and other forcing, such as sinusoidal or exponential, may be obtained by the relatively easy device of obtaining corresponding currents. A galvanometer with an ω_n of the order of 1 radian per second responds slowly enough so that the response may be followed visually and timed with a stop watch.

The constant k is equal to BLa, where B is magnetic flux density in the gap in which the coil turns, L is the total length of coil wire cutting the flux, and a is the average radius of the coil. k was mentioned above as torque per unit current; it is also electromotive force E per unit of angular velocity $\dot{q}$. That is, k enters the two equations

$$E = k\dot{q} \qquad (4\cdot88)$$

$$u = ki \qquad (4\cdot89)$$

Now, if one considers input voltage E_i rather than input current i, the fact is that only the difference $E_i - E$ is available to force current through the coil. The coil actually has electrical resistance R and inductance L. However, since L is small and since including it makes the galvanometer a third-order system, it will be neglected for present purposes. Then the relation between E_i, E, and i is

$$E_i - E = iR \qquad (4\cdot90)$$

By means of the three Eqs. 4·88, 4·89, and 4·90, Eq. 4·87 may be expressed in different variables. For instance, from Eqs. 4·88 and 4·90 it follows that $i = (E_i - k\dot{q})/R$. Putting this into Eq. 4·87 gives

$$\frac{I}{S}\ddot{q} + \frac{R_m + (k^2/R)}{S}\dot{q} + q = \frac{k}{RS}E_i \qquad (4\cdot91)$$

Comparison of Eqs. 4·87 and 4·91 shows a difference in the damping term, indicating that under voltage forcing the mechanical system shows an effective damping which is greater by the term k^2/R than the damping under current forcing. But what does this mean? If a voltage is applied to the galvanometer, there is also a current, and vice versa. So, what is the difference between Eqs. 4·87 and 4·91? Perhaps an example will help to clarify the difference. Suppose a certain constant current is flowing up to $t = 0$, when the current is interrupted and the coil terminals are left open-circuit. For convenience call this the open-circuit step function. On the other hand, suppose that, when the current is interrupted at $t = 0$, the coil terminals are left short-circuited together. Call this the short-circuit step function. Which of the Eqs. 4·87 and 4·91 applies in these cases?

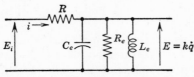

FIG. 4·22. Equivalent circuit of galvanometer.

It is clear that, in the open-circuit forcing, what one does is to establish, for $t > 0$, a known current, namely zero current; and that, in the short-circuit forcing, it is the voltage which is held at a known value, namely zero. Hence, Eq. 4·87 applies to the open-circuit step function and Eq. 4·91 to the short-circuit step function. This is quite reasonable when one considers that the term k^2/R must account for the extra energy dissipated electrically in R, by the current that flows in the short circuit. In general, if the time dependence of the voltage E_i is known, Eq. 4·91 applies; and, if the current i is known, Eq. 4·87 applies.

To establish the relation between E and i, it is only necessary to substitute E for q from Eq. 4·88 into Eq. 4·87, obtaining

$$i = \frac{I}{k^2}\dot{E} + \frac{R_m}{k^2}E + \frac{S}{k^2}\int E\,dt \qquad (4\cdot92)$$

This may be recognized at once as the equation of an electrical circuit having capacitance, resistance, and inductance in parallel, as in Fig. 4·22, since the terms on the right represent the currents through C_e, R_e, and L_e, respectively. Hence, electrically speaking, the circuit of Fig. 4·22 is completely equivalent to the actual galvanometer, provided the elements in parallel have the values

$$C_e = \frac{I}{k^2}$$

$$R_e = \frac{k^2}{R_m} \qquad (4\cdot93)$$

$$L_e = \frac{k^2}{S}$$

The open-circuit and short-circuit step functions mentioned above provide an interesting exercise in the inverse problem. Equations 4·87 and 4·91 show that the two forcings would yield the same ω_n but different ζ's. Let ζ_0 and ζ_s denote the values obtained in the open-circuit and short-circuit cases, respectively. Assume that, in addition to ω_n, ζ_s, and ζ_0, one knows R and the direct-current sensitivity, $\sigma = q/i_{dc}$. Both R and σ are usually given as manufacturer's specifications.

Since $\zeta_s = [R_m + (k^2/R)]/2\sqrt{IS}$ and $\zeta_0 = R_m/2\sqrt{IS}$, and considering that $\sigma = q/i_{dc} = k/S$,

$$\zeta_s - \zeta_0 = \frac{\sigma^2 \omega_n}{2R} S \qquad (4\cdot94)$$

$$\frac{\zeta_s}{\zeta_0} = 1 + \frac{\sigma^2 S^2}{R R_m} \qquad (4\cdot95)$$

Solving Eq. 4·94 for S,

$$S = \frac{2R(\zeta_s - \zeta_0)}{\sigma^2 \omega_n} \qquad (4\cdot96)$$

and Eq. 4·95 for R_m,

$$R_m = \frac{\sigma^2 S^2 \zeta_0}{R(\zeta_s - \zeta_0)} \qquad (4\cdot97)$$

In addition,

$$k = \sigma S \qquad (4\cdot98)$$

and

$$I = \frac{S}{\omega_n^2} \qquad (4\cdot99)$$

Thus Eqs. 4·96 to 4·99 solve what might be called the complete inverse problem for the galvanometer, giving the four elements k, I, S, and R_m needed to specify the equivalent circuit of Fig. 4·22 and Eqs. 4·93.

4·12   U-tube.   As a final example of a second-order physical system, a liquid-filled U-tube, such as is used for manometers, will be considered.   The tube may be regarded as a hydraulic model and is particularly interesting in relation to the first-order hydraulic systems discussed in Chapter 3.

Figure 4·23 shows a diagram of the tube and a pneumatic forcing apparatus to provide sinusoidal forcing.   The dotted line across the tube indicates the equilibrium position of the fluid column.   The displacement of the fluid from this position is the re-

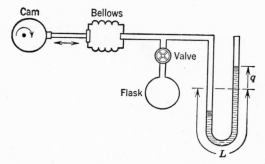

FIG. 4·23.   U-tube and forcing apparatus.

sponse q. L is the total length of the fluid column.   Otherwise the notation is as in Section 3·6.

The differential equation of the tube may be obtained by adding the pressures which act on the fluid column and equating the sum to the forcing pressure.   Thus

$$LD\ddot{q} + AR\dot{q} + 2gDq = p \qquad (4·100)$$

where the first term on the left represents the pressure due to acceleration of the fluid against its inertia, the second represents resistance of the tube, and the third represents the hydrostatic pressure of the displaced length, $2q$.   Equation 4·100 becomes the standard form of Eq. 4·5, with $q_f = p/2gD$, $\zeta = AR/D\sqrt{8gL}$, and $\omega_n = \sqrt{2g/L}$.   In passing, it is interesting to note that this value of ω_n is the same as for a simple pendulum of length $L/2$.

ζ and ω_n may be found experimentally from the step-function response or from the sinusoidal response, using the forcing apparatus indicated in Fig. 4·23.   This gives a good exercise in the methods discussed in Section 4·6.   The experimentally found values may be compared with values calculated from the dimensions of the tube and properties of the liquid. With a tube of 3.5-millimeter internal diameter and a water column of total length $L = 112$ centimeters, calculated values are $\zeta = 0.30$ and $\omega_n = 4.2$ radians per second, and observed values of $\zeta = 0.32$ and $\omega_n = 3.9$ radians per second were obtained. The observations were made visually, with stop-watch timing. With this procedure and the above value of L, the accuracy was not very good because things happened too fast. If L could be made three or four times as large, somewhat better agreement could be expected.

With a slightly larger and shorter tube ($d = 4.3$ millimeters, $L = 72$ centimeters) filled with mercury instead of water, calculated values of $\zeta = 0.018$ and $\omega_n = 5.25$ radians per second and observed values of $\zeta = 0.2$ and $\omega_n = 5.35$ radians per second were obtained. The large discrepancy in ζ is due to an increase in effective R because of turbulence, as discussed in Section 3·6. The much larger density of mercury makes the Reynolds number large, giving turbulence at a correspondingly lower speed.

CHAPTER

5

Sinusoidal Forcing of Linear Systems

5·1 Differential equation and gain ratio. The discussion of first-order and second-order systems in the preceding chapters has illustrated the close relation between the differential equation of a linear system and its gain ratio for sinusoidal forcing. The purpose here is to examine this relation on a more general basis, and in particular to extend it to nth-order linear systems.

The relation can be brought out more clearly by adopting a different convention for indicating differentiation. Let multiplication by p denote differentiation.[1] Then the standard forms of Eqs. 3·1 and 4·5 become

$$(\tau p + 1)q = q_f \tag{5·1}$$

and

$$\left(\frac{p^2}{\omega_n{}^2} + \frac{2\zeta p}{\omega_n} + 1\right)q = q_f \tag{5·2}$$

In general, for an nth-order system the equation would be

$$D(p)q = q_f \tag{5·3}$$

where $D(p)$ is a polynomial of the nth degree in p. Moreover,

$$D(r) = 0 \tag{5·4}$$

is the auxiliary Eq. 2·9. And finally, the gain ratio $\mathbf{G}$ is given by

$$\mathbf{G}(\omega_f) = \frac{1}{D(j\omega_f)} \tag{5·5}$$

---

[1] This notation should be used carefully, with a clear understanding that it is simply a convenient way of writing derivatives. For a discussion of the use of symbols as "operators," see Jeffreys and Jeffreys, *Methods of Mathematical Physics*, Cambridge University Press, 1946, Chapter **7**.

Thus this one polynomial form, represented by D, plays three roles in the response of physical systems.   Taken as a polynomial in the differential operator p, it expresses the differential equation in the form of Eq. 5·3; in the second place, with the algebraic number r as its variable, it forms the auxiliary Eq. 5·4; and its third role is to form the gain ratio, according to Eq. 5·5.

According to the discussion in Section 2·4, the error of a system is defined as $q - q_d$, where the reference quantity q_d, the quantity to be duplicated, may or may not be the same as q_f.   Hence Eqs. 5·3 and 5·5 are not sufficiently general in form to cover all relations between q and q_d.   The required generalization may be obtained as follows.   Let $N(p)$ also be a polynomial in p.   Then D and N are two polynomial forms—D being of the nth degree and N of degree n or less.   (In what follows, it is simplest to think of N as being of the nth degree; polynomials of lower degree can always be obtained by assigning zero values to the proper parameters of N.   Note that the total number of parameters is now $2n$, n for D and n for N.)   Also, let q_n denote a noise quantity—its significance will be explained below.   Now the differential equation

$$D(p) \cdot q = N(p) \cdot q_d + q_n \qquad (5 \cdot 6)$$

is a sufficiently general relationship between q and q_d to cover cases of practical interest—for example, the circuit of Fig. 2·1 or the liquid level control of Fig. 4·20.   The noise q_n might be defined by saying that it is any quantity to which the response, according to the criterion of ideal response, should be zero.   That is, noise is any undesired, disturbing forcing.   Examples of q_n are u/S in Eq. 3·26 and $\dot{f}_i/V$ in the expression for q_f in Section 4·9.   Although q_n is very important, as will become evident in Chapters 7 and 8, for the present discussion it may be neglected (considered equal to zero), and the differential equation taken as

$$D(p) \cdot q = N(p) \cdot q_d \qquad (5 \cdot 7)$$

With this relation between q and q_d the gain ratio for sinusoidal forcing is

$$\mathbf{G}(\omega_f) = \frac{N(j\omega_f)}{D(j\omega_f)} \qquad (5 \cdot 8)$$

Notice, however, that for Eq. 5·7 the auxiliary equation is still Eq. 5·4.   The polynomial N does not enter into the auxiliary equation and so is of no significance in the transient response q_t.

5·2   The sinusoidal problem.   Many aspects of technology, particularly of electrical engineering, are concerned with physical systems almost entirely in terms of sinusoidal forcing and sinusoidal response.   Transmission of electrical power by alternating current, for instance, is concerned almost exclusively with sinusoids of a single frequency; other forcings are of interest only in relation to such relatively rare occurrences as switching operations, lightning surges, and breakdowns.   In electrical communication by telephone, radio, or television, the forcing and response are not, strictly speaking, purely sinusoidal, but they are essentially sinusoidal; and the operation of such systems can best be explained and understood in terms of purely sinusoidal functions.   Furthermore, the experimental work of making test or maintenance measurements on systems is often most conveniently performed in terms of sinusoids.

An additional mathematical reason for the importance of sinusoids is the fact that the stability of a system is specified in terms of sinusoidal response, as shown in Section 6·5.

So it is worth while to consider, as a special limited part of the general problem of response of physical systems, the sinusoidal problem—that is, the problem of response of physical systems under the assumptions that sinusoids are the only functions available for representing forcing or response, and that only the forced response need be considered.   The sinusoidal problem can then be analyzed into sub-problems, just as was done for the general problem in Section 1.4.   Thus the direct sinusoidal problem is: given a known system with $q_d = q_{da}e^{j\omega_f t}$, what is q?   The converse sinusoidal problem is: given a known system with $q = q_a e^{j\omega_f t}$, what is q_d?   The inverse problem is: given q_a and q_{da}, what are the parameters of the system?   And the design problem is: how to design a system with specified gain and phase characteristics.

Of these four types, the direct and converse problems are particularly simple, because of the relation by definition, $\mathbf{G} = q_a/q_{da}$— and by hypothesis $\mathbf{G}$ is known in both these problems.   With the inverse problem and the design problem, however, matters are more complicated.   Indeed it is advisable at this point to reconsider, on a rather general basis, these problems and the relations between them.

As treated in the preceding two chapters, the inverse problem was based on the implied assumption that the order of the system was known, and so the problem consists of finding a known number of parameters. Similarly, the design problem has been mentioned as though it might be a question of designing a system of a given order. Both problems may, of course, be given the broader meaning that goes with regarding the system's order as unknown or to be determined.

So long as only first- and second-order systems are to be treated, the distinction between the broader and narrower definitions of these problems is not too important. For the inverse problem, first-order response may be regarded as a limiting case in the more general picture of second-order response. So a reasonable practice would be to assume any system to be second-order; if then the evidence is that it is heavily overdamped, the question may be decided as to whether it may be treated as first-order. In the design problem, it would also be reasonable to use second-order systems as basic, and first-order systems as an approximation justifiable under certain conditions.

From the more general viewpoint of nth-order systems, however, it is better to take the broader definitions of inverse and design problems. Thus the inverse problem is to determine, from the observed response to a known forcing, the order n of the system and the values of $2n$ parameters; and the design problem is to choose, for the purpose of meeting specified performance requirements, both the order n of the system and the design of this nth-order system. This statement shows the close relation between the two problems, and also the difference between them. In both it is a question of determining n and the values of $2n$ parameters; but the design problem must go beyond this to specify the properties of the system. For, as discussed in Section 2·3 and illustrated by many subsequent examples, entirely different systems may have the same parameters. So far as response of the system is concerned, the design problem would in general be complete when the parameters are specified. Of course, response is only one of the factors in the complete design picture. (See, for instance, discussion on specifications of measuring instruments, Section 7·3.)

The inverse problem and some aspects of the design problem are discussed in Chapter 6 on Higher-Order Systems. Returning here to the sinusoidal inverse problem and the sinusoidal design problem, if the latter is considered only in relation to response, then both may be expressed as follows: given a certain amount of information about $\mathbf{G}$, how does one find n and the $2n$ parameters? In the inverse problem the knowledge of $\mathbf{G}$ is derived from observation; in the design problem, from specification.   In the inverse problem the determinations of n and the parameters furnish information about a system already in existence; in the design problem these determinations form the basis for proceeding with the design of a system yet to be built.   But these differences do not show in the analysis, and the two problems may be treated together.

The coefficients of the polynomial form D are the parameters B, introduced in Eq. 2·6.   That is,

$$D(p) = B_n p^n + B_{n-1} p^{n-1} + \cdots + B_1 p + 1 \qquad (5\cdot9)$$

The coefficients of the polynomial form N may be represented by small b's; thus

$$N(p) = b_n p^n + b_{n-1} p^{n-1} + \cdots + b_1 p + 1 \qquad (5\cdot10)$$

The problem may now be stated: given G and ϕ, determine n, $b_1 \cdots b_n$, and $B_1 \cdots B_n$.   It may be solved by a systematic procedure which is a generalization of the ideas introduced in Chapters 3 and 4 in solving the inverse problem with sinusoidal forcing for first-order and second-order systems.

If p is replaced by $j\omega_f$ in Eqs. 5·9 and 5·10 and the resulting expressions for N and D put in $\mathbf{G} = N/D$, the result is

$$\mathbf{G} = G\cos\phi + jG\sin\phi =$$

$$\frac{(1 - b_2\omega_f^2 + b_4\omega_f^4 \cdots) + j(b_1\omega_f - b_3\omega_f^3 + b_5\omega_f^5 \cdots)}{(1 - B_2\omega_f^2 + B_4\omega_f^4 \cdots) + j(B_1\omega_f - B_3\omega_f^3 + B_5\omega_f^5 \cdots)} \qquad (5\cdot11)$$

Multiplying through this expression by D and then equating real and imaginary parts leads to the two equations:

$$G\cos\phi(1 - B_2\omega_f^2 \cdots) - G\sin\phi(B_1\omega_f - B_3\omega_f^3 \cdots)$$
$$= 1 - b_2\omega_f^2 \cdots \qquad (5\cdot12)$$

$$G\sin\phi(1 - B_2\omega_f^2 \cdots) + G\cos\phi(B_1\omega_f - B_3\omega_f^3 \cdots)$$
$$= b_1\omega_f - b_3\omega_f^3 \cdots \qquad (5\cdot13)$$

If known values of G, ϕ, and ω_f are put into these equations, they become simultaneous equations in the unknown B's and b's.   For an nth-order system the simplest procedure would be to take n values of ω_f and n corresponding values of G and of ϕ and put them into Eqs. 5·12 and 5·13, thus obtaining $2n$ simultaneous equations in the $2n$ unknowns, b_1 to b_n and B_1 to B_n. n is the minimum sufficient number of frequencies. One is free to choose more than n frequencies; for instance, one might take $2n$ different frequencies and apply them alternately to Eq. 5·12 and to Eq. 5·13. In any case one must be sure to have a total of $2n$ equations, with each unknown appearing in at least one of the equations. (The reader who recalls the second-order sinusoidal problem as treated in Chapter 4 may question the need for $2n$ frequencies, since that problem was solved with G and ϕ known at only one frequency. Note, however, that the problem then was to find q_a/q_{fa}, equivalent here to assuming b_1 and b_2 equal to zero. In general, another frequency is needed to determine b_1 and b_2.)

The foregoing discussion is all right except for one thing. It is based on knowledge of n, which is one of the unknowns. How is the value of n determined? The best answer to this question appears to be as follows: assuming $n = 1$, find b_1 and B_1; then choose several other frequencies than the ones that served to determine b_1 and B_1, and see whether G and ϕ fit the first-order formula based on b_1 and B_1; if they fit, the system is first-order; if they do not fit, assume $n = 2$, find b_1, b_2, B_1, and B_2, and again check at other frequencies. (If one recognizes first-order gain or phase characteristics on sight, he would know at a glance whether $n = 1$. So in general one would not start by assuming $n = 1$, but $n = m + 1$, where m is the highest order for which one is sure of being able to recognize gain or phase characteristics.) By continuing in this way, one arrives eventually at the correct value of n, at which time one also has the values of b_1 to b_n and B_1 to B_n. Of course, a considerable amount of extra work will have been done along the way, as compared with that needed in case n is known. Facility in using determinants to handle systems of simultaneous equations is a great help in performing this extra work quickly and accurately. For example, a quick check on whether a system is of order n might be made by taking $n + m$ values of frequency and, without solving for the B's and b's, applying the test for consistency of the $2n + 2m$ equations so obtained. The $2n + 2m$ equations in the $2n$ unknowns are consistent (i.e., a single set of values for the unknowns fits all the equations) if certain conditions are satisfied by determinants of the equations. These cannot be explicitly stated here but may be found in books on theory of equations.[1]

Another important aspect of the sinusoidal problem is the question as to what limitations, if any, are to be put on the polynomial forms N and D in Eqs. 5·7 and 5·8. One such limitation which is commonly introduced is to specify that the degree of N shall not be greater than n, as was done above in introducing Eq. 5·6. This assumption is generally considered to relate to the stability of the system, and so is treated, along with other aspects of the stability question, in Section 6·5. Otherwise, N and D may for present purposes be considered any polynomial forms with real coefficients, positive or negative. This will include unstable as well as stable systems. In fact, the chances are rather small that a given N and D, arbitrarily written down, would pertain to a stable system; for from this point of view the stable systems are in a small, select class.

Another important question concerning **G** as given by Eq. 5·8 is whether there are any general relations between G and ϕ, considering that N and D may be any polynomial forms. This question cannot be treated here in full, but some aspects of it are taken up in the next section.

5·3 Distortion. In Section 2.4 it was mentioned that in some physical systems the criterion of minimum error is replaced by the criterion of minimum distortion. This is very largely true of those systems to which the sinusoidal problem is applied. In most of these devices the instantaneous difference between q and q_d is unimportant; what is important is that whenever q does get around to duplicating q_d it should duplicate it accurately. This is commonly expressed by saying that the **waveform** of q should be the same as that of q_d. For example, in a long-distance telephone conversation there may be a delay of a second between the instant a sound is uttered and the instant it is reproduced in the listener's ear. This does not matter, so long as the reproduced sound is an accurate duplicate of the uttered sound. To take a more extreme example, a sound-recording system may involve a delay of years between original and reproduced sound; here again, the criterion of minimum distortion applies.

[1] Cf. Dickson, *New First Course in the Theory of Equations*, New York, John Wiley and Sons, 1939, pp. 134–135.

It requires some careful thinking to appreciate the different viewpoints associated with minimum error and with minimum distortion, and yet to realize the close analytical kinship between them. For instance, sinusoidal forcing of a measuring instrument, such that the response is correct except for 180 degrees phase difference, is subject to very serious error; but such response might be considered to have zero distortion, since in many "sinusoidal" systems the reversal of waveform corresponding to 180 degrees phase shift is of no consequence. The discussion and examples that follow may help to distinguish these viewpoints.

A matter of great practical importance is the relation between distortion and G; in other words, the question of how the gain and phase characteristics may be specified for minimum distortion. One can see quite readily that the conditions for zero distortion are that the gain characteristic shall be flat (i.e., have the same value for all frequencies) and that the phase characteristic shall be proportional to frequency. For then each sinusoid in the forcing will appear in the response with the proper relative amplitude and shifted along the time axis by the same fixed time interval. This time interval, or **delay,** is equal to the phase divided by ω_f. For a system satisfying the condition for no phase distortion, this value ϕ/ω_f is the same as the slope of the phase characteristic. In general, however, the slope is different from ϕ/ω_f, and the widely disseminated statement that the delay is equal to the slope of the phase characteristic may be seriously wrong. It must be understood that the phase shift must not only be a straight line but that the intercept of the line must be zero or some multiple of 2π (or, if reversal of waveform is of no consequence, some multiple of π). Distortion due to departure of the gain characteristic from flatness is called **gain distortion;** that due to departure of the phase characteristic from a straight line of the proper intercept is called **phase distortion.**

Consideration of some examples may help to fix these ideas. The amplifier circuit of Fig. 4·14, for instance, has gain and phase characteristics given by Eqs. 4·68 and 4·69. As long as the quantity $[\beta - (1/\beta)]/2\zeta$ is small compared to 1, the gain characteristic is flat and the phase shift is near zero. The gain characteristics corresponding to different ζ-values are given in Fig. 4·16, showing that for large ζ the flat portion of the characteristic extends over a considerable range of frequencies. As far as the phase characteristics are concerned, Eq. 4·69 shows that at low frequencies ϕ is positive and at high frequencies it is negative; in the middle frequency range it is nearly zero, thus approximating a straight line passing through the origin—the condition for minimum phase distortion.

Another example is furnished by the second-order gain and phase characteristics of Figs. 4·4 and 4·5. The gain characteristic is seen to be approximately flat up to a maximum frequency if ζ is about 0.6; and the phase characteristic is most nearly a straight line for this same ζ-value. Thus minimum distortion for sinusoidal forcing and minimum error for other forcings all indicate an optimum ζ in the neighborhood of 0.6.

Now one would like to have some systematic way of taking given characteristics, such as those of Figs. 4·4 and 4.5 or those of Eqs. 4·68 and 4·69, and from them predicting the amount and the nature of the distortion that would be inflicted on any given waveform of q_d; or, in the inverse sense, a way of taking a given waveform of q_d and the more or less distorted waveform of q, and from the observed distortion deducing something about the gain and phase characteristics. Unfortunately, these important problems have not been given any very good solutions. In the direct sense, one can proceed by the methods of Fourier analysis (cf. Section 5·6) to analyze the waveform of q_d into its component sinusoids, affect each of these components by the proper gain and phase effects corresponding to its particular frequency, and then add all the affected sinusoids together to obtain the waveform of q. With a sufficient background of experience and knowledge of these direct problems, one is in a position to make some fairly accurate guesses in the inverse direction. Altogether, a great deal of intensive work on these problems has been done and has been reported principally in the journals on communications engineering.

5·4 Impedance. A distinguishing feature of physical systems, compared to other systems of which the response might be studied, was suggested in Section 1·5 to be the fact that the forcing of any physical system involves the flow of some form of energy into the system. Although the forcing and the response are usually expressed as quantities other than energy or power, the fact remains that any forcing-response process may be thought of as a power transmission problem. This focuses attention on the fact that, for any given choice of q, there is a **complementary**

quantity q^*, such that the product qq^* is the power transmitted past that point in the system where q is measured or specified. Familiar examples of q, q^* pairs are voltage and current, and force and velocity.

This feature, that q and q^* apply to the same point in the system, is in contrast to the relation between forcing and response, which are implicitly visualized as applying at different points in the system. In Fig. 5·1(a), for instance, q_f is applied at the input end of a system and q is observed at its output end. Since the

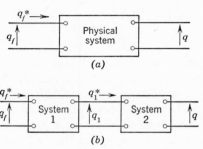

FIG. 5·1.   Complementary quantities.

forcing means that energy is flowing into the system, there is a quantity q_f^* at the input end. At the output end, however, if the system is isolated (not connected to another system), q^* will be zero, since the transmitted power is zero and q in general is not zero. If the system is analyzed into two component systems, as in Fig. 5·1(b), power is transmitted between the component parts, and the product of the two quantities q_1 and q_1^* represents this power. (Alternatively, Fig. 5·1(b) can be thought of as representing two systems connected together, rather than as a single system analyzed into two components.)

Now the problem of treating the relation between q_f and q_f^*, or between q_1 and q_1^*, is in principle no different from that involving q and q_f. For a linear system the same kind of relation holds as was given in Eq. 5·7; that is, for any complementary quantities q and q^*,

$$q = \frac{N(p)}{D(p)} q^* \qquad (5·14)$$

or, adopting the single symbol Z for N/D,

$$\frac{q}{q^*} = Z(p) \tag{5.15}$$

This **impedance operator** $Z(p)$ is reserved exclusively for the relation between complementary quantities, pertaining to the same point in a system; to express the relation between forcing at one point of a system and response at another point, the term **transfer impedance operator** and symbol $Z_t(p)$, may be used. Thus Eq. 5·7, put in form similar to Eq. 5·15, becomes

$$\frac{a}{q_d} = Z_t(p) \tag{5.16}$$

If the concepts of Eqs. 5·15 and 5·16 are applied to the sinusoidal problem, by replacing p with $j\omega_f$, one obtains the **impedance** $Z(j\omega_f)$ for which the plain symbol Z will be used; and the **transfer impedance**, $Z_t(j\omega_f)$, which is none other than the gain ratio **G** of Eq. 5·8. It must be emphasized that Z_t refers to the transfer impedance of the isolated system; that is, under the condition that $q^* = 0$. (Since the forms of $Z_t(p)$ and $Z_t(j\omega_f)$ are the same, both may sometimes for convenience be referred to by the shortened term, transfer impedance.)

Before proceeding further, it may be well to comment on the dimensions of q^*, Z, and Z_t. The convention followed thus far has been that for any one problem all q-symbols should have the same dimensions. As noted in the discussion (Section 2·4) on introducing q and q_f, it is usually possible to include in the definitions a constant which gives q and q_f the desired dimensions. As a general rule this procedure could be applied to make q and q^* of the same dimensions and so make Z, like Z_t, dimensionless. An exception occurs in writing the impedance operator for a single element, such as an electrical inductance. If L represents the inductance, E the voltage, and i the current, the relation is $E/i = Lp$; and there is no conveniently available constant of the dimensions of resistance with which to multiply i so as to give it the same dimensions as E. Because of such exceptions it will be assumed that q and q^* are not of the same dimensions but are of complementary dimensions, such that their product is power. Z is therefore not dimensionless but has the dimensions of q^2/power or power/q^{*2}.

Another question relating to dimensions is whether there is any general rule to help decide which of a given pair of quantities shall be denoted by q and which by q^*. Conventional usage decrees, in an electrical problem, that impedance denote the ratio of voltage to current. The reciprocal ratio is given another name, admittance. The attempt is made to carry over this usage to other systems, such as mechanical, by means of analogies. If force is analogous to voltage and velocity to current, mechanical impedance is force/velocity. In some problems this works out, but in others the reciprocal analogy (force to current, velocity to voltage) must be used. In preference to this somewhat precarious structure of ideas, the

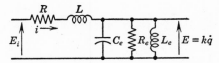

FIG. 5·2.   Third-order equivalent of galvanometer.

point of view recommended here is to select q according to the convenience of the particular problem, define q^* accordingly, and let q/q^* be the impedance. (Or, perhaps a new term should be coined for the general ratio q/q^*; one possibility [1] is "immittance," a hybrid of impedance and admittance.)

As an exercise in the use of impedance, the galvanometer discussed in Section 4·11 will be considered, this time not neglecting the inductance of the coil winding. This inductance is shown as L in the diagram of Fig. 5·2, which is the same as Fig. 4·22, except that L does not appear in the latter.

Let Z_e represent the impedance of the three equivalent elements C_e, R_e, and L_e in parallel. These three impedances are, respectively, $1/j\omega_f C_e$, R_e, and $j\omega_f L_e$. Combining these three according to the reciprocal relation for impedances in parallel,

$$\frac{1}{Z_e} = \frac{1}{1/j\omega_f C_e} + \frac{1}{R_e} + \frac{1}{j\omega_f L_e} \qquad (5\cdot17)$$

A time-saving form of this rule for parallel impedances, which is just as easy to remember as the above reciprocal relation, is this:

[1] Cf. Bode, *Network Analysis and Feedback Amplifier Design*, New York, D. Van Nostrand Company, 1945, p. 15.

the impedance of n impedances in parallel is equal to the (product of all n impedances) divided by (the sum of the n possible products of the impedances taken $n - 1$ at a time).

By whatever rule it is obtained, the expression for Z_e in the present example may be written

$$Z_e = \frac{j\omega_f L_e}{1 - \omega_f^2 L_e C_e + j\omega_f(L_e/R_e)} \qquad (5 \cdot 18)$$

Now the total impedance through which the current i of Fig. 5·2 flows is $R + j\omega_f L + Z_e$; or

$$Z = \frac{E_{ia}}{i_a} = R + j\omega_f L + \frac{j\omega_f L_e}{1 - \omega_f^2 L_e C_e + j\omega_f(L_e/R_e)} \qquad (5 \cdot 19)$$

The voltage amplitude E_a is equal to $Z_e i_a$, which with Eq. 5·19 gives the transfer impedance, or gain ratio.

$$\mathbf{G} = Z_t = \frac{E_a}{E_{ia}} = \frac{Z_e}{Z} =$$

$$\frac{j\omega_f \dfrac{L_e}{R}}{1 - \omega_f^2\left(L_e C_e + \dfrac{L L_e}{R R_e}\right) + j\omega_f\left(\dfrac{L_e}{R} + \dfrac{L}{R} + \dfrac{L_e}{R_e} - \omega_f^2 \dfrac{L L_e C_e}{R}\right)} \qquad (5 \cdot 20)$$

The three Eqs. 5·18, 5·19, and 5·20, as they stand, represent aspects of the sinusoidal problem applied to the galvanometer circuit. But merely by replacing $j\omega_f$ by the differential operator p, these equations become the general differential equations appropriate to any form of forcing. Equation 5·18 would become the differential equation relating the total current, through the equivalent elements, C_e, R_e, and L_e, and the voltage across these elements. Equation 5·19 would relate the input voltage E_i and the input current i. Finally, Eq. 5·20, relating E_i and E, will be written out here, giving the third-order differential equation,

$$\frac{E}{E_i} = \frac{p\dfrac{L_e}{R}}{\dfrac{L L_e C_e}{R}p^3 + \left(L_e C_e + \dfrac{L L_e}{R R_e}\right)p^2 + \left(\dfrac{L + L_e}{R} + \dfrac{L_e}{R_e}\right)p + 1}$$

$$(5 \cdot 21)$$

This example illustrates the close and simple relation between the impedance, representing the sinusoidal response, and the impedance operator, representing the differential equation and therefore the response to any forcing. It must be emphasized that this simple relation exists only for linear systems with constant coefficients. Therefore, to be prepared for the study of other systems, one must hold to the differential equation as being the basic expression of the physical laws. The simple relation of the sinusoidal impedance to the differential equation is a great convenience and help in studying simple and higher-order systems. In particular, as the above example shows, if one has a "circuit diagram" of the system and is skilled in writing impedance relations for such diagrams, it is easy to obtain the differential equation relating any two quantities of the system.

5·5 Impedance and discrimination criteria. To illustrate the application of performance criteria, other than minimum error or minimum distortion, two criteria closely related to sinusoidal forcing will be discussed. First it may be well to summarize the situation with respect to minimum error and minimum distortion. These criteria apply to those physical systems designed as duplicators—that is, systems in which the response q is to be the duplicate of a quantity q_d. If the duplication is to be as nearly as possible instantaneous, performance is measured in terms of error; if the duplication is supposed or permitted to be delayed, error is unimportant and only distortion matters.

A system with small error is characterized by a differential equation which is approximately $q = q_d$, all other terms being small. In some equations instead of q and q_d it may be one of their derivatives which are approximately equal; the equation of the amplifier circuit of Fig. 4·14, for example, is approximately $\dot{q} = \dot{q}_d$, where $q_d = G_1 E_i$ (cf. Eq. 4·56). Thus it is easy to see in a differential equation the terms which should be made small so as to obtain minimum error. Unfortunately, it is not so easy to see in a differential equation the conditions to be met to provide minimum distortion. In some cases these conditions are the same as for minimum error, but this is not always true. By contrast, it is possible to specify concisely (see Section 5·3 above) the conditions on **G** that give minimum distortion. Hence, really serious work on minimum-distortion duplicators calls for extensive study of gain and phase characteristics, rather than of differential equations as such.

A defining feature of the gain characteristic of any duplicator is flatness over some range of frequencies. The mercury-in-glass thermometer discussed in Chapters 2 and 3 is flat over frequencies starting at zero; the amplifier of Fig. 4·14 is flat over a range of frequencies centered about some value, with the gain dropping to zero both at low and at high frequencies. The corresponding defining feature of the phase characteristic is that over some range of frequencies it approximates a straight line with the proper intercept. If the system is minimum error, the intercept is zero; if minimum distortion, zero or some multiple of 2π. The terms "flatness" and "straightness" may serve to denote these minimum distortion properties of **G**.

Now, as examples of systems that are not designed to be duplicators, consider systems whose impedances are designed for specified values and systems designed for specified shapes of gain and phase characteristics, or more briefly, systems of **specified impedance** and systems of **specified discrimination**. Some systems are designed especially to create an impedance which is very large, or very small, or very nearly equal to some constant value, or negative, or changing in a certain way with frequency, etc. Similarly, other systems are designed especially to create a transfer impedance which has a specified frequency dependence, other than flatness and straightness. The term "discrimination" thus implies a transfer impedance or gain ratio which is intentionally designed to have features other than, or in addition to, flatness and straightness.

As an example of a problem in specified impedance, consider the military problem of hiding a submerged submarine against detection by sounding devices. If the acoustic impedance (ratio of sound pressure to sound volume velocity) of the submarine is exactly the same as that of the sea water, the submarine is hidden, for it can be responsible neither for reflection nor for undue absorption of the probing sound. Thus the impedance of the submarine surface must be matched to that of the water over such frequency ranges as the enemy searcher might use.

Perhaps the most familiar examples of systems designed for specified discrimination are the **filters** of electrical and acoustical engineering. These involve a wide variety of performance criteria, depending on the relative importance of how sharply the filter should discriminate against certain frequencies and how much distortion can be tolerated in the frequencies which are passed.

No attempt is made here to treat these two problems, impedance and discrimination. The published literature on them is large. The purpose in mentioning them is simply to present them as important examples of the exceptions to the main trend of thought in this book, the problems of the duplicator criteria.

5·6 Fourier analysis. In the preceding sections of this chapter considerable use has been made of the idea of the sum of a number of sinusoids. Particularly in the relation between forcing and forced response much use has been made of the essential property of linear systems that "the forced response to the sum of several forcings is the sum of the forced responses to each of the forcings considered individually." This property is also applied to all sorts of forcings other than sinusoidal, but the sinusoids are especially significant because of those characteristics which may be included in the term "Fourier analysis."

The key result of Fourier analysis is the fact that an arbitrary function of time may be represented as the sum of sinusoids. The formulas and rules for doing this will be set down here in some detail.

For this discussion the arbitrary time function may be thought of as a forcing, $q_f(t)$. If $q_f(t)$ is periodic, the component sinusoids will differ in frequency by finite amounts; in fact, they will have frequencies which are all integral multiples of a single **fundamental frequency.** If $q_f(t)$ is not periodic, the component sinusoids differ in frequency only by infinitesimal degrees. This means that a periodic function is represented by a **Fourier series,** and a nonperiodic function by a **Fourier integral.**

(A borderline case, which is of mathematical interest, is furnished by the so-called "almost periodic" functions. An example of such a function is $\cos t + \cos \sqrt{2}t$; this is almost like the periodic function $\cos t + \cos (7t/5)$, but, since $\sqrt{2}$ is irrational, the function is not truly periodic.)

The formulas for Fourier series and integrals may be written using the complex number notation for sinusoids, or using only real numbers. In the complex notation the Fourier series is

$$q_f(t) = \sum_{k=-\infty}^{\infty} C_k e^{jk\omega_f t} \qquad (5\cdot 22)$$

where

$$C_k = \frac{\omega_f}{2\pi} \int_0^{2\pi/\omega_f} q_f(t) e^{-jk\omega_f t}\, dt \qquad (5\cdot 23)$$

In these formulas, k is the running index, taking on all integral values, and ω_f is the fundamental angular frequency.

The Fourier integral, for nonperiodic q_f, is

$$q_f(t) = \int_{-\infty}^{\infty} C(\omega') e^{j\omega' t}\, d\omega' \qquad (5\cdot 24)$$

where

$$C(\omega') = \frac{1}{2\pi} \int_{-\infty}^{\infty} q_f(t) e^{-j\omega' t}\, dt \qquad (5\cdot 25)$$

Here ω' denotes a continuously variable frequency, running through all real values.

In real numbers the formulas corresponding to Eqs. $5\cdot 22$ to $5\cdot 25$ are

$$q_f(t) = A_0 + \sum_{k=1}^{\infty} (A_k \cos k\omega_f t + B_k \sin k\omega_f t) \qquad (5\cdot 26)$$

or

$$q_f(t) = A_0 + \sum_{k=1}^{\infty} C_k \cos (k\omega_f t + \theta_k) \qquad (5\cdot 27)$$

where

$$A_0 = \frac{\omega_f}{2\pi} \int_0^{2\pi/\omega_f} q_f(t)\, dt \qquad (5\cdot 28)$$

$$A_k = \frac{\omega_f}{\pi} \int_0^{2\pi/\omega_f} q_f(t) \cos k\omega_f t\, dt \qquad (5\cdot 29)$$

$$B_k = \frac{\omega_f}{\pi} \int_0^{2\pi/\omega_f} q_f(t) \sin k\omega_f t\, dt \qquad (5\cdot 30)$$

$$\left. \begin{array}{l} C_k = \sqrt{A_k{}^2 + B_k{}^2} \\[2ex] \theta_k = -\tan^{-1} \dfrac{B_k}{A_k} \end{array} \right\} \qquad (5\cdot 31)$$

and the Fourier integral,

$$q_f(t) = \int_0^{\infty} [A(\omega') \cos \omega' t + B(\omega') \sin \omega' t]\, d\omega' \qquad (5\cdot 32)$$

or

$$q_f(t) = \int_0^\infty C(\omega') \cos\left[\omega't + \theta(\omega')\right] d\omega' \qquad (5\cdot33)$$

where

$$A(\omega') = \frac{1}{\pi} \int_{-\infty}^{\infty} q_f(t) \cos \omega't\, dt \qquad (5\cdot34)$$

$$B(\omega') = \frac{1}{\pi} \int_{-\infty}^{\infty} q_f(t) \sin \omega't\, dt \qquad (5\cdot35)$$

$$\left.\begin{array}{l} C = \sqrt{A^2 + B^2} \\[2mm] \theta = -\tan^{-1}\dfrac{B}{A} \end{array}\right\} \qquad (5\cdot36)$$

By these formulas any waveform, periodic or not, may be expressed as the sum of sinusoids. From the viewpoint of this book the chief motive for thus expressing functions is to be able to treat the problem of minimum distortion; for, as noted in the preceding section, this problem is more readily apprehended by means of the gain ratio **G** than by means of the differential equation itself. Many practical applications involve strong distinction between gain distortion and phase distortion; this is particularly true of all aspects of acoustic engineering, for the ear itself is relatively insensitive to phase distortion. For the adequate treatment of such problems an indispensable tool is the ability to think of functions, and to treat them analytically, as sums of component sinusoids.

The two aspects of Fourier analysis are **analysis** and **synthesis**. Analysis is the breaking down of a given waveform into its Fourier components, that is, finding the amplitudes and phases of the sinusoids of which it is composed. This process is often called, particularly with reference to the amplitudes, "finding the frequency spectrum of the function." Synthesis is concerned with putting together sinusoids of known amplitudes and phases and finding the resultant waveform. Put more briefly, the analyzing problem is: given a waveform, find its spectrum; and the synthesizing problem is: given a spectrum, find the waveform. Both problems can be carried out by calculation, but, because the calculations may be quite tedious, machines of both types, harmonic analyzers and harmonic synthesizers, have been built.

CHAPTER

6

Higher-Order Systems

6·1 Transient response. The problem of finding complete solutions of an nth-order linear differential equation with constant coefficients was discussed in Section 2·8. To that extent, therefore, the direct problem for higher-order systems has been covered. Several aspects of the problem which were simply mentioned there, however, need to be considered in detail.

As with simple systems, the problem of finding q for a known system and a known q_f consists of the two problems of finding the transient response q_t and the forced response q_r. q_t is the solution of the homogeneous equation obtained by putting $q_f = 0$ in the complete equation

$$D(p) \cdot q = q_f \qquad (6 \cdot 1)$$

Finding this solution involves finding the roots of the auxiliary equation

$$D(r) = 0 \qquad (6 \cdot 2)$$

In these equations D is a polynomial form of degree n. These equations are the same as Eqs. 2·6 and 2·9, or, in the notation used here, Eqs. 5·3 and 5·4.

The algebraic problem of expressing the roots of Eq. 6·2 in terms of the parameters of D can still be solved for $n = 3$ and $n = 4$ but becomes impossible for n greater than 4. Actually, even for third- or fourth-order systems the expressions giving the roots in terms of the parameters are so voluminous that as a practical matter it is not feasible to write out complete expressions for the response, corresponding to Eqs. 3·4 and 4·20. So all higher-order systems are on the same basis in that calculation is the only practical way of getting the roots of Eq. 6·2. In these calculations one has the choice, if $n < 5$, of using either the algebraic formulas or the general numerical methods; for $n > 4$, only the numerical methods are available.[1]

For numerical computation of the roots of Eq. 6·2, a variety of methods may be used. The two most generally useful ones are probably Newton's method and the root-squaring method associated with the name of Graeffe.[2] The various methods are discussed in a number of books, particularly those devoted mainly to numerical analysis. A discussion of the third-order problem is included in the next section of this chapter.

Although the numerical calculation of roots is a valuable technique to have available for application to an individual problem, from the broad point of view such calculation must be regarded as unrewarding, since it contributes essentially nothing to a general understanding of response. One would like therefore to proceed with the general discussion of nth-order systems without depending on detailed knowledge of the roots.

It is interesting to regard the transient response in analogy with a Fourier series. Equation 2·8, which is a general expression for q_t, may be written

$$q_t = \sum_{k=1}^{n} C_k e^{r_k t} \qquad (6·3)$$

Comparing this with the Fourier series written with complex number notation, as in Eq. 5·22, renders the analogy apparent. The Fourier series and the transient response are made up by adding together functions from a set, each multiplied by an appropriate constant. The set of functions for a Fourier series is made up of the trigonometric functions with frequencies integrally related to a fundamental frequency; and the multiplying constants are determined by the desire to have the series approximate a given function over an interval. In the series representing q_t, the function set consists of the exponentials $e^{r_k t}$, where r_k is a root of the auxiliary equation; and the multiplying constants are determined by the desire to have q_t and its derivatives assume specified values at specified times.

---

[1] A discussion of the formulas for the cases $n = 3$ and $n = 4$ may be found in Chapter V of Dickson, *New First Course in the Theory of Equations*, New York, John Wiley and Sons, 1939.

[2] Cf. Chapter VI, Whittaker and Robinson, *Calculus of Observations*, London, Blackie and Son, Ltd., 1932.

Between the two series there are, of course, many differences which will not be enumerated here. Emphasis is on the idea that q_t can be thought of as the sum of typical functions, namely, exponentially damped sinusoids. (From a broad point of view this description may be thought of as including the simple, non-oscillatory exponentials.) In retrospect, it is now clear that the concept of simple systems could not well have been restricted to first-order systems, since the possibility of complex roots does not exist for such systems. But with the understanding of simple systems, including the second-order case, it may be said that there is nothing new involved in the transient response of higher-order systems, in the sense that the familiar exponentials of the first- and second-order responses will suffice, though more than two of them may be needed. Thus one may say, for example, that the transient response of a third-order system will consist of the sum of a first-order transient and a second-order transient; or, in general, that the transient response of any order system will consist of the sum of a number of first-order and second-order transients. This idea is illustrated in the detailed discussion of third-order systems given in the next section.

6·2 Third-order systems. For a third-order system, if one assumes that the roots of the auxiliary Eq. 6·2 are known, the differential Eq. 6·1 may be written:

$$\left[(\tau p + 1)\left(\frac{p^2}{\omega_n{}^2} + \frac{2\zeta}{\omega_n} p + 1 \right) \right] q = q_f \qquad (6\cdot4)$$

The convenience of notation using ζ and ω_n is here subject to the same limitation regarding stability mentioned in Section 4·7 in connection with Table 4·2.

With the differential equation in this form the transient response is

$$q_t = e^{-\zeta \omega_n t}\left(C_1 \cos \omega t + \frac{C_2}{\sqrt{1 - \zeta^2}} \sin \omega t \right) + C_3 e^{-t/\tau} \quad (6\cdot5)$$

that is, it is the sum of a first-order transient and a second-order transient. The three constants C_1, C_2, and C_3 are determined by initial conditions on q, $\dot{q}$, and $\ddot{q}$. From Eq. 6·5, the expressions for $\dot{q}_t$ and $\ddot{q}_t$ are

$$\frac{\dot{q}_t}{\omega_n} = e^{-\zeta\omega_n t}\left[(C_2 - \zeta C_1)\cos \omega t - \right.$$

$$\left.\frac{(1 - \zeta^2)C_1 + \zeta C_2}{\sqrt{1 - \zeta^2}}\sin \omega t\right] - \frac{C_3}{\omega_n \tau}e^{-t/\tau} \quad (6\cdot6)$$

and

$$\frac{\ddot{q}_t}{\omega_n{}^2} = e^{-\zeta\omega_n t}\left\{[(2\zeta^2 - 1)C_1 - 2\zeta C_2]\cos \omega t + \right.$$

$$\left.\frac{2C_1\zeta(1 - \zeta^2) + C_2(2\zeta^2 - 1)}{\sqrt{1 - \zeta^2}}\sin \omega t\right\} + \frac{C_3}{\omega_n{}^2\tau^2}e^{-t/\tau} \quad (6\cdot7)$$

Hence the initial values (at $t = 0$) of q_t, $\dot{q}_t$, and $\ddot{q}_t$, given the symbols Q_i, $\dot{Q}_i$, and $\ddot{Q}_i$, are

$$Q_i = C_1 + C_3$$

$$\frac{\dot{Q}_i}{\omega_n} = -\zeta C_1 + C_2 - \frac{C_3}{\omega_n \tau} \quad\quad (6\cdot8)$$

$$\frac{\ddot{Q}_i}{\omega_n{}^2} = (2\zeta^2 - 1)C_1 - 2\zeta C_2 + \frac{C_3}{\omega_n{}^2\tau^2}$$

These equations, solved for C_1, C_2, and C_3, give

$$C_1 = \frac{Q_i\left(\dfrac{1}{\omega_n{}^2\tau^2} - \dfrac{2\zeta}{\omega_n\tau}\right) - \dfrac{2\zeta}{\omega_n}\dot{Q}_i - \dfrac{\ddot{Q}_i}{\omega_n{}^2}}{\dfrac{1}{\omega_n{}^2\tau^2} - \dfrac{2\zeta}{\omega_n\tau} + 1} \quad (6\cdot9)$$

$$C_2 =$$

$$\frac{Q_i\left(\dfrac{\zeta}{\omega_n{}^2\tau^2} - \dfrac{2\zeta^2 - 1}{\omega_n\tau}\right) + \dfrac{\dot{Q}_i}{\omega_n}\left(\dfrac{1}{\omega_n{}^2\tau^2} - 2\zeta^2 + 1\right) + \dfrac{\ddot{Q}_i}{\omega_n{}^2}\left(\dfrac{1}{\omega_n\tau} - \zeta\right)}{\dfrac{1}{\omega_n{}^2\tau^2} - \dfrac{2\zeta}{\omega_n\tau} + 1}$$

$$(6\cdot10)$$

$$C_3 = \frac{Q_i + \dfrac{2\zeta}{\omega_n}\dot{Q}_i + \dfrac{\ddot{Q}_i}{\omega_n{}^2}}{\dfrac{1}{\omega_n{}^2\tau^2} - \dfrac{2\zeta}{\omega_n\tau} + 1} \quad (6\cdot11)$$

These equations are the equivalent, for third-order systems, of Eqs. 3·3 and 4·17; comparison of the three cases—first-, second-, and third-order—is instructive as to the increasing complexity of higher-order systems.   In this comparison, note should be taken that, complicated though they are, Eqs. 6·9, 6·10, and 6·11 still do not give the constants directly in terms of the parameters of the system, since τ, ζ, and ω_n are directly related to the roots of the auxiliary Eq. 6·2 rather than to the parameters of the differ-

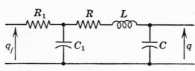

FIG. 6·1.   Third-order electrical system.

ential Eq. 6·1.   To use the parameters to express C_1, C_2, and C_3 would lead to such bulky equations that, as noted earlier, their usefulness would practically vanish.

The above equations may be applied, for example, to the electrical circuit of Fig. 6·1.   Taking q as the output voltage and q_f as the input voltage, the differential equation is

$$[LCC_1R_1p^3 + (CC_1RR_1 + LC)p^2 + (CR + C_1R_1 + CR_1)p + 1]q$$
$$= q_f \quad (6·12)$$

Of course, to use Eq. 6·5 one must have some way of putting Eq. 6·12 in the form of Eq. 6·4—that is, some way of finding the roots of the auxiliary equation.   To do this it is necessary to assign numerical values to the circuit elements.   Let these values be

$$L = 1 \text{ henry}$$
$$C = 0.25 \text{ microfarad}$$
$$C_1 = 0.57 \text{ microfarad}$$
$$R = 500 \text{ ohms}$$
$$R_1 = 700 \text{ ohms}$$

With these values, Eq. 6·12 becomes

$$(B_3p^3 + B_2p^2 + B_1p + 1)q = q_f \quad (6·13)$$

with

$$B_3 = 10^{-10} \text{ (second)}^3$$
$$B_2 = 3.0 \times 10^{-7} \text{ (second)}^2 \quad (6·14)$$
$$B_1 = 7.0 \times 10^{-4} \text{ second}$$

The auxiliary equation, in the notation of Eq. 6·13, is

$$B_3 r^3 + B_2 r^2 + B_1 r + 1 = 0 \qquad (6 \cdot 15)$$

A rough estimate of the roots of this equation may be had from the chart of Fig. 6·2. This chart is based on the transformation of Eq. 6·15 into

$$A_3 S^3 = A_1 S + 1 \qquad (6 \cdot 16)$$

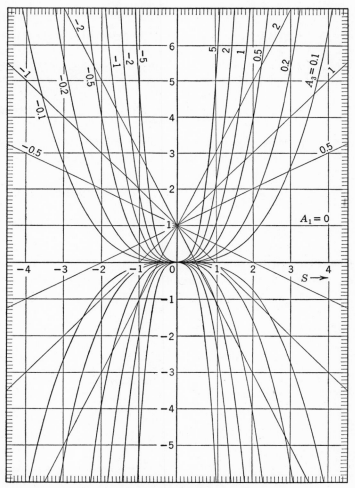

FIG. 6·2.   Chart for solving cubic.

where

$$S = B_3^{1/3} r + \frac{B_2}{3B_3^{2/3}} = B_3^{1/3}\left(r + \frac{B_2}{3B_3}\right)$$

$$A_3 = \frac{27B_3^2}{9B_3 B_2 B_1 - 27B_3^2 - 2B_2^3} \tag{6·17}$$

$$A_1 = \frac{9B_3^{2/3}(B_2^2 - 3B_3 B_1)}{9B_3 B_2 B_1 - 27B_3^2 - 2B_2^3}$$

In this transformation the symbol $B_3^{1/3}$ represents the real cube root of B_3.

With the numerical values of Eqs. 6·14 the values of A_3 and A_1 according to Eqs. 6·17 are

$$A_3 = -2.0$$
$$A_1 = 1.725 \tag{6·18}$$

For these values Fig. 6·2 shows only one intersection, meaning that there is only one real root. The value of this root is seen to be about -0.45. For this value of S the first of Eqs. 6·17 gives $r = -1.97 \times 10^3$ as an approximation for the real root. Making use of this value, one can get equally rough approximations of the two complex roots. If one is interested in more precise values, however, the more time-saving procedure is to obtain first a more precise value of S. This may be done, for example, by Newton's method of approximation.

The Newton method involves writing Eq. 6·16

$$f(S) = 2S^3 + 1.725S + 1 = 0 \tag{6·19}$$

and also the derivative

$$f'(S) = 6S^2 + 1.725 \tag{6·20}$$

Now if S_0, in this case -0.45, is an approximate value of the real root, a better approximation is

$$S_1 = S_0 - \frac{f(S_0)}{f'(S_0)} \tag{6·21}$$

In the present problem $f(S_0) = 0.041$ and $f'(S_0) = 2.94$. Hence $S_1 = -0.45 - 0.014 = -0.464$. The process can be continued, but for present purposes the value -0.464 may be taken as sufficiently accurate. The corresponding value of r is -2.0×10^3 $(\text{second})^{-1}$.

With this value for $-1/\tau$ in Eq. 6·4, the values of ζ and ω_n may be found by dividing the polynomial $(10^{-10}r^3 + 3.0 \times 10^{-7}r^2 + 7.0 \times 10^{-4}r + 1)$ by $(0.5 \times 10^{-3}r + 1)$. The result is $2 \times 10^{-7}r^2 + 2 \times 10^{-4}r + 1$; thus

$$\tau = 0.5 \times 10^{-3} \text{ second}$$

$$\omega_n = 0.224 \times 10^4 \text{ radians per second} \qquad (6\cdot22)$$

$$\zeta = 0.224$$

Thus Eq. 6·12 has been resolved into the factored form of Eq. 6·4. As a consequence, Eqs. 6·5, 6·9, 6·10, and 6·11 may be used to write the transient response. To avoid getting into a discussion of forced response, the subject of a later section, the only example quoted here will be response to a step forcing, for which the forced response is a constant, and $\dot{Q}_1$ and $\ddot{Q}_1$ are zero.

The values of Eqs. 6·22 used in Eqs. 6·9 to 6·11 give the constants

$$C_1 = 0.285(Q_1 - Q_2)$$

$$C_2 = 0.702(Q_1 - Q_2) \qquad (6\cdot23)$$

$$C_3 = 0.715(Q_1 - Q_2)$$

in which Q_2 represents the constant forcing and also the forced response.

The complete response may therefore be written

$$\frac{Q_2 - q}{Q_2 - Q_1} = e^{-500t}(0.285 \cos 2180t + 0.721 \sin 2180t) + 0.715e^{-2000t}$$

$$(6\cdot24)$$

in analogy with Eqs. 3·6 and 4·24. Figure 6·3 shows a plot of this third-order response and also dotted line plots of the first-order and second-order component transients. It is seen that after 2 milliseconds the third-order response becomes essentially identical with the second-order component. In fact, the entire response curve is, at a glance, not too different from a second-order response to a constant.

For comparison, Fig. 6·4 gives the response of a system with the same ζ and ω_n, but with $\tau = 2 \times 10^{-3}$ second. Here the second-order component is suppressed and the first-order dominates.

These examples show that resolution of a higher-order system into components is useful because it permits one to apply to such

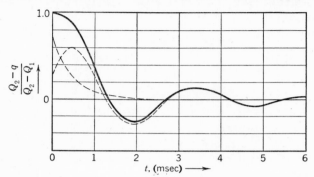

FIG. 6·3.   Third-order response to constant.

systems some of the intimate knowledge of first- and second-order systems gained in Chapters 3 and 4.   For instance, an experimental observation of response to constant forcing may be used to obtain a rough solution of the inverse problem for third-order systems, if the second-order component is oscillatory as in Figs. 6·3 and 6·4.

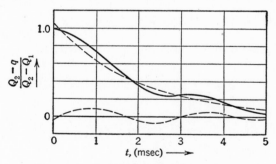

FIG. 6·4.   Response of modified system.

The method of finding ζ and ω_n based on Fig. 4·9 may be applied here with fair accuracy, since one can visually separate the first-order and second-order components approximately.

The concept of component systems has been introduced on the purely mathematical basis of the roots of the auxiliary equation;

but in many situations the component systems are also closely related to physical reality. The circuit of Fig. 6·1, for example, is the same, as far as response is concerned, as the circuit of Fig. 6·5. This circuit is made up of component circuits, separated by an isolating amplifier. An ideal isolating amplifier has the following characteristics: zero output impedance, infinite input impedance, constant voltage gain of unity, and zero phase shift

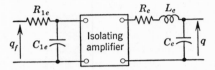

FIG. 6·5. Equivalent resolved system.

(cf. Section 6·3 of this chapter). With such an amplifier the differential equation of the circuit is

$$[L_eC_eC_{1e}R_{1e}p^3 + (C_eC_{1e}R_eR_{1e} + L_eC_e)p^2$$
$$+ (C_eR_e + C_{1e}R_{1e})p + 1]q = q_f \quad (6·25)$$

Comparing this equation with Eq. 6·12 shows them to be the same, provided the equivalent elements have proper numerical values. The choice of these equivalent values is governed by the requirements

$$C_{1e}R_{1e} = \tau$$

$$\frac{1}{\sqrt{L_eC_e}} = \omega_n \quad (6·26)$$

$$\frac{R_e}{2\sqrt{L_e/C_e}} = \zeta$$

To match the numerical values of Eqs. 6·22, for instance, one possible set of values is

$$C_{1e} = 1.0 \text{ microfarad}$$
$$R_{1e} = 500 \text{ ohms}$$
$$R_e = 1000 \text{ ohms} \quad (6·27)$$
$$L_e = 1 \text{ henry}$$
$$C_e = 0.2 \text{ microfarad}$$

These values may be compared with those first introduced into Fig. 6·1. The values do not differ greatly. It follows that a more

or less accurate guess for the real root of the system of Fig. 6·1 is
the value $-1/(C_1R_1)$; the guess is more accurate the more nearly
the time constant CR_1 is negligible compared to the others, CR
and C_1R_1.

It is evident that the values given in Eqs. 6·27 correspond to
only one of an infinite number of possibilities, since the five circuit
elements are subject only to the three conditions of Eqs. 6·26.
Thus there are infinitely many resolved circuits equivalent in
transfer impedance to the one original unresolved circuit. Conversely, it may be shown that to any one resolved circuit there are
equivalent an infinite number of unresolved circuits. That is, the
association of resolved and unresolved circuits is not unique.

The significance and usefulness of the resolution of systems into
component simple systems are investigated further in the following
section.

6·3 Component systems. The electrical circuit used as an
example in the preceding section serves well in illustrating the
resolution of a higher-order system into component simple systems.
It is easy to visualize the circuit (Fig. 6·1) being separated into
an R_1-C_1 first-order circuit followed by an L-R-C second-order

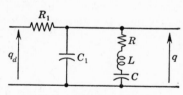

Fig. 6·6.   Rearranged system.

circuit; and much the same set
of numerical values renders the
resolved system equivalent to
the original. In general, however,
physical systems do not so easily
fall into the resolved form.   In
fact, this same circuit, slightly rearranged as in Fig. 6·6, represents
a much less obvious problem.   The differential equation for this
circuit is $q/q_d = N(p)/D(p)$, with $D(p)$ as in Eq. 6·12, and

$$N(p) = LCp^2 + CRp + 1 \qquad (6·28)$$

An equivalent resolved system is shown in Fig. 6·7.   This would
be hard to arrive at intuitively or visually but is fairly easy on a
mathematical basis.

A system for which it is still harder to visualize the components
is the nuclear chain reactor, which was treated as a second-order
system in Chapter 4 and is treated as a higher-order system in
Section 6·6.

Whether easy or hard to visualize, the resolution of a system is always mathematically feasible. More specifically, the transfer impedance of any nth-order system may be represented as the product of n_1 first-order transfer impedances and n_2 second-order

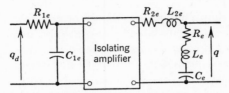

FIG. 6·7.   Resolved equivalent of rearranged system.

transfer impedances, where $n_1 + 2n_2 = n$. For the example of Figs. 6·6 and 6·7,

$$Z_t = \frac{LCp^2 + CRp + 1}{LCC_1R_1p^3 + (CC_1RR_1 + LC)p^2 + (CR + C_1R_1 + CR_1)p + 1}$$

$$= \frac{1}{C_1eR_{1e}p + 1} \cdot \frac{L_eC_ep^2 + C_eR_ep + 1}{(L_e + L_{2e})C_ep^2 + C_e(R_e + R_{2e})p + 1} \quad (6·29)$$

Diagrammatically the mathematical equivalent of any nth-order system may be represented as a succession of component simple systems separated by isolating amplifiers. For those systems for which these mathematical components can be more or less directly related to actual physical components, the question naturally

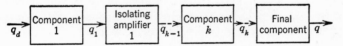

FIG. 6·8.   Resolved nth-order system.

arises as to the significance of the isolating amplifiers—why they are necessary and what would happen if they were omitted.

Consider the kth component in the chain of Fig. 6·8. By the transfer impedance Z_{tk} of this system is meant the ratio q_k/q_{k-1}, under the condition that $q_k{}^* = 0$—that is, that no power transfer occurs from this system to the next component system. This accounts for one of the specifications put on the isolating amplifier, that of infinite input impedance. This means that no power is drawn from the system feeding the amplifier, and therefore that the transfer impedance of that system is indeed Z_{tk}. This condition applied to all the components insures that

$$\frac{q}{q_d} = Z_{t1} \cdot Z_{t2} \cdots Z_{tk} \cdots = Z_t \qquad (6 \cdot 30)$$

Thus the infinite input impedance of the following amplifier helps the kth component to transfer correctly the signal delivered to it. For the amplifier to pass on the correct signal requires that it have $\mathbf{G} = 1$—constant gain of unity and zero phase shift, the conditions for zero error. These conditions can be specified for open-circuit operation of the amplifier, or for operation into its actual impedance load in the system. If it is an open-circuit specification, the further condition must be imposed on the amplifier of zero output impedance. The need for this may be understood by reference to Fig. 6·9. Here Z_{ik} represents the input impedance of the kth component system,

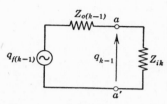

FIG. 6·9. Illustrating Thevenin's theorem.

and the points a-a' the input terminals of this system. Now by a generalization of a proposition of electrical circuit theory known as Thevenin's theorem, everything to the left of a-a' may be replaced by a source, $q_{f(k-1)}$, in series with an impedance $Z_{o(k-1)}$. The value of $q_{f(k-1)}$ is that which would be measured at a-a' if these points were left open-circuited, and $Z_{o(k-1)}$ is the impedance measured at a-a' under open-circuit conditions. When a-a' are connected to Z_{ik}, the actual value, q_{k-1}, will be

$$\frac{q_{k-1}}{q_{f(k-1)}} = \frac{Z_{ik}}{Z_{o(k-1)} + Z_{ik}} \qquad (6 \cdot 31)$$

Hence, if $q_{f(k-1)} = Z_{t(k-1)}q_{k-2}$, the desired condition is $q_{k-1} = q_{f(k-1)}$, and it follows from Eq. 6·31 that $Z_{o(k-1)}$ must be zero.

Having in mind this picture of the nature and role of the isolating amplifiers, it becomes possible to discuss the system with the amplifiers omitted. Let Z_{ik} as before denote the input impedance to the kth component; but let $Z_{o(k-1)}$ now denote the impedance measured directly at the output of the $(k - 1)$ component, rather

than the output of an amplifier following it.   Now Eq. 6·31 shows
that the desired value of unity will be approximated if $Z_{o(k-1)}$ is
small compared to Z_{ik}.   If this condition,

$$\frac{Z_{o(k-1)}}{Z_{ik}} \ll 1 \tag{6·32}$$

is satisfied at any point a-a' in a system when the system has been
broken at that point into two components, the transfer impedance
of the entire system is the product of the transfer impedances of
the components.   An equivalent statement of the condition,
applied to the system before it has been opened at a-a', is that the
power transferred past a-a' be small compared to the power level
at a-a'.

Let this test be applied for example to the circuit of Fig. 6·1.
Take the points a-a' across the capacitor C_1.   Then the R_1-C_1
system has the transfer impedance operator $1/(C_1 R_1 p + 1)$, and
the output impedance $Z_o = R_1/(1 + j\omega_f C_1 R_1)$; the R-L-C system
has the transfer impedance operator $1/(LCp^2 + CRp + 1)$, and
the input impedance $Z_i = R + j\omega_f L + (1/j\omega_f C)$.

Hence the ratio is

$$\frac{Z_o}{Z_i} = \frac{j\omega_f CR_1}{-j\omega_f^3 LCC_1 R_1 - \omega_f^2(LC + CC_1 RR_1) + j\omega_f(RC + R_1 C_1) + 1} \tag{6·33}$$

Because of its frequency dependence, this will be small at frequencies near zero and also at high frequencies; in between, however,
there is a frequency range where its value will be small only if

$$\frac{CR_1}{RC + R_1 C_1} \ll 1 \tag{6·34}$$

But this is exactly the condition shown in Section 6·2 above to
be needed to make the original system and the resolved system
identical.

There are points in many physical systems where condition 6·32
is well satisfied.   One example is the input to a vacuum tube; quite
often the impedance of the input grid circuit is high compared to
the impedance feeding it.   Another example is the detection of
mirror rotation by deflection of light in a photocell; here the power
represented in deflecting the light beam is essentially zero compared

to the power involved in rotating the mirror. When condition 6·32 is satisfied only to a rough approximation, it is still, in general, worth while to proceed with the resolution into components. For the picture of the resolved system, rough though it may be, contributes immediately to understanding of the system and furthermore serves as a first approximation toward a more precise determination, when it is needed, of the roots of the auxiliary equation.

The convenience and usefulness of the resolved system in working direct or inverse problems of higher-order systems has perhaps been sufficiently indicated in Section 6.2. The discussion there was based on the implication that the only way of accomplishing the resolution was by tedious numerical determination of roots. The point of the preceding paragraphs is that by their very nature some systems are almost resolved as they stand.

One other application of impedance measurement at internal points a-a' may be indicated. Let Z_{t1} be transfer impedance from input to a-a', and Z_{t2} be transfer impedance from a-a' to output. Let q_1 be the value of response at a-a' in normal operation (i.e., system not opened at a-a'). Then, as in Eq. 6·3,

$$q_1 = Z_{t1} q_d \frac{Z_i}{Z_o + Z_i} \qquad (6·35)$$

where Z_i is impedance measured from a-a' toward output, and Z_o is impedance toward input. Then

$$q = Z_{t2} q_1 = Z_{t1} Z_{t2} \frac{Z_i}{Z_o + Z_i} q_d = Z_t q_d \qquad (6·36)$$

where Z_t is the overall transfer impedance of the system. The relation

$$Z_t = \frac{Z_i}{Z_o + Z_i} Z_{t1} Z_{t2} \qquad (6·37)$$

is useful where measurement of Z_t is difficult and the four quantities on the right can be measured more conveniently.

6·4 Complete Response. The relations among q, q_d, and q_f are

$$D(p)q = N(p)q_d = q_f \qquad (6·38)$$

The original version of the direct problem was: given q_f and D, find q. The generalized version is: given q_d, N, and D, find q.

This may be reduced to the original version by carrying out the operation $N(p)$ on q_d, thus obtaining q_f. (Note that this problem in q_d and q_f is the same as the converse problem in q and q_f.) Since q_d is generally given as an analytical formula, it is at most a matter of a few differentiations to obtain q_f.

It therefore suffices to discuss the relation $Dq = q_f$; and, as noted at the start of this chapter, this goes very much as for simple systems. In the matter of finding forced response q_r, the

TABLE 6·1

FORCED RESPONSE OF HIGHER-ORDER SYSTEM TO VARIOUS FORCINGS

	q_f/Q_2	q_r/Q_2
1	1	1
2	$\dfrac{t}{B_1} + A$	$\dfrac{t}{B_1} + A - 1$
3	$\left(\dfrac{t}{B_1}\right)^2 + A\,\dfrac{t}{B_1} + B$	$\left(\dfrac{t}{B_1}\right)^2 + (A - 2)\left(\dfrac{t}{B_1}\right) - A + B + 2 - 2\,\dfrac{B_2}{B_1{}^2}$
4	$e^{\sigma_f t}$	$\dfrac{e^{\sigma_f t}}{1 + B_1\sigma_f + B_2\sigma_f{}^2 + \cdots + B_n\sigma_f{}^n}$

same procedure may be used as was used for simple systems. In Table 6·1 are given a few results on forced response applicable to higher-order systems. The symbols B_1, B_2, $\cdots$, B_n are used for the parameters, as in Eq. 2·6. The results apply to any order of system, provided of course that the B's are given correct values. Item 3 for instance, applied to first-order systems, requires $B_2 = 0$. The complex exponential, item 4, includes the real exponential, the sinusoid, and the exponentially damped sinusoid, as in Chapters 3 and 4.

Values of q_r from this table, in conjunction with Eqs. 6·9, 6·10, and 6·11, solve the direct problem for third-order systems. The same type of treatment given third-order systems in Section 6·2 may also be worked out for systems of still higher order.

A result of some intrinsic interest, which at the same time serves as an illustration of results that may be worked out in the theory of nth-order systems, is the response to an impulse. The results obtained for first-order and second-order systems in Section 3·1 and Section 4·5 may be included in the general statement: for an nth-order system, the effect of an impulse is to add a term I/B_n to the initial value of the $(n - 1)$ derivative of q, where B_n is the last parameter in the series, $B_1, B_2, \cdots, B_n$. That this statement does in fact apply to higher-order systems as well as to simple systems may be shown by considering as for simple systems the limiting form of the sum $\sum_{i=1}^{n} r_i{}^{n-1} C_i e^{r_i t}$, which represents the derivative in question. The constants C_i determined in terms of the roots $r_1, \cdots, r_n$ by the initial conditions, are expressed in determinants

$$C_i = \frac{A_i}{\Delta} \qquad (6·39)$$

where

$$\Delta = \begin{vmatrix} 1 & 1 & \cdots & 1 \\ r_1 & r_2 & \cdots & r_n \\ r_1{}^2 & r_2{}^2 & \cdots & r_n{}^2 \\ \cdot & \cdot & & \cdot \\ \cdot & \cdot & & \cdot \\ \cdot & \cdot & & \cdot \\ r_1{}^{n-1} & r_2{}^{n-1} & \cdots & r_n{}^{n-1} \end{vmatrix} \qquad (6·40)$$

and A_i is a minor of unity in Δ, multiplied by Q_2, the height of the pulse. Now it is possible to write

$$\lim_{T \to 0} (\Sigma r_i{}^{n-1} C_i e^{r_i T}) = I \left(\frac{r_1 r_2 \cdots r_n}{\Delta} \right) \lim_{T \to 0} \frac{\Sigma b_i e^{r_i T}}{T} \qquad (6·41)$$

where b_i is r_i times the minor of $r_i{}^{n-1}$ in Δ.

Since $\Sigma b_i = 0$, to satisfy initial conditions, the limit must be evaluated by differentiating numerator and denominator with respect to T. This gives

$$\lim_{T \to 0} \frac{\Sigma b_i e^{r_i T}}{T} = \Sigma r_i b_i \qquad (6·42)$$

But the sum on the right is by definition of the b_i the determinant Δ. Hence Eq. 6·41 is

$$\lim_{T \to 0} (\Sigma r_i{}^{n-1} C_i e^{r_i T}) = I \cdot r_1 r_2 r_3 \cdots r_n \qquad (6·43)$$

In this brief sketch of the proof, a factor $(-1)^n$ has been omitted by neglect of signs. This should appear in Eq. 6·43, where it would make the term on the right identical with I/B_n. By similar arguments it may be shown that other initial values, of derivatives of order lower than $n - 1$, are unaffected by the impulse.

6·5   Stability. Because of the increased difficulty for higher-order systems of finding actual values of the auxiliary equation's roots, it is natural that much attention has been given to finding properties of the roots without knowing their values. The property of greatest practical significance is degree of stability. Mathematically this property of the roots is measured by the sign and magnitude of the real parts of the roots. Negative real parts mean stability; positive real parts mean instability. Fortunately, the degree of stability of the roots can be investigated rather easily, compared to numerical calculation of roots.

The question concerns the roots of the algebraic equation

$$D(r) = B_n r^n + B_{n-1} r^{n-1} + \cdots + B_1 r + 1 = 0 \quad (6·44)$$

Since the roots in general may be complex, it is necessary to carry out a general discussion of the roots in terms of the complex r-plane, which includes all possible complex values (and therefore also all real values) of the variable r. Given the n real numbers B_1 to B_n, where in the complex plane will the n roots of Eq. 6·44 lie? One way of answering this question was made available by the mathematician Cauchy about a hundred years ago. He established a method for saying how many roots of Eq. 6·44 lie in any given portion of the r-plane. The method is as follows.

In Eq. 6·44 r is the independent complex variable and D is the dependent variable. As r varies in the r-plane, D varies in the D-plane. r and D may be referred to as vectors in their respective planes. Consider now a certain area of the r-plane, bounded by a contour C_1. As the r-vector traces this contour C_1, the dependent vector D will also trace some contour C_2 in the D-plane. Cauchy showed that, for each root of Eq. 6·44 lying in the area bounded by C_1, the vector D will make one revolution about the origin. Hence the number of roots in a given portion of the r-plane may be counted by counting the revolutions of the D-vector as the r-vector traces the contour surrounding the area in question.

In regard to stability, the portion of the r-plane of interest is the half-plane to the right of the axis of imaginaries. Let

$r = \rho + j\omega$. Then the contour C_1 is chosen, as shown in Fig. 6·10 to start at 0, go along the negative ω-axis to $-\infty$, circle with infinite radius around the arc abc to the $+\infty$ end of the ω-axis, and then come back to the origin. Figure 6·11 shows how the D-vector for a stable second-order system moves as r traces the contour C_1 of Fig. 6·10. Corresponding portions of the contours C_1 and C_2

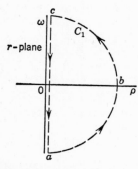

FIG. 6·10.   Contour in   FIG. 6·11.   Contour in D-plane.
        r-plane.

are similarly labeled 0-a-b-c. The angles turned through by the D-vector for the successive portions of C_2 are:

portion $0a$: $-\pi$
portion abc: $+2\pi$
portion $c0$: $-\pi$

In general, for an nth-order system, the corresponding tabulation would be:

portion $0a$: $-A$
portion abc: $+n\pi$
portion $c0$: $-A$

Now the second-order system of Fig. 6·11 has a net angle of $(-\pi + 2\pi - \pi)$, or zero, and therefore is stable. For the nth-order system to be stable requires that its net angle be zero, or

$$n\pi - 2A = 0 \qquad (6·45)$$

where A is the angle turned through by the D-vector as r moves from 0 to c along C_1. Or, to make a more complete statement of the result, an nth-order system has n_p roots with positive real parts, where

$$n_p = \frac{n\pi - 2A}{2\pi} \qquad (6\cdot46)$$

The form of this result makes it clear that one does not need to plot all the contour C_2, but only the portion $0c$, corresponding to the variation of ω from 0 to $+\infty$. For the calculation of this plot Eq. 6·44 becomes

$$D(j\omega) = (1 - B_2\omega^2 + B_4\omega^4 \cdots) + j\omega(B_1 - B_3\omega^2 + B_5\omega^4 \cdots) \qquad (6\cdot47)$$

Figure 6·12 gives such plots for stable systems from $n = 1$ to $n = 4$. It is seen that in each of these plots A satisfies the stability requirement of Eq. 6·45. Since this equation requires $A = +n(\pi/2)$, a convenient form in which to express and remember the stability condition is: *the D-vector must turn n quadrants in the positive direction as ω goes from 0 to $+\infty$.*

To illustrate the variety of forms the contour may take, depending on the relative signs and magnitudes of the parameters, the ten different possibilities for a third-order system are shown in Fig. 6·13. In each one, the contour starts from the point 0, corresponding to the real value $D = 1$.

The drawing of rough sketches such as these is very easy with

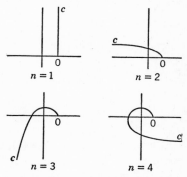

FIG. 6·12. D-contours for stable systems.

the help of Eq. 6·47 and requires only a few points near the origin to establish the nature of the contour. In return, the amount of information contained in such sketches is considerable. In a sense, Fig. 6·13 tells the whole story of third-order systems—in particular, the story of the effect on stability of changes in any of the parameters. For example, consider the transition from case (a) to case (b) to case (c), as a result of decreasing the value of B_1. Starting with a stable system, the point at which the contour intersects the negative real axis moves in toward the origin and eventually passes through the origin. The value of B_1 for which this occurs is the value that would give the auxiliary equation two purely imaginary roots. This represents the transition from stable to unstable conditions. As B_1 is still further reduced, the contour looks as shown for case (b), with the hump above the real axis becoming smaller until finally, for $B_1 = 0$, it disappears; then, as B_1 takes on negative values of increasing magnitude, the

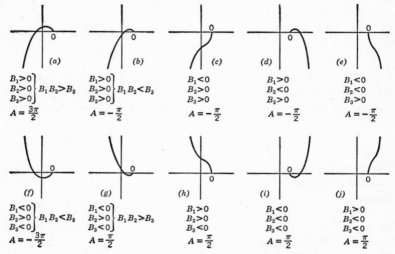

FIG. 6·13. D-contours for third-order systems.

contour appears as in case (c), with the point of inflection moving farther and farther from point 0.

Similarly, cases (a), (b), and (d) show effects of progressive decrease in B_2. The case of $B_2 = 0$ in this sequence is represented by a straight vertical line through the point 0.

Considering that of the ten cases only one, case (a), represents a stable system, the relative rarity of stability is apparent. Of course, the exactly opposite case, of all three roots in the right half of the r-plane, is equally rare, being represented only by case (f).

The condition for stability is that all parameters be positive, and in addition that $B_1 B_2 > B_3$. Similar rules for stability can be stated for any nth-order system. These rules, associated with the names of Routh and Hurwitz, need not be elaborated here, since they involve about as much calculation as a sketch of the

D-contour and do not yield as much information. The rules are, in fact, a part of this information implicit in the geometrical features of the contour for a stable system and may therefore be deduced in any given case from consideration of Eq. 6·47 and the contours. The rule that all parameters must be positive may be thus deduced, as well as the other relations. Thus for $n = 3$, Fig. 6·13 shows that one of the stability conditions is that when the imaginary part of *D* vanishes the real part shall be negative. The imaginary part vanishes for $\omega^2 = B_1/B_3$. For this value of ω the real part is $1 - (B_1B_2/B_3)$, and for this to be negative requires $B_1B_2 > B_3$. For $n = 4$, the stable contour shown in Fig. 6·12 indicates that there are two stability conditions in addition to all positive parameters: one, that when the imaginary part vanishes, the real part shall be negative, and two, that when the real part vanishes (the second time) the imaginary part shall be negative. Either of these conditions leads to the relation

$$B_1(B_2B_3 - B_4B_1) > B_3{}^2$$

which is one of the relations arrived at by Routh's rule; and, assuming B_1 positive, this includes the other result of Routh's method,

$$B_2B_3 > B_4B_1$$

Therefore, if one remembers the simple geometrical shape of a stable *D*-contour and in addition the simple rule that all parameters must be positive, the rest of the story in any given case may very easily be worked out from these two as first principles, with the help of Eq. 6·47.

Calculation and plotting of the *D*-contour is most readily done by the use of Eq. 6·47, which gives the complex number *D* in cartesian form. Experimental work, however, might furnish *D* in polar form,

$$D = \mathbf{G}_D = G_D e^{j\phi_D} \tag{6·48}$$

since often it is gain and phase shift that are measured. Hence there is sometimes an advantage in presenting the information given in the *D*-contour in terms of G_D and ϕ_D. If G_D and ϕ_D are given, it is easy to plot the *D*-contour. Conversely, if the contour is given, one can plot the G_D and ϕ_D characteristics, provided the values of ω are known corresponding to various points of the contour.

At this point it is well to comment again on the important role of sinusoidal functions. The variation of r along the ω-axis gives D the form of a sinusoidal gain function, and it is the variation of this gain which determines the stability of the system. Thus the sinusoidal behavior of the system is inextricably bound up with its general transient behavior.

There is one more phase of the stability question which needs discussion. This concerns the role of the numerator $N(p)$ of the general transfer impedance operator $Z_t(p) = N(p)/D(p)$. Since the roots of the auxiliary equation are given entirely by the parameters of D, N does not enter into the transient stability. There remains, however, the forced response. As shown in Eq. 6·38, $q_f = Nq_d$. Hence for q_f to be a finite function, there must be limitations on N, on q_d, or on both. If q_d is any of the functions listed as forcing in the Tables 3·1 and 4·1 of forced responses, $N(p)$ can involve derivatives of arbitrarily high order, without making q_f infinite. Suppose, however, that q_d were to have pulse forcing. The derivative of q_d would then be infinite where the pulse instantaneously returns to zero, so that q_f and hence q would be infinite. For all forcings, then, and particularly if q_d is discontinuous or otherwise "pathological," care must be taken that $N(p) \cdot q_d$ remains finite. Otherwise there appears to be no need for restricting $N(p)$ in any way.

6·6 Examples. The three examples to be discussed here are a current control, an engine speed control, and the nuclear chain reactor. These systems all have interesting features in relation to resolution into components.

The current control system is of the kind that can be used for a heavy direct current, such as the current in the magnet of a cyclotron. A schematic diagram is given in Fig. 6·14. The load is represented as a resistance R in series with an inductance L. q is chosen to be the current through this load. A shunt of resistance R_s in series with the load gives a control voltage, $E_s = R_s q$, which is the input to the control amplifier. The output of this amplifier is a voltage E_1, which establishes a field current in an exciter generator (possibly an amplidyne). This in turn excites the field of the main generator with a voltage E_2. The voltage output of the main generator is E_3.

In writing the equations for the system, a number of approximations will be made—none of which, however, does severe violence to reality. The exciter, the generator, and the load are assumed to act as isolated first-order systems of time constants τ_1, τ_2, and τ_3, respectively. The amplifier time constants are assumed to be negligibly small compared to those of the generators and load,

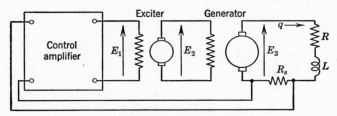

FIG. 6·14.   Current control system.

so that the amplifier acts as a zero-order system. Under these conditions the following equations apply:

$$(\tau_1 p + 1)E_2 = A_1 E_1 \tag{6·49}$$

$$(\tau_2 p + 1)E_3 = A_2 E_2 \tag{6·50}$$

$$(\tau_3 p + 1)q = \frac{E_3}{R} \tag{6·51}$$

$$E_1 = -A R_s (q - q_d) \tag{6·52}$$

In these equations, A, A_1, and A_2 are dimensionless constants representing the voltage gains across the amplifier, the exciter, and the generator, respectively. $R_s q$ is the voltage input to the control amplifier, which operates according to Eq. 6·52—its output is proportional to the departure of q from q_d. In Eq. 6·51, τ_3 may be taken equal to L/R, considering $R_s \ll R$.

If the above four equations are multiplied together and the factor $E_1 E_2 E_3$ divided out, the resulting equation may be written

$$\left(\frac{\tau_1 \tau_2 \tau_3}{1 + K_f} p^3 + \frac{\tau_1 \tau_2 + \tau_2 \tau_3 + \tau_3 \tau_1}{1 + K_f} p^2 + \frac{\tau_1 + \tau_2 + \tau_3}{1 + K_f} p + 1 \right) q$$

$$= \frac{K_f}{1 + K_f} q_d \tag{6·53}$$

with K_f defined by

$$K_f = \frac{A A_1 A_2 R_s}{R} \tag{6·54}$$

Before proceeding with Eq. 6·53, consider the open system, without any feedback from R_s to the input of the amplifier, so that E_1 becomes proportional simply to q_d. The equation of this system is obtained by putting $q = 0$ in Eq. 6·52 and proceeding as above. This gives

$$[\tau_1\tau_2\tau_3 p^3 + (\tau_1\tau_2 + \tau_2\tau_3 + \tau_3\tau_1)p^2$$
$$+ (\tau_1 + \tau_2 + \tau_3)p + 1]q = K_f q_d \quad (6\cdot55)$$

Let B_1, B_2, and B_3 denote the parameters in Eq. 6·55. Then it is clear that the open system satisfies the stability condition

$$B_1 B_2 > B_3 \quad (6\cdot56)$$

For substituting their values in terms of τ_1, τ_2, and τ_3, it can be seen that

$$\frac{B_1 B_2}{B_3} = 3 + \left(\frac{\tau_1}{\tau_2} + \frac{\tau_2}{\tau_1}\right) + \left(\frac{\tau_1}{\tau_3} + \frac{\tau_3}{\tau_1}\right) + \left(\frac{\tau_2}{\tau_3} + \frac{\tau_3}{\tau_2}\right) \quad (6\cdot57)$$

So, if τ_1, τ_2, and τ_3 are all positive, as they would be for the components shown in Fig. 6·14, $B_1 B_2/B_3$ is certain to be greater than 1.

Consider now the parameters of the closed system of Eq. 6·53. For this system to be stable requires

$$\frac{B_1 B_2}{B_3} > 1 + K_f \quad (6\cdot58)$$

So the question is: how big is K_f? Looking at Eq. 6·53, it is seen that under static conditions

$$q = \frac{K_f}{1 + K_f} q_d \quad (6\cdot59)$$

So, to obtain a good approximation to the ideal duplicator criterion of $q = q_d$, it is necessary that K_f be quite large compared to unity. For instance, if static error is to be held to 0.1 per cent, K_f must be about 1000, and therefore $B_1 B_2/B_3$ must be greater than 1000. Equation 6·57 shows that this can be achieved only by having time constants of different orders of magnitude. (If $\tau_1 = \tau_2 = \tau_3$, for example, $B_1 B_2/B_3 = 9$.) Assuming τ_3, the time constant of the load, to be fixed at a value of something like 10 seconds, the only hope of combining stability with low static error lies in making τ_1 small, perhaps by use of an amplidyne or an electronic exciter. (τ_2, the time constant of the main generator, presumably is fixed.)

Note that the open system is a resolved third-order system, satisfying Eq. 6·55. Introducing feedback changes the system equation to Eq. 6·53, the roots of which may be very different from τ_1, τ_2, and τ_3. Thus, if the closed system is resolved, its components would not correspond at all closely to the components of the open system.

The next example to be considered is also a control system—the centrifugal, or "flyball," governor on an engine. (This example may be compared with the speed control discussed in Section 3·8.) Again, some simplifying assumptions are applied. The engine is represented simply as a flywheel of moment of inertia I. The governor itself is assumed to have mass M and damping C as well as a spring constant K. It therefore satisfies a second-order differential equation,

$$M\ddot{x} + C\dot{x} + Kx = F \qquad (6·60)$$

where x is displacement of the governor sleeve and F is force applied to the sleeve because of the rotating balls.

The equation of the engine is

$$I\dot{q} = u + u_n \qquad (6·61)$$

where q is the angular velocity of the engine, u is the torque developed by the engine, and u_n is the noise torque, or disturbance, to which it is hoped the response will be small.

The connection between Eqs. 6·60 and 6·61 is twofold: first, the torque u depends on the displacement x of the governor sleeve; and second, the force F is a function of the speed q. The simplest assumptions will be used for these dependences, namely,

$$F = S_g(q - q_d) \qquad (6·62)$$

and

$$u = -S_e x \qquad (6·63)$$

where q_d is the speed desired, and S_g and S_e are constants. Equation 6·62 can be regarded as an approximation valid over a small range of q near q_d; in general, centrifugal force is proportional to the square of angular velocity.

Combining Eqs. 6·60 to 6·63 to eliminate x, F, and u, the equation in q is found to be

$$\left(\frac{IM}{S_eS_g}p^3 + \frac{IC}{S_eS_g}p^2 + \frac{IK}{S_eS_g}p + 1\right)q = q_d$$

$$+ \left(\frac{M}{S_eS_g}p^2 + \frac{C}{S_eS_g}p + \frac{K}{S_eS_g}\right)u_n \quad (6·64)$$

The forcing is seen to consist of the reference quantity plus terms in u_n and its derivatives. It is clear that the error will be small

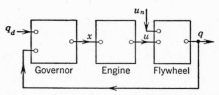

FIG. 6·15.   Diagram of governor-controlled engine.

if the product S_eS_g is large.   On the other hand, the stability condition is

$$\frac{IKC}{M} > S_eS_g \quad (6·65)$$

Hence S_eS_g may be made indefinitely larger only as M is made correspondingly smaller or the product IKC larger. It is particularly interesting to note that, if I, K, and M were fixed, an increase in C would promote stability.

Figure 6·15 gives a schematic diagram of the system. The displacement x of the governor sleeve may be considered to move a throttle on the engine. In Eq. 6·63, the engine is assumed to respond instantaneously to the throttle actions. This is one of the assumptions which may not be in strict accord with reality. Another assumption is that the displacement x is given as in Eq. 6·60, independent of u—that is, independent of how the engine is running. This assumption implies that the spring (of stiffness K) is strong compared to any possible reaction of the engine on the throttle mechanism.

It is interesting to compare this system with the current control discussed above, particularly in the differences between open and closed system operation. The open current control (without feedback) was seen to be a third-order system with forcing proportional to q_d (Eq. 6·55); with feedback (Eq. 6·53) the system still operates as a third-order system with forcing proportional to q_d, though the parameters are reduced in value. The equation for open operation of the governor-engine system, obtained by putting $q = 0$ in Eq. 6·62, is

$$\left(\frac{MI}{S_e} p^3 + \frac{CI}{S_e} p^2 + \frac{KI}{S_e} p\right) q = S_g q_d + \left(\frac{M}{S_e} p^2 + \frac{C}{S_e} p + \frac{K}{S_e}\right) u_n$$

$$(6\cdot66)$$

or

$$\left(\frac{M}{K} p^2 + \frac{C}{K} p + 1\right) q = \frac{S_g S_e}{KI} \int q_d \, dt + \int \left(\frac{M}{K} p^2 + \frac{C}{K} p + 1\right) \frac{u_n}{I} dt$$

$$(6\cdot67)$$

so that here the transition from closed to open operation changes the order from third to second and makes the forcing proportional to the time integral of q_d.

The third and final example of higher-order system to be discussed here is the nuclear chain reactor, already discussed as a second-order system in Section 4·10. The system was treated as second-order on the basis of lumping all the delayed neutron emitters into a single group. If, instead of one group of such fission fragments, an arbitrary number $(n - 1)$ of such groups is considered, the two Eqs. 4·80 and 4·81 are replaced by n equations

$$\dot{q} = (\rho_p - \rho_d)q + \sum_1^{n-1} \rho_{ek} f_k + s \qquad (6\cdot68)$$

$$\dot{f}_k = -\rho_{ek} f_k + \rho_{dk} q \qquad (6\cdot69)$$

The index k runs through integral values from 1 to $n - 1$; hence there are $n - 1$ equations of the form 6·69. The quantity ρ_d is approximately equal to the sum, $\Sigma \rho_{dk}$. The n Eqs. 6·68 and 6·69 may be reduced to a single nth-order equation by substituting in Eq. 6·68 $f_k = \rho_{dk} q/(p + \rho_{ek})$ from Eq. 6·69, giving

$$\dot{q} = (\rho_p - \rho_d)q + \sum_1^{n-1} \frac{\rho_{ek} \rho_{dk}}{p + \rho_{ek}} q + s \qquad (6\cdot70)$$

If the denominators in the sum were all multiplied out, the equation would involve derivatives of q up to the nth, derivatives of s up to $n - 1$, and derivatives of ρ_p up to $n - 1$. No attempt will be made here to deal with so general a problem. Instead, the transient response, assuming ρ_p to have after $t = 0$ some fixed value ρ_{p2}, will be considered.

The auxiliary equation is

$$r + \rho_d - \rho_{p2} = \sum_{1}^{n-1} \frac{\rho_{ek}\rho_{dk}}{r + \rho_{ek}} \tag{6.71}$$

Because of the particular form in which this equation is obtained, a graphical solution of it is possible, offering considerable advantage over the standard approach to solution of the auxiliary equation. Figure 6·16 shows this graphical method. The roots are given by the intersections of the straight line $y = r + \rho_d - \rho_{p2}$ with the multi-branch hyperbola $y = \Sigma(\rho_{ek}\rho_{dk})/(r + \rho_{ek})$. For an nth-order system, there are n branches, n intersections, and so n real roots. In Fig. 6·16 only a few branches are indicated. The last branch in the negative r-direction will not cross the r-axis but will approach it asymptotically from the minus y-side, just as the last branch in the positive r-direction approaches the r-axis from the positive y-side.

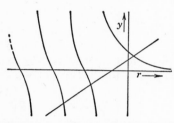

FIG. 6·16. Graphical solution of auxiliary equation.

The solution illustrated in Fig. 6·16 shows one positive root and $n - 1$ negative roots. It therefore represents an unstable system. The transition from stability to instability occurs at $\rho_d - \rho_{p2} = \Sigma\rho_{dk}$; or to the approximation that $\rho_d = \Sigma\rho_{dk}$, at $\rho_{p2} = 0$. On this latter basis, positive ρ_{p2} would mean one positive root and negative ρ_{p2} would mean all negative roots.

To carry out fully the calculation of response for any specified initial conditions, the determination of the constants would be carried out along the lines indicated for the second-order approximation in Section 4·10. This aspect of the problem will not be elaborated here. The example of the chain reactor is included here mainly to emphasize the fact that occasionally, because of the particular mathematical details, a higher-order system may be dealt with more easily than by the standard approaches described earlier in this chapter. The device of Fig. 6·16 is not in general available for solving the auxiliary equation of an nth-order system. But, being available for the reactor, it does make the mathematical treatment of the reactor that much easier.

CHAPTER

7

Measuring Instruments

7·1 Physical systems and measurements. Repeatedly in the preceding pages there have been statements that a certain quantity was "known," or hypotheses that began "given a certain quantity." Each such allusion was an implicit reference to a process of measurement, for it is only by the processes of measurement that physical quantities can be known or given. Hence the concept of measurement occupies a fundamental place in the response of physical systems and, indeed, in all of physics.

Assuming that measurement involves the use of instruments, and that instruments are physical systems which like other physical systems require measurements to be understood, one is in danger of falling into the infinite regression: instruments are needed to make measurements to understand instruments to make measurements to understand instruments ····. The way out of this trouble is by the introduction of standards. It would be too long a story here to give the interesting and important account of how, starting with a few standards, the complex structure of physical measurements is built up, encompassing the possibility of measuring all the numerous physical quantities. But this basic role of measurement has been mentioned here in order to emphasize the fact that there are two aspects of the relation between measuring instruments in particular and physical systems in general. One aspect is the fact that instruments are physical systems to which the methods of study given in this book may be applied. The other aspect is the fact that instruments are intimately involved in those concepts and processes of measurement which make the whole study of physical systems possible.

The remainder of this chapter may seem to be more directly and explicitly concerned with the first-mentioned aspect, but the second aspect, the fundamental role of measurement, will also come to the fore occasionally, especially in some of the discussions on error.

7·2   Instruments as physical systems.   How do measuring instruments fit the general pattern of physical systems?   It seems reasonable to identify q with the **reading** of the instrument, and q_f (or, in general, q_d) with the **true value** of the quantity being measured.   These definitions fit in with the criterion for perfect performance of a duplicator, namely, $q = q_d$.   Thus if one's watch indicates twelve noon at exactly the instant when it really is twelve noon, the watch is performing satisfactorily.   However, a little thought about this homely example will generate some questions.   What is meant by reading in this instance—the numbers measuring the positions of the hands, or the numbers telegraphed from eye to brain after a more or less hurried glance at the watch face?   What is the meaning of "when it really is twelve noon"?

The exact definition of q is somewhat arbitrary.   But the simplest and most useful definition is to say that the reading q is the absolutely final numerical result of the measurement after all corrections, conversions, or other operations have been carried out.   If the position of the watch hands is exactly at noon, but the visual reading (perhaps because the watch is viewed at an angle) is 11:59, then the reading is 11:59.   If in addition the owner of the watch remembers that it is 5 minutes slow and mentally adds the 5 minutes, then the reading is 12:04.

The definition of q may seem misleading on the basis that "it's no fault of the watch if the owner doesn't look at it carefully or if he doesn't remember whether it's fast or slow."   A little reflection, however, shows that it is at least partly the fault of the watch.   A good watch is easy to read correctly, even in a hurry.   Also, a good watch runs neither fast nor slow; it runs right.   Everything considered, the discussion of instrument accuracy is materially simplified by defining the reading q as the final result, obtained in close duplication, presumably, of the true value of q_d.

The problem of defining q is merely the making of a more or less arbitrary choice of what should be called the reading of an instrument.   The problem of understanding just what is meant by the true value q_d is considerably more subtle and elusive.   A fuller insight into the nature of this concept will, it is hoped, be afforded by some of the later sections of this chapter. However, a preliminary statement of the principal idea will be given here. Belief in the reality of the true value is profession of faith in the possibility of making a more or less accurate measurement. A few examples will illustrate this.

Consider a jar full of beans. The concept of the true value of the number of beans in the jar is real only because one can visualize a measurement process which would establish this true value. Does this mean, if the beans have been counted once and found to be 5083 in number, that $q_d = 5083$? Not at all! Maybe there was a mistake—one cannot guarantee this value. In fact, the concept of the true value really does not depend on whether the beans were counted or whether they ever will be counted. It is the *possibility* of an accurate count that lends reality to the true value. Such a count can be visualized even for a more difficult quantity such as the number of people in the United States at a specified instant. Even though no means exists for making the count, it can be conceived in the imagination; and that is all that is needed to give substance to the concept of the true value.

What is the true value of the thickness of a rug? Here there is difficulty beyond that encountered in the counting problem. One can imagine a perfectly definite true value for the number of beans in the jar. But there is difficulty even in imagining a definite value of the rug thickness. The concept of thickness itself is somewhat vague in this case, partly because different parts of the rug might have different thicknesses and partly because the thickness measured at any one place would depend on how it was measured. In spite of the difference between a rug and a sheet of metal foil, exactly the same difficulties exist for measurement of the foil thickness. In fact, these two problems are involved in any measurement: one, understanding the concept of the quantity to be measured; and two, understanding the concept of a "true" method of measurement from which the concept of the true value follows.

In summary, then, the true value of a physical quantity is based first of all on a definition of the quantity. Next comes the concept of a true, or perfect, or correct, process of measuring the quantity. The true value is the result of a perfect measurement. It must be emphasized that all three—definition, measurement, value—exist only in the imagination. One can never "find" the true value of a physical quantity. But the more nearly an actual measurement approaches the perfect measurement, the more nearly will the result of that measurement duplicate the true value.

7·3 Instrument specifications. The technology of measuring instruments has grown very rapidly until it has assumed rather startling proportions. Not even the most casual review of this enormous field can be made here. Instruments are to be discussed here mainly in the general terms of physical systems, with only such references to the details of instrumentation as are needed to establish clearly the place of instruments, and of the measurement process, in the general picture. This point of view necessarily involves omission of many phases of instrumentation of very great importance to instrument designers, manufacturers, and users—such matters as cost, appearance, convenience, ruggedness, etc.

The term "instrument specifications" is therefore introduced here in the limited sense of "specifications required to describe an instrument as a physical system." As these specifications are discussed below, the reader will note that in the main they apply to any duplicator as well as to instruments. In fact the subject of instrumentation is more and more coming to be understood as including, besides measuring instruments, the two other chief types of duplicators—regulators and servos.

To specify an instrument, in the limited sense mentioned, it is necessary to give a quantitative evaluation of three factors: **accuracy, range,** and **efficiency.** Each of these three specifications will receive detailed treatment in subsequent sections, but brief (and only partially satisfactory) definitions will be given here.

Accuracy measures the degree to which an instrument satisfies the duplicator criterion, $q = q_d$. It is therefore expressed in terms of the error, $q - q_d$. The general form of the quantitative definition is $1 -$ (fraction), the numerator of the fraction being some measure of estimated error, and the denominator being some measure of the reading. Different possibilities and their meanings are discussed in Section 7·6.

Range has two aspects: **scale range** and **frequency range.** Scale range measures the difference between (or the ratio of) the largest and smallest readings that may be obtained with the instrument. Frequency range gives the frequencies over which measurements may be made with a specified accuracy.

Efficiency measures the effect of q_d*. It is therefore very closely related to impedance (Section 5·4). Efficiency is defined as the reading q divided by the power input to the instrument. That is, efficiency is the ratio $q/(q_d q_d*)$. Since $q = q_d$ approximately, this definition is nearly the same as $1/q_d*$.

The remainder of this chapter is devoted to a discussion of these three instrument specifications. The above order in which the three were introduced and defined is the order of importance in which the average instrument user would probably rank them. This order will be reversed in the following sections, because efficiency and range can be disposed of with comparatively brief discussions, whereas accuracy needs to be discussed at great length.

All instruments used to measure a given physical quantity q will be said to belong to the same **class.** For example, all instruments which measure temperature belong to the class of thermometers. Obviously, specifications are significant only for comparative rating of instruments in the same class. For instruments of any given class, any one of the three desirable qualities—high accuracy, wide range, high efficiency—can be indefinitely increased only at the expense of one or both of the others. Practical design is therefore a compromise of these three and, in the commercial field at least, of other factors of cost, appearance, etc.

7·4 Efficiency. The familiar voltmeter, with its specification of ohms per volt, gives one illustration of an efficiency specification. Similarly, ammeter efficiency could be specified in mhos per ampere. In the terminology preferred here, however, a voltmeter of 20,000 ohms per volt may be said to have an efficiency, at a reading of 1 volt, of 20,000 volts per watt; and an ammeter having a resistance of 0.1 ohm would have an efficiency, at a reading of 1 ampere, of 10 amperes per watt. It is clear that the numerical value of efficiency must be specified at a particular reading, since in general q_d* varies with q.

The units of efficiency are always the same as q units per watt. Thus this use of the word "efficiency" is closely similar to, but not identical with, the general engineering usage of "output power divided by input power." Where necessary to avoid confusion, the present usage may be distinguished by the longer name "instrument efficiency."

The above examples of voltmeter and ammeter are typical of the simpler problems of defining efficiency. There are two respects in which the concept might be broadened. First, there is the question of "reactive power input" versus "resistive power input." The direct-current voltmeter and ammeter have essentially pure resistive input—that is, under equilibrium direct-current conditions the input power is all dissipated in the resistance of the coil circuit. Only when the instruments are connected or disconnected, or when the value of q_d is changing, do the reactive circuit elements, such as coil inductance, have an effect. Of course, in some unusual applications of these instruments these transient conditions might be important. But in the usual application one can think of the input power as purely resistive.

With some other instruments, such as alternating-current meters, however, the reactive power input may be as important as the resistive. Even though reactive power does not represent a net flow of energy into the instrument, the instantaneous flow may itself be of significance. For many instruments, moreover, the power transfer (resistive or reactive) is zero except at the beginning and end of a measurement. A simple example is the spring balance. If the spring constant is K, the energy stored in the spring by a mass M, after it has come to rest, is $M^2 g^2 / 2K$. The potential energy lost by the mass is $M^2 g^2 / K$. But there is no convenient way of converting either of these energies into power, so that the definition of efficiency seems not to apply. However, the ratio (q^2/energy), which is here proportional to K/g^2, is a measure of the same *idea* of efficiency which was put into the definition of (q/power).

It appears desirable therefore to let the meaning of efficiency be broad enough to cover total power, resistive or reactive, and transient or steady. Such a broadening means that efficiency cannot, in general, be specified in terms of a single number; and conversely, when efficiency is given as a single number it is to be assumed that only resistive power is being considered.

The second respect in which the concept of efficiency might be broadened may be understood by considering why efficiency, in any case, is important. High efficiency is desirable because it means that using the instrument to make the measurement will not disturb the system being measured. Such disturbance may come from too low an impedance, since then the input power is relatively large and consequently capable of having an appreciable effect. As a result the measurement may show load error, meaning error due to the change in effective q_d due to the load (i.e., power input) of the instrument itself. Another result may be disturbed functioning of the system being measured, as when a low-impedance voltmeter is connected to a delicately adjusted electronic circuit. However, the disturbance may not always be solely a function of input power, and the question is whether efficiency should include a measure of such disturbance.

As an example which illustrates the kind of disturbance which may occur, consider the hot-wire anemometer used to measure turbulence of air flow in wind tunnels. This device consists of a very fine wire carrying an electrical current which heats it. When this wire is exposed to the air stream, the velocity fluctuations in the flow cause the wire to be more or less cooled. The resultant changes in temperature of the wire are measured in terms of the wire's electrical resistance. Now although this wire be mounted on as small a support as is feasible, nevertheless the introduction of the instrument into the stream is bound to have some effect on those very details of instantaneous velocity which the instrument is supposed to measure. The effect of the hot wire assembly in changing the flow patterns it is supposed to measure is related in somewhat obscure fashion to such things as the size and shape of the assembly and its supporting elements, the shape and dimensions of the channel in which the flow occurs, and the physical properties of the air. The disturbance of the flow might be partially described in terms of power, but a complete quantitative specification is pretty clearly out of the question.

As this example illustrates, efficiency is closely related to such qualitative factors as simplicity, convenience, and ease of use—all of which were ruled out of consideration at the start of Section 7·3. Nevertheless, even where it is hard to draw a sharp line limiting the scope of efficiency, and still harder to give a numerical specification of it, the broad concept of efficiency retains its usefulness in helping to assure the design or selection of an instrument best suited to a particular problem.

A widely used method of avoiding load error and disturbance is to build the instrument into the system. Then, although the values of q_d and the functioning of the system are indeed affected by the presence of the instrument, they are permanently and consistently affected in a way that may be allowed for in the design.

Measurement of electrical resistance will be considered as a final example in the definition and meaning of efficiency. The ordinary ohmmeter operates by sending a small current through the resistance to be measured. Since q here is in ohms, the units of efficiency are ohms per watt, which is dimensionally the same as $1/(\text{amperes})^2$. That is, $q_d{}^*$ is the square of the current. Thus efficiency is inversely proportional to the square of the current sent by the ohmmeter into the resistor. Note that in this example there is a net continuous transfer of energy *from* the instrument *into* the system being measured. In most measurements the direction of power flow is the opposite. This energy transferred to the resistor may change its temperature and therefore its resistance—a typical example of the value of q_d being altered because of the instrument.

7·5 Range. To discuss scale range, it is first necessary to clarify the concept of the scale itself. It is worth noting that the scale may be considered a distinguishing feature of instruments. If a physical system has a scale, it may be an instrument; if it does not have a scale, it is not an instrument. To help understand just what the scale is and what its function is, consider the instrument divided functionally into two parts, as shown in Fig. 7.1. The instrument is shown to consist of a **mechanism** and a **scale.** The output of the mechanism is the displacement of an **index.** (The

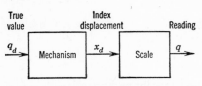

FIG. 7·1. Instrument mechanism and scale.

mechanism is not necessarily mechanical; it may involve pneumatic, hydraulic, or electrical, as well as mechanical, elements.) The index is usually a pointer, though it may be something else, such as a row of lights. (If the index is not a pointer, the term index displacement and more particularly the symbol x_d may still be used to refer to the indication given by the index.) The scale is the means by which the displacement x_d is interpreted to mean a certain number of units of q. That is, it converts the index displacement into the reading. Corresponding to the definition of q as the absolutely final result of the measurement, the definition of the scale must be taken in the broad sense of including not only an array of index marks and numbers, but also all the charts, correction formulas, or other factors which enter into the process of obtaining the final reading q.

Where it is desirable to refer to the reading taken directly from the index, the further notation of Fig. 7·2 may be used. Here the scale is considered in two parts: the index scale which yields an index reading x_r, and the scale convertor which converts the index reading into the final reading q. As an example, consider a cathode-ray oscilloscope used to measure voltage. The deflection of the luminous spot would be x_d. Unless the 'scope had been specially calibrated, the index reading x_r would also be deflection, say in inches. Then by means of the scale converter, which would probably be a formula involving constants of the circuit being measured and the 'scope's sensitivity and gain setting, the value x_r would be converted into q in volts.

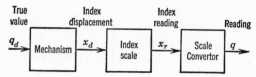

FIG. 7·2.   Further analysis of scale.

As another example, consider a multi-range ammeter with a single set of numbers on the index scale and a range switch multiplying by factors of 10. Then for a given reading x_d would be index displacement in inches, x_r would be amperes read from the index scale, and the convertor would be the range switch position by which x_r is converted to the reading q in amperes, equal to x_r multiplied by the proper power of 10.

Instruments for which x_r is dimensionally and numerically equal to q—that is, which have no scale convertor—are said to be **direct-reading.**

Now **scale range** Q_s may be defined as the difference between the largest reading possible and the smallest reading possible with the particular instrument. **Index scale range** Q_{is} is the range of the index scale in terms of q, without switching. Thus, if the ammeter mentioned above had an index scale range of 0 to 50 milliamperes and had three range switch positions giving multiplication by 1, 10, and 100, the scale range of the instrument would be 0 to 5 amperes.

The use of zero as the lower limit in such statements of range is misleading, since zero cannot actually be read accurately, but only some approximation to zero. A measure of range which is better in this respect is the **specific range,** a dimensionless quantity defined as Q_s/Q_c, where Q_c is the **least count.** Q_c is defined as the increment in q corresponding to the smallest increment in index reading x_r which can be detected with certainty by watching the index displacement x_d.

Comparing the multi-range ammeter described above with a single-range meter going from 0 to 5 amperes, assuming the two meters have index scales of the same shape and size, it is clear that, although both meters have the same scale range, the multi-range meter would have a much smaller least count on its lowest range and therefore a much higher specific range. In other words, if the least count of the multi-range instrument is taken as the smallest detectable change in x_r on its lowest scale, this value is $\frac{1}{100}$ of the least count for the single-scale instrument. The definition of least count Q_c proposed here is thus to be understood as meaning the smallest detectable change in q on any part of the instrument's scale under any condition. Admittedly, this definition is arbitrary, but the definition of specific range based on this definition of Q_c is believed to be a useful one.

If the instrument has a logarithmic scale—one in which the displacement of the index is proportional to the logarithm of q—the ratio of least count to scale reading is essentially constant for all values of q. For this particular kind of instrument, a good definition of specific range would be the ratio q/Q_c. If this definition were then applied to instruments with linear scales, the value would vary all the way from 1 at the bottom of the range (near zero on most scales) up to the value Q_s/Q_c at the top of the range. So from this point of view the definition adopted here, namely Q_s/Q_c, may be thought of as maximum specific range.

Since wide range can usually be achieved only at the expense of other desirable qualities, the desired or needed range should be given careful attention. In some instances wide range is not only unnecessary but actually objectionable. For example, the frequency meters used to monitor commercial electric power frequencies obviously need only a very limited range in the immediate vicinity of 60 cycles per second. For other instruments, of course, wide range is essential. An example of this sort is furnished by the sound level meter, which is expected to measure sound pressures varying by factors as large as 10,000 or even

100,000. Generally speaking, it is a difficult design undertaking to achieve wide range without sacrificing accuracy.

In extending width of range, the designer is sooner or later led to consider some scheme of switching. This by no means is a cure-all for the difficulties involved in achieving wide range, but it is often a practical and convenient method of increasing the useful range of a single instrument. The most serious objection is the fact that in many applications a continuous range is necessary or desirable—the step-wise operation involved in switching from one range to another being more or less objectionable.

Aside from the problems involved in obtaining wide range, there is always difficulty in obtaining extreme ranges—that is, ranges which cover either very small values of q_d or very large values. It is a matter of practical experience that for every class of instrument there is a common, every-day range of values for which instruments are readily available; but by going far enough in either direction beyond this range it becomes increasingly difficult to obtain ready-made means of measurement. This is true of temperature, pressure, voltage, current, mass, time, length—of practically any physical quantity one wishes to name. The factors which make measurement difficult in the extreme ranges differ for different quantities. But, if any generalization is worth while here, it would be that the principal difficulty at high ranges is caused by limitations in the physical properties of materials of which instruments may be made; and the principal difficulty at low ranges is some form of noise.

The concept of noise plays a very important role in the response of physical systems. In Eq. 5·6 the symbol q_n was introduced for noise, with the understanding that it was any forcing to which the desired response is zero or as near zero as one can get. Now, as q_d becomes smaller, it eventually reaches magnitude comparable with q_n; and finally the spurious response to q_n overshadows the response to the true value q_d. Various schemes have been developed for reducing the response to q_n (cf. Chapter 8), but no scheme is fully successful. For noise is an inevitable reflection of a basic feature of physical nature—a kind of "graininess," or statistical irregularity. The physical quantities, which seem to pour like a continuous fluid at their higher values, take on, as their magnitudes are reduced, some of the properties of a collection of Mexican jumping beans.

This is graphically illustrated by the problem of measuring very small electrical currents, such as occur in instruments for measuring radioactivity. A commonly used method is to let the current flow through a resistor and measure the resultant voltage across the resistor by means of a vacuum tube circuit. Now for very small currents both the resistor and the vacuum tube must be considered, in addition to their usual functions, to be sources of noise voltage q_n. The resistor generates thermal agitation noise due to the random thermal motion of the electrons in its interior. The effect increases with increasing temperature of the resistor. The formula is

$$q_n = \sqrt{4kTR\,\Delta f} \tag{7·1}$$

where T is the absolute temperature of the resistor, R is its resistance, k is Boltzmann's constant (1.38×10^{-23} joule per degree) and Δf is the frequency range over which the voltage is measured.

The vacuum tube acts as a source of noise because the current it carries consists of electrons randomly distributed in time. For convenience in comparing it with the resistor noise, this noise may also be specified in terms of an equivalent resistance R_e. For triode tubes $R_e \approx (T/T_0 g_m)$, where g_m is the mutual conductance of the tube, T_0 is room temperature, and T is temperature of the tube's cathode. The proportionality factor is approximately unity but depends somewhat on electrode geometry and on saturation characteristics of the cathode. Typical values of the various factors give as an approximate rule for triodes

$$R_e = \frac{2.5}{g_m} \tag{7·2}$$

For pentode tubes there is additional noise due to screen grid current. The approximate rule for pentodes, corresponding to Eq. 7·2, is

$$R_e = \frac{I_p}{I_p + I_g}\left(\frac{2.5}{g_m} + \frac{eI_g}{2kT_0 g_m{}^2}\right) \tag{7·3}$$

where e is the electron's charge, I_p is the plate current, and I_g is the screen grid current.

These noise voltages are present in the resistor and the vacuum tube at all times, whether the signal being handled is large or small.

The point is simply that they become significant only when the voltage to be measured becomes small enough to be comparable with them in magnitude. This example of small current measurement is typical of the limitations which the "atomicity" of nature puts on the measuring process.

The other aspect of range, in addition to scale range, is frequency range. To define frequency range, it is necessary to pick some measure of the error introduced in the response because the forcing frequency is too high or too low. There is no generally accepted way of doing this for instruments in general, or for physical systems in general. There is, however, a fairly widely used agreement on the meaning of frequency range for systems for which gain distortion is the important criterion. This is based on departure from flatness of the gain characteristic and sets a limit to the frequency range at that frequency for which the gain, relative to unity, is $1/\sqrt{2}$. Frequency range thus defined is commonly called band width and as such was discussed for the amplifier example treated in Section 4·8. Figure 4·15 gave band width versus ζ. Frequency range could be similarly defined in terms of phase distortion, or in terms of error. Though such definitions have been proposed for individual problems, there is apparently as yet no wide usage of most of them (cf. first paragraph of Section 7·10).

Perhaps the most general statement of frequency range is to say that it is the range of frequency over which the dynamic error stays within acceptable limits. The definition of "acceptability" will of course vary from one instance to another (cf. Section 7·10).

7·6 Accuracy. The third, and perhaps the most important, specification of an instrument is its accuracy. To define accuracy, it is convenient to adopt the symbol Δq for error; that is, by definition

$$\Delta q = q - q_d \qquad (7·4)$$

Now **accuracy** means the absence of, or at least the smallness of, **error**. On this much there is general agreement; but on the question of just how to express accuracy quantitatively there have been various suggestions. The definition to be proposed here is given by the expression $1 - (\Delta Q_m/Q_s)$, where Q_s is the full scale range of the instrument and ΔQ_m is the estimated maximum error that occurs anywhere over that range.

Another useful concept is **specific accuracy,** which is the accuracy at a particular reading q. It is defined as $1 - (\Delta q_m/q)$, where Δq_m is the estimated maximum error at that reading.

It is often convenient to state accuracy or specific accuracy in percentages.

The word "uncertainty" is rather widely used in relation to error. It is sometimes used to denote the estimated total error, sometimes the probable random error (cf. Eq. 7·22), and sometimes the residual (cf. Eq. 7·23) of a given reading in a series of readings. To avoid confusion it therefore seems better not to use the word at all.

The measurement process involves more than just the instrument; it involves the way the instrument is used. If an instrument is specified as having a certain percentage accuracy, this means that if the instrument is in "normal condition" and is used in a "normal manner" the error will be within the specified limit. Thus specification of accuracy implies something about the instrument and something about the way the instrument is used in making the measurement. One can therefore speak of the "accuracy of an instrument" and of the "accuracy of a measurement," or of "instrument errors" and of "measurement errors." These two terms will be used for two different analyses of errors.

The term **instrument errors** refers to a classification of errors in relation to the instrument itself. It is the kind of classification of interest to the instrument designer who wishes to design an accurate instrument; or to an instrument serviceman who must diagnose and repair some trouble in an instrument which is giving larger errors than it should. From this point of view errors may be classified in five groups: mechanism, scale, environmental, dynamic, and reading errors. From the discussions to be given below it will be clear that the first two groups, mechanism and scale errors, actually include the other three. The only excuse for separating these three for individual treatment is that they constitute important, clearly defined groups. Environmental and dynamic errors relate primarily to the mechanism; reading error relates primarily to the scale.

The term **measurement errors,** on the other hand, implies a classification of errors in relation to the measurement process and so is of primary interest to the instrument user. From this standpoint errors may be grouped into random errors and determinate errors.

The following sections deal first with the various groups of instrument errors and then with measurement errors. It must be understood that these *two* discussions deal with *one* subject, the totality of errors affecting measurements. The difference is in the point of view.

7·7   Mechanism error. According to the picture of an instrument given in Fig. 7·1, proper functioning of the instrument requires first that the index displacement x_d be properly related to q_d, and second that the reading q be properly related to x_d. Any defect in the first relationship is called **mechanism error.** That is, mechanism error is any error resulting from imperfection or fault of the instrument mechanism. The actual causes of such errors are numerous and varied. Mechanical factors which may be responsible include dry friction between moving elements, hysteresis in elastic members, poor fit between gears or between shafts and bearings, etc. Electrical sources of this kind of error would include the electronic noise in vacuum tubes, imperfect insulation against voltage differences, and magnetic hysteresis.

The load error discussed in connection with efficiency may be included as a mechanism error, since it may be regarded as due to the fact that the instrument efficiency of the mechanism is not infinite.

From the nature of these causes it is clear that mechanism error can be minimized only by careful design and good construction in the first place, including correct calibration (cf. next section), followed by careful use so as to protect the instrument from overloading, mechanical shock, dirt, humidity, corrosive vapor, or any other treatment that might render the mechanism less satisfactory than it originally was.

7·8   Scale error. Just as mechanism error has been defined as error due to imperfection in the instrument mechanism, **scale error** is that due to faults in the scale, causing a defect in the second relation mentioned at the start of section 7·7. Scale errors would generally arise in the process of **calibration,** although there is also the possibility of post-calibration effects such as accidental damage, wear, expansion, or warping of the scale.

The important process of instrument calibration must now be considered in detail. With the terms introduced in previous sections one can describe calibration as the process of fitting together the relation between x_d and q_d on the one hand and the relation between q and x_d on the other hand. One may define **deflection** sensitivity S as dx_d/dq_d. Similarly, **scale sensitivity** S_s may be defined as dq/dx_d. (The single word "sensitivity" is commonly employed in instrument technology as a fundamental criterion of instrument performance. It is usually given the meaning of what is here called deflection sensitivity. The present treatment does not emphasize sensitivity as an end in itself but only as one of the factors that determine instrument accuracy.) The first step of calibration then is to **fix the scale**; that is, to determine S and S_s in such a relationship to each other that their product, which is dq/dq_d, is equal to 1. This requires

$$SS_s = \frac{dq}{dq_d} = 1 \qquad (7 \cdot 5)$$

Even though this equation is rigorously satisfied, the instrument may still have scale error, since integration of $dq = dq_d$ gives $q = q_d + k$, where k is the constant of integration. The operation of making this constant equal to zero is necessary to satisfy the second condition of calibration, namely,

$$k = 0 \qquad (7 \cdot 6)$$

This step is often described as **setting the zero** or as elimination of error in the zero of the instrument.

These two steps of fixing the scale and setting the zero constitute the calibration process. It should be pointed out that fixing the scale can be done either by making S_s to fit a given S or by modifying S to fit a given S_s. This latter procedure is less common but is employed in some less-expensive instruments where it is cheaper to stamp out large numbers of standard scales and incorporate simple linkage adjustments within the mechanism.

The actual procedures of fixing the scale and setting the zero always involve, in addition to the instrument being calibrated, either a reference instrument or a standard. The calibration process may in fact be described as the process of adjusting the given instrument so that it compares as closely as possible with the reference instrument or standard.

Sometimes the best that can be done toward satisfying Eq. $7 \cdot 5$ is to make SS_s equal to a constant, not necessarily unity. Then, even if the zero is correctly set, the instrument will not give $q = q_d$, but q proportional to q_d with the proportionality factor unknown. The instrument may be said to have received a relative rather than absolute calibration. Although such an instrument is useful for making comparative measurements on samples to which it can be applied, its reading cannot be compared with those obtained from other instruments. An example of this situation occurs with radioactivity counters. A given counter will not count all, but only a certain fraction, of the actual disintegrations in the specimen it is measuring. If the results obtained with this counter are to be compared with those of other counters, this fraction must be known—the instrument must have an absolute calibration. On the other hand, for comparing the activities of different specimens the counter may be used with the fraction unknown—with only a relative calibration—since the unknown proportionality factor affects all measurements equally.

Additional difficulty is given to the calibration process by the necessity of establishing and holding **calibration conditions.** Unfortunately, every instrument mechanism responds to physical quantities other than the one particular quantity it was designed to measure. Thus many instruments are sensitive to temperature changes even though they are not thermometers. The effects of such spurious forcing lead in general to environmental errors, the subject of the following section. It must be noted here, however, that the calibration process must be carried out under fixed calibration conditions, since, if this is not done, the instrument will inevitably be subject to environmental error larger than necessary. Calibration must be carried out with those physical quantities to which the instrument is sensitive held within fixed known limits. If, under these fixed conditions, Eqs. 7·5 and 7·6 are satisfied to the desired approximation, the accuracy of the instrument under conditions other than the calibration conditions can be held close to this optimum performance either by including in the mechanism design **compensating** features to make it insensitive to the spurious quantities or by including methods of **correcting** the scale for the new conditions.

Under calibration conditions, consideration should be given not only to quantities other than q_d but also to q_d itself. The range of q_d used in calibration should, of course, correspond fairly closely with the full range of the instrument scale. Also, the time dependence of q_d should be of the general character for which the instrument is supposed to serve. These considerations will be further discussed in the following two sections.

7·9   Environmental error. This is the error due to the effect on q of factors other than q_d. As previously noted, environmental error may be minimized by careful calibration under fully specified calibration conditions; by designing into the instrument mechanism so-called compensation, elements which tend to correct or offset incipient environmental error; and by including, as parts of the (broadly defined) scale, correction charts or other means for correcting readings taken under environmental conditions substantially different from calibration conditions. Good compensation for a wide range of environmental factors is, of course, highly desirable, but the cost and complexity involved frequently lead to substitution of the less desirable "correction of index reading."

Thus, in choosing or specifying an instrument, an important consideration affecting its accuracy is its susceptibility to environmental errors. This can be estimated only on the basis of rather full knowledge—first, of the number and kind of quantities to which the instrument is sensitive; second, of the calibration conditions under which the scale is supposed to read correctly; and third, of the degree to which the instrument is compensated against, or furnished with corrections for, an unavoidable environmental effect.

7·10   Dynamic error. Dynamic error may be defined as that which is due to the time dependence of q_d. Because of the many different forms this time dependence may take, it is difficult to give any single quantitative estimate of the dynamic error to be expected from a given instrument. The concept of frequency band width, discussed at the end of Section 7·5, provides one means of presenting information on the dynamic error to be expected for certain forms of time dependence. It is also common practice to make use of the step-function response to specify dynamic error, by specifying response time and overshoot. **Response time** is defined as the time after application of the step forcing at which the response has made a specified fraction (often 90 per cent) of the required change. **Overshoot** is defined as the maximum amount, usually expressed as a percentage of the step magnitude, by which the response exceeds the required change. Small response time and small overshoot are desirable attributes, meaning in general that the dynamic error of the instrument will be small. One must remember, however, that small response time is a relative term, and that any instrument will give a large dynamic error when used outside its normal frequency range.

First-order systems have no overshoot and have small response times in proportion as their time constants are small. Second-order systems have small response times if they have large values of ω_n, and small overshoot if ζ is near 0.6.

Dynamic error is similar to environmental error, since it can be specified in terms of $\dot{q}_d$ and $\ddot{q}_d$, etc., as being factors, other than q_d, to which q is sensitive. Consequently, the calibration conditions must include specification of the time dependence of q_d; for example, a direct-current voltmeter cannot be calibrated with 60-cycle supply. Conversely, an electronic voltmeter with a resistance-coupled amplifier cannot be calibrated in terms of a direct-current battery voltage. Therefore it is necessary to distinguish between **static calibration** and **dynamic calibration**.

Instruments which read correctly at zero frequency (examples are direct-current electrical instruments, ordinary pressure gages, thermometers, weight scales) may be statically calibrated; i.e., it is correct to calibrate them with an essentially unchanging value of q_d (this means that the reading is taken with q_d held at a fixed value for a time long compared to the instrument's response time). The need for dynamic calibration arises with certain instruments which read incorrectly, or not at all, at zero frequency. One illustration of such an instrument would be an alternating-current voltmeter fed by a resistance-coupled amplifier of the type discussed in Section 4·8. (The circuit is given in Fig. 4·14.) The gain for sinusoidal forcing was given by Eq. 4·67 which may be written

$$\mathbf{G} = G_1 \frac{j2\zeta\beta}{1 - \beta^2 + j2\zeta\beta} \qquad (7\cdot7)$$

where G_1 is the gain at mid-frequency. From this expression it is clear that at zero frequency ($\beta = 0$) this circuit has no output at all and hence cannot be calibrated with direct current. It should, of course, be calibrated at or near the frequency corresponding to $\beta = 1$, where the gain is equal to G_1. Depending on the width of its frequency range (which is larger, the larger ζ is made), the instrument would have more or less dynamic error at given low frequencies and at given high frequencies.

A mechanical system which behaves quite analogously can be described in relation to the subject of vibration measuring instru-

ments.   The principle of the "seismic mass" used in vibration instruments is indicated in Fig. 7·3.   The body whose vibration is
to be measured has rigidly fastened to it a rigid frame.   The displacement x (or a time derivative of x) of this frame relative to
specified axes therefore is the reference quantity q_d.

The mass M is coupled to the frame through a spring of force
constant K and a dashpot of damping constant C.   The displacement of the seismic mass M, relative to the frame, is measured

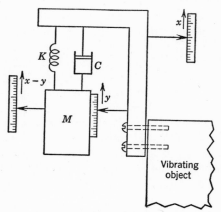

FIG. 7·3.   The seismic mass.

by y.   Under these circumstances the differential equation of the
system is

$$-M(\ddot{x} - \ddot{y}) + C\dot{y} + Ky = 0 \qquad (7\cdot8)$$

or

$$\frac{\ddot{y}}{\omega_n{}^2} + \frac{2\zeta}{\omega_n}\dot{y} + y = \frac{\ddot{x}}{\omega_n{}^2} \qquad (7\cdot9)$$

with $\omega_n = \sqrt{K/M}$ and $\zeta = C/2\sqrt{KM}$.

Assuming that the scale reading is proportional to the displacement y, one can for purposes of the discussion here take $q = y$.   If
the instrument is used as an accelerometer, one defines q_d to be
$\ddot{x}/\omega_n{}^2$, and the differential equation 7·9 becomes

$$\frac{\ddot{q}}{\omega_n{}^2} + \frac{2\zeta}{\omega_n}\dot{q} + q = q_d \qquad (7\cdot10)$$

This equation reduces to $q = q_d$ when $\dot{q}$ and $\ddot{q}$ are zero, which means that the accelerometer can be statically calibrated. More generally, it means that the accelerometer has reasonably small dynamic error over a range of frequency whose upper limit is in the vicinity of $\beta = 1$.

If the system of Fig. 7·3 is to be used as a velocimeter, q_d is defined to be $\dot{x}/2\zeta\omega_n$, in which case Eq. 7·9 becomes

$$\frac{\ddot{q}}{\omega_n{}^2} + \frac{2\zeta}{\omega_n}\dot{q} + q = \frac{2\zeta}{\omega_n}\dot{q}_d \qquad (7\cdot11)$$

Here static calibration would obviously not apply, but the possibility of having $q = q_d$ is seen to exist over that frequency range for which the second term in Eq. 7·11 is much larger than the first and third terms. This is exactly the condition for the amplifier discussed above. In fact, the sinusoidal gain deduced from Eq. 7·11 would be identical, except for the constant G_1, with Eq. 7·7. In other words the velocimeter, just like the resistance-coupled amplifier, must be calibrated in the middle of its frequency range, and it will show dynamic error toward both ends of this range.

If the system of Fig. 7·3 is to be used as a displacement meter by defining $q_d = x$, Eq. 7·9 could lead to $q = q_d$ only at frequencies where the first term overshadows the second and third. This is true at frequencies large compared to the mid-frequency, and hence the displacement meter is calibrated at frequencies well above $\beta = 1$. (Theoretically, it should be calibrated at infinite frequency.) Towards zero frequency it shows increasing dynamic error.

In connection with Fig. 7·3 it is convenient to mention another problem which, though not particularly pertinent to the subject of measuring instruments, furnishes an instructive example of a physical system. This is the problem of vibration isolation. For this problem the quantity of interest is the absolute motion $x - y$ of the seismic mass, which now represents the body to be protected from vibration or shock. So, putting $q = x - y$, Eq. 7·9 is

$$\frac{\ddot{q}}{\omega_n{}^2} + \frac{2\zeta}{\omega_n}\dot{q} + q = q_n \qquad (7\cdot12)$$

where q_n is given by

$$q_n = x + \frac{2\zeta}{\omega_n} \dot{x} \qquad (7 \cdot 13)$$

The symbol q_n is used here because this is a typical example of forcing to which the desired response is zero. Perfect vibration isolation would mean that the absolute displacement q would remain zero regardless of the variation of x. A plot of the gain (q_a/x_a) characteristics based on Eqs. 7·12 and 7·13 shows that the gain becomes less than unity and decreases toward zero only for frequencies above $\beta = \sqrt{2}$. At lower frequencies the vibration is actually magnified—q_a is larger than x_a. Hence it is only at the higher frequencies that the system begins to satisfy the design criterion of minimum response to q_n.

The foregoing examples of the resistance-coupled amplifier and the vibration instruments illustrate the relation between calibration and the occurrence of dynamic error in instruments calibrated either statically or dynamically. The relation is like that between calibration and environmental error. Moreover, just as environmental errors can be avoided, either by compensation in design of the instrument mechanism or by scale correction, these two possibilities exist also for dynamic error. In terms of second-order systems, for instance, proper design for a desired frequency range involves optimum choosing of ω_n and ζ. The choice of ω_n determines the location of the frequency limits (converting β-values into actual frequencies), and the choice of ζ controls the width of the frequency range for specified limits of dynamic error.

The alternative process of scale correction involves, for dynamic error, the converse problem; i.e., one knows the scale reading q and the parameters of the instrument, and the problem is to calculate or in some way to determine the true reference quantity q_d. Thus the converse problem, in the particular application to measuring instruments, may be described as "correcting for dynamic error."

Since the converse problem was introduced in Chapter 1 and discussed in Chapter 3 in terms of q_f, attention is directed to the fact that only for statically calibrated instruments does $q_f = q_d$. For dynamically calibrated instruments q_f involves one or more derivatives of q_d. The converse problem, or correction of dynamic error, in these cases involves integration of q_f to arrive at q_d. To illustrate this, in addition to the amplifier and vibration measuring instruments, consider the electrical circuit of Fig. 7·4. This circuit has the same differential equation as the vibration isolation system. That is, taking q as the output voltage and q_d as the input voltage, the differential equation is of the standard second-order form (Eq. 4·5) with

$$q_f = q_d + \frac{2\zeta}{\omega_n} \dot{q}_d \qquad (7\cdot14)$$

where $\omega_n = 1/\sqrt{LC}$ and $\zeta = R/(2\sqrt{L/C})$.

Then, for the converse problem for this system, knowing q, one would find its derivatives and thus find q_f. But to finish the problem one would have to put this time dependence of q_f into Eq. 7·14 and solve for q_d. This last step is clearly like a direct first-order problem, with $\tau = 2\zeta/\omega_n$.

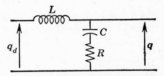

FIG. 7·4.	Electrical analogue of vibration isolation.

7·11 Reading error. This type of error arises in the process of "reading the scale," where this expression covers the full process, no matter how complicated, of translating the "position of the index" into the final best value of q. The only restriction implied is that only one measurement is involved. The process may be repeated, and the value of q thus obtained is in general slightly different, even though the true value q_d is presumably unchanged. The significance of these differences in results of repeated measurements is discussed in later sections of this chapter.

Two kinds of factors enter into the process of reading the scale: one is the so-called "personal equation" meaning the factors dependent upon the actions of the person taking the reading; the other consists of the actual physical features of the instrument which may render the occurrence of reading errors more or less probable. The steps taken by the human observer in reading the scale fall into the two categories of, first, associating the proper numerical value x_r with the index position x_d and, second, applying to the numerical value x_r thus obtained necessary conversions, corrections, or theoretical considerations.

From the above statement of the part played by the human observer in reading the scale, it follows that good instrument design directed toward minimizing reading error should emphasize certain factors. Consider first deflection sensitivity. Up to a certain point large deflection sensitivity helps to reduce reading error. But there is a point of diminishing returns which must be estimated in relation to the other causes of reading error and to the various causes of mechanism error. In addition to being reasonably sensitive, the instrument should be free from vibration, from sensitivity to position, and from all similar erratic behavior. The color, lighting, and quality of printing of the index scale should be such as to contribute satisfactory legibility. The instrument should preferably have a direct reading scale, so as to avoid the hazard of converting by means of a chart or other device. Finally, corrections should be as few and as simple as possible, so that the possibility of error in the correction process is minimized.

7·12 Measurement errors. The foregoing discussion of instrument errors was based largely on an implicit understanding of what is meant by true value and error. But, as shown by the brief discussion in Section 7·2, if one stops and really looks at the concept of true value, it is not easy to say exactly what he sees. Similarly, the concept of error requires for its comprehension a certain effort of the imagination. The discussion of measurement errors must be based on a deeper understanding of these ideas.

Consider a series of measurements, all made with q_d held fixed as nearly as possible on a single value and also with environmental conditions held fixed as nearly as possible. Assume that the person making the measurements has no other way of knowing or guessing the true value q_d. Let the results of his successive measurements be denoted by q_j, where $j = 1, 2, 3, 4 \cdots m$. If q_{aa} is the arithmetic average of the m readings, it is the value which the person would quote as his best guess of the true value. But if he were asked how close he considered this guess to be, what would he answer? For most measurements made under the above conditions, his confidence in q_{aa} would be directly related to how many measurements were made and to how closely the various q_j's repeated the same value.

On the other hand, the facts that many measurements have been made and that all the q_j's cluster very closely about a certain value do not insure that q_{aa} is very closely equal to q_d. They mean only that **random error** is probably small. If in addition **determinate error** is small, then q_{aa} is indeed a close approximation to q_d. Qualitatively, these two classes of errors may therefore be defined as follows: random errors are those whose effects on q_{aa} may be minimized by making m very large; determinate errors are those whose effect on q_{aa} is substantially independent of how large m is. Expressed in another way, random errors are random in sign and magnitude, so that if there are enough of them (if m is large enough) the effect of any one error is probably canceled by the effect of some other error; determinate errors are consistent in sign and more or less consistent in magnitude, so that the effect of a determinate error on the average of a hundred readings will probably be just as large as the effect on the average of two readings.

More quantitative definitions of random and determinate error will be given. Before proceeding in this direction, however, it is well to emphasize these two facts: first, the true value of a quantity being measured is never "found" or "established" or "known" —it is "estimated" or, more frankly, "guessed"; second, the magnitude of error must also be guessed. The theory of errors is a guide to more systematic and better informed guessing.

The more quantitative treatment of error must be given in terms of probability. The concept of probability is very similar to the concept of a derivative in differential calculus and should be just as familiar to all students of science and engineering. Both the probability concept and the derivative concept are defined as limits; and both are idealized abstractions which as such are not physically realizable but which bear a satisfactory logical relation to their physically realizable counterparts.

As a first step toward a definition of probability, consider a finite **aggregate** of elements (e.g., a series of measurements), each of which has a characteristic attribute (e.g., the reading obtained in the measurement). The word "aggregate" will always be used here with the implicit understanding that it refers to a finite collection of elements. Now a **frequency distribution** for the aggregate is obtained by counting the numbers of elements for which the attribute lies within certain ranges and expressing these counts as fractions of the whole aggregate—i.e., as relative frequencies. Thus one might count the number of persons in a population whose heights fall in intervals of 1 inch. In general, the plot of frequency distribution would look as shown in Fig. 7·5. Two features of frequency distributions should be emphasized: one, frequency distributions are discontinuous functions, since the interval along the attribute axis is always finite; and two, a given aggregate has infinitely many different frequency distributions corresponding to the infinitely many possible choices of size of attribute interval.

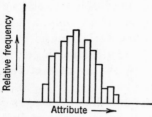

Fig. 7·5.   Frequency distribution.

Now consider what happens to the frequency distribution of an aggregate as two things happen simultaneously: the number of elements in the aggregate is made larger and larger, and the size of the attribute interval is made smaller and smaller. One would expect the discontinuities in the relative frequency distribution to become less and less conspicuous, so that the relative numbers in any interval would become more and more nearly proportional to the width of the interval. The ultimate limit of this process yields an aggregate of infinitely many elements, which by way of definition is called a **collective,** and, instead of the discontinuous frequency distribution, a continuous probability function, the ordinate of which for any attribute is defined to be the **probability density** of that attribute.

The probability of an attribute's being in a given interval is approximately equal to the ordinate of the curve at the middle of the interval multiplied by the width of the interval, the approximation being better and better as the interval width is made smaller and smaller. Thus

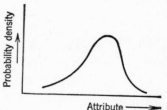

Fig. 7·6.   Probability function.

probability in a collective corresponds to relative frequency in an aggregate.

A probability function might look, for instance, as shown in Fig. 7·6. The area under the entire curve of Fig. 7·6 is equal to unity. This property of the probability curve derives from the similar property of the frequency distribution, provided by specifying that the counts be expressed as fractions of the total aggregate. Assuming that all elements are counted, the sum of these fractions must obviously be unity. (This may be emphasized by calling the distribution a *relative* distribution.) For any finite interval along the attribute axis, the corresponding area under the probability curve represents the probability of the attribute's having a value in that interval.

The above definition was given in terms applicable to a continuously varying attribute. Many applications of probability are to collectives for which the attribute takes on only discrete values. The above definition can also apply to these situations, with the modification that the process, of taking successively smaller intervals along the attribute axis does not need to be continued indefinitely but only so far as to insure that only one value of the attribute falls within each interval. In the experiment of tossing a coin, for example, the attribute has only two possible values, heads and tails. Thus only two intervals on the attribute axis are needed, one for heads and one for tails. The probability function is therefore discontinuous and so might look the same as a frequency distribution. Probability of tossing heads with a coin, for instance, is the limit, as the number of tosses goes toward infinity, of the ratio of the number of heads tossed to the total number of tosses.

Unfortunately, the language of probability has been used loosely, even by mathematicians and physicists. The reader is cautioned to remember that the term "probability" in a technical quantitative sense has meaning only for situations to which a quantitative definition as given above can be applied. This warning can be epitomized by a paraphrase of the Chinese laundryman's slogan —"No collective, no probability." If one finds it difficult to visualize clearly the notion of collective applicable to the quantity in question, he is not in position to use the probability concept.

The term "probability" refers, then, to the hypothetical distribution of an attribute in a collective. Since one can never have full experimental knowledge of a collective, including as it does an infinite number of elements, one can never know experimentally the probability of an event. Does this render the probability concept useless? No, for exactly the same situation applies to the concept of a derivative. Velocity is defined as the limit, as Δt approaches zero, of the difference ratio $\Delta x / \Delta t$. But experimentally Δt never approaches indefinitely near to zero. There is always a finite interval of time representing the smallest time interval that can be detected experimentally. But for mathematical reasons it is simpler to deal with the limit, the derivative, than with the physically realizable difference ratio. Similarly, in probability theory it is simpler to deal with the collective and its properties than with the physically realizable aggregate.

The problem in probability theory which is of particular interest here is the following. Given full knowledge of a certain aggregate, how does one proceed to make intelligent guesses about the corresponding collective? That is, given a certain aggregate of readings, what can be guessed about the collective consisting of an infinite number of such measurements? The full scope of this problem cannot be handled here. But, by assuming that the distribution of the random errors in the collective follows a certain special mathematical formula, the problem is reduced to such size that its chief features can be outlined. The special form assumed for the distribution is the one which is commonly called the normal law of errors (also frequently called Gaussian distribution). The conditions for validity of the normal law are discussed in the next section.

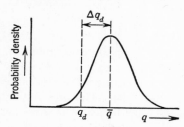

Fig. 7·7.   Normal probability of readings.

The implications of this assumption may be brought out by reference to Fig. 7·7. This shows the assumed readings, of infinite number forming the collective, distributed symmetrically about a certain $\bar{q}$, according to the curve of the normal law, the formula for which will be given in the next section. This value $\bar{q}$ is the limit of the arithmetic mean q_{aa} of m readings as m approaches infinity. That is, by definition,

$$\bar{q} = \lim_{m \to \infty} q_{aa} = \lim_{m \to \infty} \frac{\sum_{j=1}^{m} q_j}{m} \qquad (7·15)$$

One of the properties of the normal distribution is that it is symmetrical about $\bar{q}$ as thus defined.

Now the random error of an individual reading q_j is given the symbol Δq_{rj} and is defined as

$$\Delta q_{rj} = q_j - \bar{q} \qquad (7\cdot16)$$

The determinate error of the (infinite) series of measurements is given the symbol Δq_d and, as indicated in Fig. 7·7, is defined as

$$\Delta q_d = \bar{q} - q_d \qquad (7\cdot17)$$

Note that this definition of determinate error can be given only in terms of the collective and has no meaning for a single reading.

7·13   Random error.   Based on the assumption of the normal law, the theory of random error may now be explored in some detail.   Corresponding to the probability of readings shown in Fig. 7·7, the normal probability of random errors, defined by Eq. 7·16, is as shown in Fig. 7·8. The curves are symmetrical about zero, which means that the average random error is zero.   Two curves are shown, the solid curve representing a more precise series of measurements than the dotted curve.

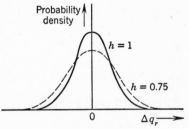

Fig. 7·8.   Normal probability of random error.

Precision means smallness of random error, compared to accuracy which means smallness of total error.

The mathematical formula for the normal law is

$$P(\Delta q_r) = \frac{h}{\sqrt{\pi}} e^{-h^2(\Delta q_r)^2} \qquad (7\cdot18)$$

where $P(\Delta q_r)$ is the probability of a random error Δq_r. h is called the **modulus of precision,** for, the larger h is, the more precise the measurements—the more sharply peaked is the probability curve and the smaller are the random errors.   Besides h, which has meaning only for the normal law, several more general measures of precision may be used.   These are the **probable error,** Δq_{rp}; the **root-mean-square error,** Δq_{rm}; and the **average error,** Δq_{ra} (average of magnitude).   These quantities are defined for any probability function $P(\Delta q_r)$ by the following equations:

$$\int_0^{\Delta q_{rp}} P(\Delta q_r)\, d\Delta q_r = \frac{1}{2}\int_0^\infty P(\Delta q_r)\, d\Delta q_r = \frac{1}{4} \qquad (7 \cdot 19)$$

$$\Delta q_{ra} = \frac{\displaystyle\int_0^\infty \Delta q_r P(\Delta q_r)\, d\Delta q_r}{\displaystyle\int_0^\infty P(\Delta q_r)\, d\Delta q_r} \qquad (7 \cdot 20)$$

$$= 2\int_0^\infty \Delta q_r P(\Delta q_r)\, d\Delta q_r = \frac{0.5642}{h}$$

$$(\Delta q_{rm})^2 = \frac{\displaystyle\int_0^\infty (\Delta q_r)^2 P(\Delta q_r)\, d\Delta q_r}{\displaystyle\int_0^\infty P(\Delta q_r)\, d\Delta q_r} = \frac{1}{2h^2} \qquad (7 \cdot 21)$$

These definitions are applied to the normal law by using Eq. 7·18 for $P(\Delta q_r)$. Thus, using a table of the probability integral $\int_0^x e^{-x^2}\, dx$ to solve Eq. 7·19 for Δq_{rp}, one finds

$$\Delta q_{rp} = \frac{0.4769}{h} \qquad (7 \cdot 22)$$

The probable error is that value of Δq_r which divides the area under the curve from zero to ∞ into two equal parts. Errors of magnitude greater than Δq_{rp} and less than Δq_{rp} are therefore equally probable.

For converting the modulus of precision and the various measures of error into each other, Table 7·1 is helpful.

TABLE 7·1

CONVERSION FACTORS FOR MEASURES OF PRECISION

	Δq_{rp}	Δq_{ra}	Δq_{rm}	$1/h$
Δq_{rp}	1.000	0.8543	0.6745	0.4769
Δq_{ra}	1.1829	1.000	0.7979	0.5642
Δq_{rm}	1.4826	1.2533	1.000	0.7071
$1/h$	2.0966	1.7726	1.4142	1.000

The picture drawn thus far of the theory of random errors, involving Figs. 7·7 and 7·8 and Eqs. 7·15 to 7·22, describes only the hypothetical collective of an infinite number of measurements. Nothing has yet been done to relate this hypothetical concept to the physically realizable aggregate of a finite number of measurements. So it is appropriate at this point to turn to the consideration of a finite number m of readings, q_1, q_2, $\cdots$, q_m. The symbol q_{aa} has already been introduced for the arithmetic average of these m readings. Now define the **residual** Δq_{Rj} of a given reading as

$$\Delta q_{Rj} = q_j - q_{aa} \tag{7·23}$$

The residuals Δq_{Rj} must not be confused with the errors Δq_{rj}. The literature on random errors is regrettably full of such confusion. Whereas the numerical difference between the known Δq_{Rj} and the estimated Δq_{rj} may or may not be appreciable in a given series of measurements, the logical distinction is always very important. The residuals are derived from the known readings which are elements of an aggregate; the errors are derived from the elements of an estimated, or guessed, collective, of which the known aggregate is presumed to be a sample.

The central problem of the theory of random errors may now be expressly stated: given m known readings and their residuals Δq_{Rj}, how does one use them to guess the collective of which the readings are a sample? This is a particular version of a widely occurring problem in statistical probability: given m elements drawn at random as a sample from a collective, what can one guess about the collective? Assuming that the random errors are distributed according to the normal law, an answer to this problem is given by the formula,

$$\Delta q_{rp} = 0.6745 \sqrt{\frac{\Sigma(\Delta q_{Rj})^2}{m-1}} \tag{7·24}$$

which gives the guess of the collective of which the m readings with residuals Δq_{Rj} are a sample. Any of the other measures of the collective may be derived from Δq_{rp} by using the factors of Table 7·1. The probable error Δq_{rp} was used in Eq. 7·24 to specify the collective because it is most widely used for this purpose.

The next step is to use the m readings to guess $\bar{q}$. The best guess here is that $\bar{q} = q_{aa}$, the arithmetic average. Next comes the crucial question: how good is this guess? Or, what is the probable error in q_{aa}? The answer is given by the formula

$$\Delta q_{rpa} = 0.6745 \sqrt{\frac{\Sigma(\Delta q_{Rj})^2}{m(m-1)}} \qquad (7 \cdot 25)$$

It must be emphasized that the two probable errors given by Eqs. 7·24 and 7·25 refer to entirely different collectives. The first collective, specified by Eq. 7·24, has as elements the errors of an infinite number of single measurements. The collective to which Eq. 7·25 applies has as elements the errors of an infinite number of arithmetic averages, each of which is the q_{aa} based on a series of m measurements. The meaning of Eq. 7·24 is: having made m measurements with residuals Δq_{Rj}, the probability is just one-half that the next measurement made would have an error greater than the Δq_{rp} given by this equation. The meaning of Eq. 7·25 is: having made m measurements with residuals Δq_{Rj}, the probability is just one-half that another series of m measurements would yield a q_{aa} differing from $\bar{q}$ by more than the Δq_{rpa} given by this equation. Note that the ratio $\Delta q_{rpa}/\Delta q_{rp}$ is equal to $1/\sqrt{m}$ or, in words, the probable error of the arithmetic average is $1/\sqrt{m}$ times the probable error of a single observation.

The value q_{aa} is thus obtained as the best estimate of the value $\bar{q}$, which, neglecting determinate error, is the same as the true value q_d. Moreover, by means of Eq. 7·25 an estimate is given of the probable error in q_{aa}. Therefore the result of the measurement should be expressed as $q_{aa} \pm \Delta q_{rpa}$. The practical question remains as to how many significant figures should be used in writing q_{aa} and Δq_{rpa}. The relative probable error in Δq_{rpa}—that is, the probable error in Δq_{rpa} divided by Δq_{rpa}—may be denoted by $\Delta^2 q_{rpa}$ and is given by

$$\Delta^2 q_{rpa} = \frac{0.477}{\sqrt{m}} \qquad (7 \cdot 26)$$

This equation shows that Δq_{rpa} should never be written with more than two significant figures unless m is greater than 23; for, with this value of m, Δq_{rpa} is uncertain to 1 part in 10. Similarly, unless m is greater than 6, more than one significant figure in Δq_{rpa} can hardly be justified.

So, to express a measurement numerically, one should use Eq. 7·26 to limit the number of significant figures in Δq_{rpa}, and then limit the significant figures in q_{aa} so that the last significant figure is in the same decimal place as the last significant figure of Δq_{rpa}.

Much of the usefulness of the application of probability theory to errors comes from the possibility of obtaining satisfactory accuracy from a relatively small number of measurements. The values of the residuals obtained are examined to see whether there is a strong need for more measurements. Under these circumstances, it is disconcerting to find an unusually large residual. Whenever this happens, the experimenter feels some doubt as to whether the

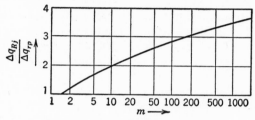

FIG. 7·9.   Chauvenet's criterion.

reading concerned was a "good" one, and the question arises whether the questionable observation should be completely omitted from the series of results. Since the normal law gives a finite probability of any given magnitude of error, no matter how large, the rejection of any observation is to this extent an arbitrary matter for which no strict justification can be given. Wide use has been made of one arbitrary rule, called Chauvenet's criterion, which says that a particular q_j may be rejected if the probability of a residual, at least as large as the particular residual in question, does not exceed $1/(2m)$. The probability in question must be obtained from the error collective estimated by considering all residuals, including the one in question. The numerical form of this criterion, as worked out from the normal law, is given in the chart of Fig. 7·9. If the ratio of the residual to the probable error is larger than the value shown by the curve, the reading may be rejected.

The foregoing discussion applies when the normal law of error can be considered a good approximation to the distribution of random errors. This is true for the majority of actual measurements, for the law is derived from an assumption which is usually fairly close to reality. The assumption is that the random error is the algebraic sum of many small errors, each of which occurs positively or negatively at random. In discussing the origin of random error in the next paragraph, it will be seen that this assumption is usually satisfied, particularly for a series of measurements carried out with q_d and environmental conditions held fixed, and with equal care being taken with each measurement of the series. Under different circumstances a somewhat different law might be more suitable. In any event the particular problem discussed here is only one of the problems in the application of probability theory to physical measurements. The purpose here has been to emphasize the fundamental nature of the probability concept and of its application to random error.[1]

Turning to consideration of the origin of random errors, one can name three chief sources: variation in the true value q_d itself; variation in the instrument and use of the instrument; and variation in sampling q_d. To illustrate these variations, think of measurements being made on a coin-shaped metal disk. If the mass is the quantity being measured, one can expect only variations in the second category; for it is hard to imagine any variation in the mass itself, and there is no need of sampling, since mass is a specific, not a statistical, quantity. However, suppose the diameter of the disk is being measured with a micrometer. Then there may well be variations of all three kinds. The diameter itself may vary in random manner, perhaps because of temperature changes due to the intermittent handling that goes with taking the measurements. In addition, the micrometer and the way it is used will introduce random errors, such as environmental errors and reading errors. And finally, the concept of the diameter of the disk is statistical in that there is not just one diameter but infinitely many; consequently, knowledge of *the* diameter of the disk is dependent on how this infinite number of diameters is sampled.

The random error due to imperfect sampling of a statistical quantity may be called **sampling error**. To illustrate the three kinds of sampling that may be needed, some further examples, in addition to the measurement of the disk diameter, will be discussed. The example of disk diameter illustrates sampling over a spatial dimension. Another example of averaging over space would

[1] For further discussion of the normal law, see Chapter 8 of Whittaker and Robinson, *Calculus of Observations*, London, Blackie and Son, Ltd., 1932.

be measurement of temperature in a room; one would like to measure the temperature at several points in the room, before claiming to know *the* temperature of the room. Measuring the length of cotton fiber illustrates the need for sampling over a numerical aggregate. The measurement of radioactive decay rate is an example of sampling over time.

The average length of fiber is an important specification of cotton quality. Instruments have been developed which measure the average length of fiber of a cotton sample selected, presumably, at random from the bale, or other large unit, of cotton which is being tested. The technique of selecting the sample to be put on the instrument is an important part of the measurement process. There is the question whether the number of fibers picked up is sufficiently large, and also the question whether the fibers are picked at random as far as their lengths are concerned. Fluctuations in the number of fibers picked up and in the randomness of their lengths will cause the successive instrument readings to exhibit typical random error.

The problem of measuring the decay rate of a radioactive element gives another interesting example of sampling error as a particular kind of random error. If the decay rate (a constant for any one material) is given the symbol λ, then in an aggregate of N atoms of this substance there will be λN disintegrations per second. Then, if time of observation, or counting time, is T, the true average count for this period, which is q_d for this problem, is

$$q_d = \lambda N T \qquad (7·27)$$

Then, if N is large compared to n and if T is small compared to $1/\lambda$, the probability of occurrence of n disintegrations in time T is given by the Poisson formula,

$$P(n) = \frac{e^{-q_d} q_d{}^n}{n!} \qquad (7·28)$$

For small n this formula gives an asymmetric distribution, but for large n it becomes identical with the normal, or Gaussian, distribution, which in the present notation would be

$$P(n) = \frac{1}{\sqrt{2\pi q_d}} e^{-(q_d - n)^2 / 2q_d} \qquad (7·29)$$

Comparison of this with Eq. 7·18 shows that here $q_d - n$ plays the role of the random error Δq_r. Thus in this example the particular random error due to sampling can definitely be shown to be distributed very nearly according to the normal law.

7·14   Determinate error.   The complete process of measurement may now be summarized as follows.   A certain number m of readings is taken.   It is then assumed that these readings are a sample from a particular collective, centered, as shown in Fig. 7·7, about some value $\bar{q}$.   The arithmetic average of the m readings, q_{aa}, is taken as the best guess of the value of $\bar{q}$.   The probable random error Δq_{rpa} in this guess is given by Eq. 7·25.   This summarizes the effect of random error.   But, as shown in Fig. 7·7, the value of $\bar{q}$, or of q_{aa}, may still differ from q_d by an amount Δq_d, the determinate error.   So the total error Δq in the result of the series of measurements is the sum of two parts:

$$\Delta q = \Delta q_{rpa} + \Delta q_d \qquad (7\cdot30)$$

This equation is the closest one can come to a quantitative definition of determinate error.

With Eq. 7·30, the formal discussion of error, in the limited scope presented here, is complete.   A few words may be added, however, about the origins of determinate error, and about the possibility of detecting and eliminating it.

Determinate error arises in situations where the error-causing imperfection is operating repeatedly or consistently in the same direction.   A simple example of an imperfection causing determinate error is an instrument pointer which has been bent and, therefore, consistently indicates a value either too high or too low.

Since by definition the scale reading q is obtained *after* all corrections have been applied, it follows that elimination of determinate error is usually very difficult.   If it is known that certain corrections should be made and these corrections are not made, this is a reading error which is determinate and which, of course, can be eliminated by applying the known correction.   Similarly, if there is any obvious imperfection in the instrument (for example, the above-mentioned bent pointer) leading to determinate error, one can estimate and correct for the effect of this imperfection.   However, under some conditions one may have no obvious reason for suspecting determinate error and yet, because of a surprising result or for other reasons, may feel the need for assurance that it does not exist.   Under such circumstances recourse may be had in well-established fields of measurement to comparison with other instruments or with basic standards. In pioneering fields where comparable instruments do not yet exist and the basic standards are not yet well established, even these methods fail, and the only procedure involves careful examination of one's own work, comparison with the work of other investigators, and theoretical study which may help to indicate most probable results or to establish reliable standards.

CHAPTER

8

Feedback Systems

8·1 Definition of feedback system. Examples have been given in Chapters 3, 4, and 6 of physical systems of the kind commonly called automatic controls or regulators. These examples were the automatic speed control of Section 3·8, the liquid level control of Section 4·9, and the current control and the governor-controlled engine of Section 6·6. All such devices belong to the class called duplicators, to which the criterion of minimum error or the criterion of minimum distortion apply. Like all duplicators, their function is to have their response duplicate a certain reference quantity q_d. But these particular four duplicators all operate by what is commonly called feedback. What is this factor which these four systems have in common?

An attempt to answer the question on mathematical grounds is not too rewarding, for each of these systems satisfies a differential equation which is derived and solved just as for systems not involving feedback. In fact, on this basis the speed control of Section 3·8 has more in common with a mercury-in-glass thermometer than with the other feedback examples.

The history of feedback sheds some light on the question. Toward the end of the eighteenth century James Watt made the first technical application of feedback by inventing the flyball governor for his steam engine. A British patent granted in 1871 is cited as the beginning of the servo art; this invention was essentially a power amplifier for giving the steam engine governor greater power for throttle adjustment. A United States patent granted in 1918 to Irving Langmuir marks the beginning of another principle application of feedback, to the electronic amplifier. These three fields of application of feedback—regulators,

174

servos, and feedback amplifiers—have all made great progress, though until recently they were almost entirely independent of each other. Although the first servos were "boosters," or power amplifiers, and did not involve feedback, the recent application of feedback to these devices has yielded such important results that there is now a tendency to use the term "servo system" to refer to any of the devices that employ feedback. The actual term "feedback" was introduced in the field of electronic amplifiers. It is used here as being the simplest and most descriptive term available for conveying the general idea involved.

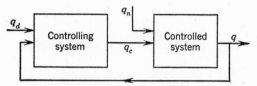

FIG. 8·1.   Diagram of feedback system.

Considering these devices, both in comparison with each other and in comparison with devices not employing feedback, one arrives at the conclusion that one of the distinctions of feedback systems is that they all may be made to fit a particular pattern, such as that of Fig. 8·1. Here a physical system with response q, instead of being directly subjected to q_d, has for input a quantity q_c, which may be called the **control quantity.** It in turn is the response of the controlling system, which has for input both q_d and q. The control quantity q_c is therefore dependent in some fashion both on q_d and on q. And it is here that one arrives at the heart of the feedback idea. A **feedback system** is to be understood here as being a system to which the pattern of Fig. 8·1 applies and in which q_c is *purposely* made such a function of q_d and q as will best enable q to satisfy some criterion of ideal performance. It is the *pattern* and the *purpose* that make a feedback system, and not the pattern alone.

To illustrate this the pattern of Fig. 8·1 will be shown to apply equally well to two physical systems which have been discussed as examples in Chapter 6, but of which only one is a feedback system. The feedback system is the governor-controlled engine, and the other system is the nuclear chain reactor. Figure 8·2 shows the pattern applied to the governor system. This figure is essentially the same as Fig. 6·15, which was drawn with the feedback pattern in mind.

The same pattern is applied in Fig. 8·3 to the nuclear chain reactor. Now it may be fairly argued that this way of looking at the reactor is not particularly illuminating as regards the

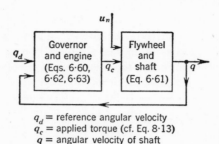

q_d = reference angular velocity
q_c = applied torque (cf. Eq. 8·13)
q = angular velocity of shaft

FIG. 8·2. Feedback diagram of governor system.

physical processes going on in the reactor. It may also be pointed out that q_d, missing from the picture, must be assumed to be zero. But these comments do not alter the fact that Eqs. 6·68 and 6·69 lead naturally to the diagram of Fig. 8·3, that is, to the diagram of a feedback system. Moreover, Fig. 8·3 suggests one way of making a reactor simulator, that is, an arrangement of electrical

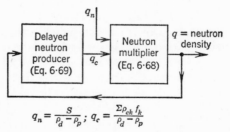

$$q_n = \frac{S}{\rho_d - \rho_p}; \; q_c = \frac{\Sigma \rho_{ek} f_k}{\rho_d - \rho_p}$$

FIG. 8·3. Reactor diagrammed as feedback system.

or other circuits that would satisfy the same differential equations as the reactor. In short, the only reason the reactor cannot be termed a feedback system is that it just happens to fit the pattern rather than having been expressly made to fit it in order to achieve a certain kind of performance. (See also the last paragraph of Section 9·5.)

One can cite other examples of physical systems in which the output acts back on the input but which should not be called feedback systems. Electrical circuits furnish many examples. Consider, for example, the stray capacitance or mutual inductance between output and input of a vacuum tube circuit. Such coupling is always present to some degree or other. If the degree is such as to result in oscillation or other noticeable trouble, it is widespread usage to say that "the trouble is due to feedback." The same expression might be employed to describe the situation with a public address system when the microphone and loudspeaker are so placed with respect to each other that the whole system oscillates. There is no quarrel here with this common meaning of feedback, implying usually the transfer of energy from a point of high power level to a point of lower power level in the system.

The point of the foregoing paragraphs is the suggestion that the specific term "feedback system" be reserved for systems in which feedback is *used*.

8·2 The feedback problem. Having assigned to the term "feedback system" the specific meaning of a system in which feedback is used, it is a simple matter to state the specific meaning of the term "feedback problem." This problem is to use feedback. Stating this more completely in the terms of Fig. 8·1, the **feedback problem** is to determine, for a given controlled system, that relationship between q_c, q_d, and q in the controlling system which will best satisfy the system's performance criterion. Inasmuch as the symbol q_d has been used for the input, in addition to q, to the controlling system, the implication has been that the overall system is a duplicator. Feedback is useful in satisfying other criteria, also, but the main discussion here will be on the duplicator criterion of minimum error.

Suppose for a starting point one considers a first-order system which, in the absence of feedback, satisfies the equation

$$\tau \dot{q} + q = q_d + q_n \qquad (8·1)$$

(Since one of the principal advantages of feedback is its reduction of noise response, it is important in all study of feedback to include q_n in the forcing.) The meaning of Eq. 8·1 is that τ is the time constant and q the response of the system which is to satisfy the performance criterion, $q = q_d$. With the application of feedback, according to Fig. 8·1, q_d is replaced by q_c in Eq. 8·1, and the feedback problem is so to relate q_c to q_d and q that the performance criterion will be best satisfied.

To demonstrate the possibilities inherent in the simplest kind of feedback, let

$$q_c = -K_f(q - q_d) \qquad (8 \cdot 2)$$

where K_f is a positive constant. Then the equation of the system is

$$\tau \dot{q} + q = -K_f(q - q_d) + q_n$$

or

$$\frac{\tau}{1 + K_f} \dot{q} + q = \frac{K_f}{1 + K_f} q_d + \frac{q_n}{1 + K_f} \qquad (8 \cdot 3)$$

From this it is apparent that if K_f is much larger than unity the effect of feedback will be threefold: one, a desirable effect of greatly reducing the effective time constant; two, a desirable effect of greatly reducing the effective noise forcing; three, an undesirable effect of slightly changing the effective value of q_d. Thus two big advantages have been achieved at the cost of one small disadvantage. Even this disadvantage can be removed by letting

$$q_c = -K_f(q - q_d) + q_d \qquad (8 \cdot 4)$$

for then the system's equation becomes

$$\frac{\tau}{1 + K_f} \dot{q} + q = q_d + \frac{q_n}{1 + K_f} \qquad (8 \cdot 5)$$

The effective value of time constant may be still further reduced by putting in q_c a term proportional to $\dot{q}$. Thus let

$$q_c = -K_f(q - q_d) + q_d + \tau_f \dot{q} \qquad (8 \cdot 6)$$

This gives for the complete equation

$$\frac{\tau - \tau_f}{1 + K_f} \dot{q} + q = q_d + \frac{q_n}{1 + K_f} \qquad (8 \cdot 7)$$

Apparently, by making τ_f equal to τ, one could eliminate dynamic error completely. There is the danger in this, however, of getting τ_f slightly greater than τ and so having an unstable system. At least a little margin must be allowed for stability.

Suppose the control quantity of Eq. 8·4 were applied to a second-order system. The result would be

$$\frac{\ddot{q}}{\omega_n{}^2(1 + K_f)} + \frac{2\zeta}{\omega_n(1 + K_f)}\,\dot{q} + q = q_d + \frac{q_n}{1 + K_f} \qquad (8\cdot8)$$

This shows that the feedback reduces the effective ζ by $1/\sqrt{1 + K_f}$ and increases the effective ω_n by $\sqrt{1 + K_f}$. The increase in ω_n is desirable; but the decrease in ζ, beyond a certain point, might be highly undesirable. This illustrates the limitation of feedback simply proportional to the error $(q - q_d)$. As shown by the example of the current control in Chapter 6, for a third-order system increasing this kind of feedback can lead to instability.

In general for an nth-order system, the differential equation is

$$(S + 1)q = q_c + q_n \qquad (8\cdot9)$$

where S is an expression in the operator p. If C is a similar expression in p, the control quantity may be assumed to be

$$q_c = -K_f(q - q_d) + q_d + Cq \qquad (8\cdot10)$$

giving for the complete equation

$$\left(\frac{S - C}{1 + K_f} + 1\right)q = q_d + \frac{q_n}{1 + K_f} \qquad (8\cdot11)$$

The problem then is to make the term $(S - C)/(1 + K_f)$ as small as possible without running into stability trouble.

The foregoing discussion in connection with Eqs. 8·1 to 8·11 is, of course, an idealized theoretical approach to the feedback problem. It represents what one would *like* to do in achieving duplicator performance by means of feedback; what one *can* do is often a somewhat different matter. The possible differences in this respect between different systems is illustrated by the current control and the engine-governor control of Section 6·6. One can discuss the current control by considering $q_c = A_1 A_2 E_1/R$. Combining Eqs. 6·49, 6·50, and 6·51 gives as the equation of the controlled system

$$(\tau_1 p + 1)(\tau_2 p + 1)(\tau_3 p + 1)q = q_c \qquad (8\cdot12)$$

which, together with the dependence of E_1, given in Eq. 6·52, gives the complete Eq. 6·53. This example therefore fits neatly into the pattern given above, of a controlled system forced by a control quantity q_c, which is given a specified dependence on q and q_d. One can go further and readily imagine an amplifier built to give q_c any other dependence on q and q_d that might be desired to improve performance.

By contrast the engine-governor system fits rather awkwardly into the above pattern. In Fig. 8·2 the control quantity is indicated to be the torque applied to the shaft and flywheel. The combination of Eqs. 6·60, 6·62, and 6·63 shows that q_c is given in this case as

$$q_c = \frac{-S_e S_g (q - q_d)}{Mp^2 + Cp + K} \tag{8·13}$$

The denominator in this expression, involving the operator p, is due to the dynamics of the control device itself—the governor. Thus Eq. 8·13 does not represent only what one would like to have in the relation between q_c and the error $(q - q_d)$; it also represents the unavoidable effect of using a governor having finite mass M and damping C.

Admitting then that the pattern of Eqs. 8·9, 8·10, and 8·11 may have to be substantially modified for practical reasons, this pattern remains nevertheless a useful guide in application of feedback to linear duplicators. The feedback problems involving parametric forcing, distributed systems, or nonlinear systems are discussed in later chapters.

8·3 Thermal examples. The example to be discussed here is a laboratory experiment based on the thermal model of house heating discussed in Section 3·5, in connection with Fig. 3·11. The Eq. 3·20 of this system was

$$(CRp + 1)T_o = T_i + RH \tag{8·14}$$

This is the same as

$$(\tau p + 1)q = q_c + q_n \tag{8·15}$$

if $\tau = CR$, $q = T_o$, and $(q_c + q_n) = (T_i + RH)$. It is interesting to note that one may choose T_i as q_n, and RH as q_c, or vice versa. Assuming for the present example that T_o is supposed to follow RH and that T_i represents noise, the choice to be made is $q_c = RH$, and $q_n = T_i$.

Since in this case q_n is the temperature of an ice-bath and therefore a known constant, it may easily be entirely eliminated.

Making $q_c = RH$ depend on T_o and T_i and on a reference temperature T_d, according to the equation,

$$RH = -K_f(T_o - T_d) + T_d - T_i \qquad (8·16)$$

then gives from Eq. 8·14

$$\left(\frac{CR}{1 + K_f}\,p + 1\right) T_o = T_d \qquad (8·17)$$

The effect of Eq. 8·16 can be obtained by means of the elements shown in Fig. 8·4. The temperature T_o is measured with a thermocouple and potentiometer. A human operator, acting as

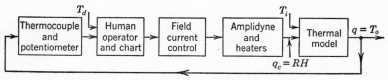

Fig. 8·4. Diagram of thermal feedback system.

part of the controlling system, uses the observation of T_o to guide his adjustment of the field current in an amplidyne, thus controlling the heat H generated in the heaters fed by the amplidyne. (A human link may be incorporated in any feedback system. The idea that feedback is always involved in automatic systems might easily arise, since practically all automatic controls do involve feedback. But the converse proposition, that all feedback systems are automatic, is far from true. In fact, many human actions fall into the feedback pattern, so that the concepts of feedback and automatism do not have so much in common as might at first appear.)

The human operator makes use of a chart or other means of "instantaneously" converting readings of the potentiometer into desired values of field current, so as to satisfy Eq. 8·16. In the laboratory model the maximum power which the amplidyne could deliver continuously into the 56-ohm heater was about 125 watts. The thermal resistance R was found to be about 0.9° C per watt. Assuming $T_d = 32°$ C, and $T_i = 4°$ C, Eq. 8·16 at $t = 0$ becomes, if the initial value of T_o is also 4° C,

$$112.5 = -K_f(4 - 32) + 32 - 4 \qquad (8·18)$$

whence $K_f = 3.0$. This is calculated for a step-function response from 4° C to 32° C, the maximum power being required at the initial instant. K_f is limited to the relatively small value of 3 by the limited power available from the amplidyne. Taking $K_f = 3$, along with $R = 0.9$° C per watt, $T_d = 32$° C, and $T_i = 4$° C, the relationship between H and T_o, according to Eq. 8·16, is

$$H = 138 - 3.33T_o \tag{8·19}$$

The value of H can be converted to amplidyne output current by dividing by the heater resistance and taking the square root, and finally to values of field current by reference to the amplidyne characteristic. Both these operations are nonlinear, but since they are incorporated into the chart which the human operator uses they do not affect the analysis presented here.

The system diagrammed in Fig. 8·4 has no provision for giving H negative values. Therefore a step-down response could not be experimentally carried through. If one had a combined heater and refrigerator that could transfer heat in either direction, this limitation would be overcome.

This example applies to the heating of a room or a house, and Eq. 8·16 could be the basis for a very nice heating control. It could be made still better, of course, by adding to the expression for q_c a term proportional to $\dot{q}$, so as to reduce still further the effective time constant of the complete system, as in Eq. 8·7.

8·4   Electronic feedback demonstrator.   A circuit which has been found very useful for purposes of demonstration and

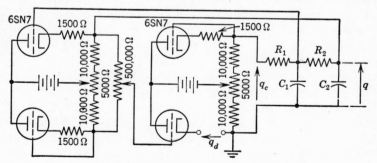

FIG. 8·5.   Circuit of electronic feedback demonstrator.

teaching is shown in Fig. 8·5. The controlled physical system is the double RC circuit made up of R_1, R_2, C_1, and C_2. This circuit was shown in Fig. 4·13 (with the addition of a resistor R_3 across the capacitor C_2), and the values of q_f, ω_n, and ζ are given in Eqs. 4·53, 4·54, and 4·55.

The voltage q_c driving the controlled circuit is the output of two bridge circuits arranged so as to give

$$q_c = -K_f(q - q_d) + \tau_f \dot{q} \qquad (8·20)$$

The voltage across R_2 is exactly equal to $C_2 R_2 \dot{q}$. Hence τ_f is $A_1 A_2 C_2 R_2$, where A_1 is the voltage gain of the first bridge (including the effect of the 0.5 megohm potentiometer setting), and A_2 is the voltage gain of the second bridge. Thus τ_f can be varied from zero up to a maximum value by changing the potentiometer setting and consequently the value of A_1.

The voltage input to the second bridge is thus $q - A_1 C_2 R_2 \dot{q}$. From this the value q_d is subtracted, since q_d appears in the cathode of the input tube. So the output of this second bridge is $-A_2(q - q_d) + A_1 A_2 C_2 R_2 \dot{q}$. Comparison with Eq. 8·20 shows $K_f = A_2$.

The equation of the complete system is

$$\left(\frac{p^2}{\omega_n{}^2(1 + K_f)} + \frac{2\zeta/\omega_n - \tau_f}{1 + K_f} p + 1 \right) q = \frac{K_f}{1 + K_f} q_d \qquad (8·21)$$

If $R_1 = 100{,}000$ ohms, $C_1 = 0.01$ microfarad, $R_2 = 500{,}000$ ohms, and $C_2 = 0.005$ microfarad, the values of ω_n and ζ are $\omega_n = 632$ radians per second and $\zeta = 1.26$. Assuming $A_2 = 8$ and the maximum value of A_1 also to be 8, the maximum value of τ_f is $64 C_2 R_2$ or 0.16. Since $2\zeta/\omega_n = 0.004$, it is clear that the effective ζ in Eq. 8·21 can be made negative by turning up the potentiometer on the output of the first bridge. A negative ζ means an unstable system, and hence oscillation. Thus, simply by changing the setting of the potentiometer one can go from effective ζ of about 0.4 well into the region of negative effective ζ.

Since the frequency and amplitude of the oscillations resulting when ζ is negative are affected by the nonlinearity of the system, this experiment also affords some insight into the behavior of nonlinear systems (cf. Section 11·3).

Instead of the particular circuit shown in Fig. 8·5 as the controlled system, other circuits can be used—first-order systems, higher-order systems, systems involving inductance, etc. The only restriction is that the circuit should end in an R_2-C_2 combination, since this is the device which permits getting an accurate term in $\dot{q}$.

The way q_d is introduced, with one terminal grounded, makes it convenient to study the response of the complete system to various q_d's.

If a finite resistance R_3 is connected (perhaps in an instrument for measuring q) across C_2, the effect is to make the voltage across R_2 equal to $C_2 R_2 \dot{q} + (R_2/R_3)q$. The resulting complete equation is

$$
\left\{ \frac{p^2}{\omega_n{}^2 \left[1 + A_2 \dfrac{1 - \dfrac{R_2}{R_3} A_1}{1 + \dfrac{R_1 + R_2}{R_3}} \right]} + \frac{\dfrac{2\zeta}{\omega_n} - \dfrac{\tau_f}{1 + \dfrac{R_1 + R_2}{R_3}}}{1 + A_2 \dfrac{1 - \dfrac{R_2}{R_3} A_1}{1 + \dfrac{R_1 + R_2}{R_3}}} p + 1 \right\} q
$$

$$
= \frac{A_2}{1 + \dfrac{R_1 + R_2}{R_3} + A_2 \left(1 - \dfrac{R_2}{R_3} A_1 \right)} q_d \qquad (8 \cdot 22)
$$

8·5 An example of negative impedance. The diagram of Fig. 8·6 indicates the nature of the example to be discussed here.

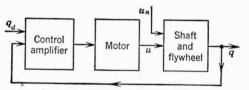

Fig. 8·6. A feedback-controlled shaft.

It is similar to several examples already discussed. The rotation of a shaft is controlled by the torque u of a motor, which in turn is governed by a control amplifier fed by the response q and the reference quantity q_d. The response q may be either the angular displacement or the angular velocity of the shaft.

If q_d remains constant for relatively long times, the system would be described as a **regulator** or **automatic control**. If the changes in q_d are frequent and relatively rapid, the system is called a

servomechanism—a "position servo" or a "velocity servo," according as q and q_d represent angular displacement or angular velocity. The mathematical treatment of these devices is similar to that already given for several examples. Let it be assumed here that the shaft experiences not only the inertia of the flywheel but also viscous friction. The equation for the shaft with q = angular velocity is then

$$\tau \dot{q} + q = q_c + q_n \qquad (8 \cdot 23)$$

where $\tau = I/C_t$, $q_c = u/C_t$, and $q_n = u_n/C_t$; I is the moment of inertia of the shaft and flywheel, and C_t is the torsional damping coefficient. (It is worth while to note that, although for clarity the flywheel is shown separate from the motor in Fig. 8·6, in many actual cases of servos or regulators the principal part of I is the rotating armature of the motor. So, although the logical picture of the boundary between the controlling system and the controlled system is as shown in Fig. 8·6, the actual physical location of this boundary is inside the motor, between its stator and its rotor.)

If the feedback relation is

$$q_c = -K_f(q - q_d) \qquad (8 \cdot 24)$$

the complete equation becomes

$$\frac{\tau}{1 + K_f} \dot{q} + q = \frac{K_f}{1 + K_f} q_d + \frac{q_n}{1 + K_f} \qquad (8 \cdot 25)$$

in close analogy to foregoing feedback examples.

But now suppose that q_d, instead of being independent of the shaft response, is made to depend on the torque applied to the output end of the shaft. In particular, suppose

$$q_d = -K_z q^* \qquad (8 \cdot 26)$$

where K_z is a positive constant having the dimensions of angular velocity divided by torque, and q^* is the torque. It must be understood that q^* is not the same as u, the torque applied by the motor to the shaft. The motor works on the *input* end of the shaft; q^* is applied on the *output* end. If one thinks of strain gages, for instance, as furnishing the q^* signal, they would be applied at the end of the shaft away from the motor, as indicated in Fig. 8·7.

Now if one grasps the shaft at point A of Fig. 8·7 and attempts to turn it manually, how does the shaft respond? The answer is obtained mathematically by substituting for q_d in Eq. 8·25 from Eq. 8·26, giving

$$\frac{\tau}{1 + K_f}\dot{q} + q = -\frac{K_z K_f}{1 + K_f}q^* + \frac{q_n}{1 + K_f} \qquad (8\cdot27)$$

This shows that, except for the dynamic error due to the term in $\dot{q}$ and the random error due to the term in q_n, the system behaves as a negative torsional impedance, according to the relation

$$\frac{q}{q^*} = -\frac{K_z K_f}{1 + K_f} \qquad (8\cdot28)$$

This means that, if one grasps the shaft and applies a clockwise torque q^*, the system responds by establishing an opposite,

FIG. 8·7.   Output end of shaft.

counterclockwise angular velocity q. This example might therefore be described as the "case of the contrary shaft."

This particular effect of negative impedance is just one of the many possibilities that could be realized by giving various forms to the two relationships, of which the particular forms used here are Eqs. 8·24 and 8·26.

These possibilities illustrate the application of feedback to purposes other than satisfaction of the duplicator criterion.

CHAPTER

Parametric Forcing

9·1 The nature of parametric forcing. In discussion of
physical systems thus far, it has been assumed that the properties
of an nth-order physical system can be specified in terms of $n + 1$
coefficients, or, as far as its dynamic behavior is concerned, in
terms of n parameters. These coefficients or parameters have
been treated moreover as constants, i.e., as not depending on time.
Actually many physical systems of technical and scientific importance must be described in terms of coefficients which are functions
of time. In such systems the time variation of the parameters
may be in place of, or in addition to, a forcing function such as
has been denoted by q_f. If there is no forcing in the sense of q_f,
the system will still respond to the time variation of the parameters. The effects of the parameter variations may be said to be
due to **parametric forcing.**

The differential equation for a physical system of the nth order
was given in Eq. 2·5, in terms of constant coefficients A_0, A_1,
A_2, $\cdots$, A_n. The equation of an nth-order physical system with
parametric forcing will look exactly the same, if it is understood
that one or more of the A's, instead of being constant, may vary
with time. Differential equations of this sort are the general linear
equations, of which linear equations with constant coefficients are
a sub-group.

Much of the mathematical simplicity inherent in equations with
constant coefficients is lost in the presence of parametric forcing.
This is especially clear in the extreme case in which all the parameters are time dependent. For such an equation the direct problem
of calculating response would be, generally speaking, difficult or
impossible; and the inverse problem would also be rather hopeless,

187

since in the parameters there could be arbitrary mixture of properties of the physical system and properties of the particular way
in which the parameters were varying with time; that is, the
inverse and converse problems would merge indistinguishably.
But, even though the degree of generality achieved with constant
coefficients cannot be hoped for here, the problems associated with
parametric forcing can be solved to some extent for a fair number
of important systems.

9·2 Linearity and parametric forcing. Since the differential equation governing a parametrically forced system may still
be a linear equation even though its coefficients are not constants,
the properties of linear differential equations still apply to linear
parametric forcing. The most important property is that of
superposition, which means that the sum of two or more solutions
of the differential equation is, in turn, a solution. In fact, the
general solution of the homogeneous nth-order linear differential
equation is the complementary function consisting of the sum of n
independent solutions, in complete analogy with the solution
denoted by q_t for the equation with constant coefficients. Furthermore, the general integral of the complete (i.e., inhomogeneous)
differential equation is the sum of the complementary function and
a particular integral.

This formal identity with the solution for constant coefficients,
however, still leaves the problem of finding these solutions (complementary function and particular integral) of the general linear
equation, and this is usually a rather difficult problem. Hence
the allusion in the preceding section to the difficulty of the direct
problem.

The property of superposition mentioned above needs to be
considered more in detail. Suppose the general linear equation is

$$D(p) \cdot q = q_f \qquad (9 \cdot 1)$$

where the coefficients in the polynomial form D may depend on
time. Let q_t and q_r as before denote, respectively, the complementary function and the particular integral. Then by definition

$$D(p) \cdot q_t = 0 \qquad (9 \cdot 2)$$

and

$$D(p) \cdot q_r = q_f \qquad (9 \cdot 3)$$

Now suppose that q_f consists of the sum of a number of functions —say, for example, the two functions q_{f1} and q_{f2}. Suppose further that two particular integrals q_{r1} and q_{r2} are known, such that

$$D(p)q_{r1} = q_{f1} \tag{9·4}$$

and

$$D(p)q_{r2} = q_{f2} \tag{9·5}$$

From addition of these equations it follows that

$$D(p)(q_{r1} + q_{r2}) = q_{f1} + q_{f2} = q_f \tag{9·6}$$

so that the function $q_r = q_{r1} + q_{r2}$ is the particular integral of Eq. 9·3. This result may be given the following generalized form: the forced response of a linear system to forcing consisting of the sum of a number of functions is the sum of the forced responses to each of the functions taken individually.

In particular, if q_f is made up of the sum of a number of sinusoids, the forced response of a system with constant coefficients will consist of sinusoids, each one of which represents the response to a particular one of the forcing sinusoids. Moreover, the corresponding sinusoids in forcing and response always have the same frequency, though in general they differ in amplitude and in phase. Thus, so far as direct forcing is concerned, the forced response of a linear system with constant coefficients never includes frequencies not present in the forcing.

With parametric forcing, however, the response will in general include many frequencies in addition to those present in the forcing. The systems discussed in the following section illustrate this.

In connection with the subject of waveform distortion, a system is commonly said to be linear if the response does not have sinusoidal components differing in frequency from those in the forcing; and the term "nonlinear distortion" is used to describe the effects on waveform of such components. For systems subject to parametric forcing this terminology is awkward; for the parametrically forced system is governed by a linear differential equation and so is logically called a linear system. This then leads to having nonlinear distortion in the response of a linear system. The awkwardness can be avoided if one adopts a term other than "nonlinear distortion" to refer to the presence in the response of nonforcing components, if these components are caused by parametric forcing. (Such components may, of course, be present in the response because of actual nonlinearity of the differential equation.) The suggestion offered here is to refer to these effects as **parametric distortion.**

9·3 Two types of microphone. Two simple examples of parametric forcing will be discussed here. Figure 9·1 shows a circuit which can represent the carbon microphone (as well as certain other physical systems such as a resistance strain gage). The microphone is shown as the resistance $r(t)$ connected in series with a fixed resistance R and a battery of voltage Q_f. As r

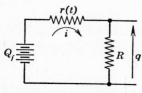

varies with time, the current i flowing in the circuit varies, and this variation can be passed to an amplifier in terms of the voltage $q = iR$. The response q is determined from the equation

FIG. 9·1.   Carbon microphone circuit.

$$\left(1 + \frac{r}{R}\right) q = Q_f \qquad (9\cdot7)$$

It is seen that this is a system of order zero, since derivatives are not involved in its equation. The equation is solved, therefore, simply by writing it

$$\frac{q}{Q_f} = \frac{1}{1 + r/R} \qquad (9\cdot8)$$

Thus, when r varies with time, q will vary with time according to Eq. 9·8. For instance, if $r = r_0(1 + m \cos \omega_f t)$, the solution given in Eq. 9·8 is

$$\frac{q}{Q_f} = \frac{R}{R + r_0} \cdot \frac{1}{1 + \dfrac{mr_0}{R + r_0} \cos \omega_f t}$$

Assuming that m is smaller than unity, the expression can be expanded in the series

$$\frac{q}{Q_f} = \frac{R}{R + r_0} - \frac{mRr_0}{(R + r_0)^2} \cos \omega_f t \cdots \qquad (9\cdot9)$$

If the modulation factor m is quite small compared to unity, the two terms of Eq. 9·9 are a good approximation to the complete response, since the terms not written down all involve higher powers of m and are, therefore, small. However, from a mathematical point of view the complete solution involves an infinite number of frequencies, and so the carbon microphone always gives a certain amount of parametric distortion. This distortion may be minimized in one or both of two ways: either by making m small, or by making r_0 small compared to R. Both methods of reducing distortion are undesirable from the point of view of obtaining a large signal which could be passed on, for instance, to a vacuum tube amplifier. (For this purpose a capacitor would be used to isolate the direct-current component of the response of Eq. 9·9 from the grid of the vacuum tube.) It is clear that the main alternating-current component of the response is made small either by making m small compared to unity, or by making r_0 small compared to R. Freedom of distortion in this system can, therefore, be achieved only at the expense of signal strength, so

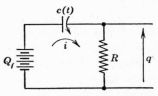

FIG. 9·2.   Condenser microphone circuit.

that the usual engineering practice is a compromise between these two requirements.

An example of a first-order system subject to parametric forcing is furnished by the condenser microphone, for which Fig. 9·2 gives the circuit diagram. Here the capacitance $c(t)$ of the microphone is a function of time, and changes in its capacitance cause current i to flow through the resistor R, thereby giving an output voltage $q = iR$. The equation for q is

$$cR\dot{q} + (1 + R\dot{c})q = Q_f R\dot{c} \qquad (9·10)$$

This may be put in the standard form of Eq. 3·1, $\tau\dot{q} + q = q_f$, by defining here a time-dependent τ as

$$\tau = \frac{Rc}{1 + R\dot{c}} \qquad (9·11)$$

together with the forcing

$$q_f = \frac{Q_f R\dot{c}}{1 + R\dot{c}} \qquad (9·12)$$

The response is given as the sum of a complementary function and a particular integral, which may still be referred to, respectively, as transient response q_t, and forced response q_r. They are given by the equations

and

$$q_t = Q_i e^{-\int dt/\tau} \tag{9·13}$$

$$q_r = e^{-\int dt/\tau} \int \frac{q_f}{\tau} e^{\int dt/\tau} \, dt \tag{9·14}$$

In Eq. 9·13, Q_i is an arbitrary constant, to be determined by an initial condition (though the determination may not be so easy as it was in Chapter 3). If τ is constant, the result embodied in Eqs. 9·13 and 9·14 is the same as that given in Eq. 3·4.

It follows from Eq. 9·14 that, if q_f has a constant value Q_2, the forced response regardless of the time dependence of τ will be $q_r = Q_2$, just as for constant τ. The only effect of parametric forcing will be on q_t. For example, suppose the condenser microphone undergoes a linear change of capacitance, such that

$$Rc = \tau_0(1 + mt) \tag{9·15}$$

Then Eq. 9·11 yields for τ,

$$\tau = \tau_0 \frac{1 + mt}{1 + m\tau_0} \tag{9·16}$$

and Eq. 9·12 yields for q_f the constant value

$$q_f = \frac{Q_f m\tau_0}{1 + m\tau_0} \tag{9·17}$$

Then the response, from Eqs. 9·13 and 9·14, is

$$q = \frac{Q_i}{(1 + mt)^{(1+m\tau_0)/m\tau_0}} + \frac{Q_f m\tau_0}{1 + m\tau_0} \tag{9·18}$$

In this particular case Q_i is given, just as in the case of constant coefficients, as $Q_1 - Q_2$, where Q_2 is the constant forcing and Q_1 is the response at $t = 0$.

Considering Eq. 9·11, the transient response given in Eq. 9·13 may be written

$$q_t = Q_i e^{-\int (\dot{c}/c)\, dt} e^{-\int dt/Rc} = -Q_i \frac{c}{C_0} e^{-F} \tag{9·19}$$

where C_0 is a constant, and where the symbol F has been introduced for $F(t) = \int dt/Rc$. Now it is clear that, if c remains positive, the function F will be a monotone increasing function of time. Hence Eq. 9·19 shows that q_t will decrease toward zero magnitude, as implied by its name.

The forced response, given in Eq. 9·14, may also be expressed in terms of F. Combining Eqs. 9·11 and 9·12 with 9·14, and using Eq. 9·19 for $e^{-\int dt/\tau}$,

$$\frac{q_r}{Q_f} = \frac{C_0}{c} e^{-F} \int \frac{\dot{c}}{C_0} e^F \, dt \qquad (9 \cdot 20)$$

Integrating by parts,

$$\frac{q_r}{Q_f} = \frac{C_0}{c} e^{-F} \left(\frac{c}{C_0} e^F - \frac{1}{RC_0} \int e^F \, dt \right) \qquad (9 \cdot 21)$$

or

$$\frac{q_r}{Q_f} = 1 - \frac{e^{-F}}{Rc} \int e^F \, dt \qquad (9 \cdot 22)$$

This form may be used, for example, to investigate the **forced** response to a periodic change of capacitance, with fundamental angular frequency ω_f. Proceeding on the assumption that this response would also be periodic, one might guess

$$\int e^F \, dt = Rce^F \left[A_0 + \sum_{n=1}^{\infty} (A_n \cos n\omega_f t + B_n \sin n\omega_f t) \right] \qquad (9 \cdot 23)$$

Differentiating this equation and dividing out e^F, one obtains

$$1 = (1 + R\dot{c}) \left[A_0 + \sum_{n=1}^{\infty} (A_n \cos n\omega_f t + B_n \sin n\omega_f t) \right]$$

$$+ \omega_f Rc \sum_{n=1}^{\infty} n(B_n \cos n\omega_f t - A_n \sin n\omega_f t) \qquad (9 \cdot 24)$$

After substituting in this expression any periodic function for $c(t)$, one could attempt to determine values for the constants A_n and B_n which would make the equation true. This will be carried out here only for the simplest form,

$$c = C_0(1 + m \sin \omega_f t) \qquad (9 \cdot 25)$$

Putting this into Eq. 9·24, and introducing the symbol β for $\omega_f R C_0$, one gets

$$1 = A_0 + A_0 m\beta \cos \omega_f t + \sum_{n=1}^{\infty} (A_n \cos n\omega_f t + B_n \sin n\omega_f t)$$

$$+ \beta \sum_{n=1}^{\infty} n(B_n \cos n\omega_f t - A_n \sin n\omega_f t)$$

$$+ m\beta \sum_{n=1}^{\infty} [\tfrac{1}{2}(n + 1)A_n \cos (n + 1)\omega_f t$$

$$- \tfrac{1}{2}(n - 1)A_n \cos (n - 1)\omega_f t + \tfrac{1}{2}(n + 1)B_n \sin (n + 1)\omega_f t$$

$$- \tfrac{1}{2}(n - 1)B_n \sin (n - 1)\omega_f t] \quad (9 \cdot 26)$$

The next step is to equate coefficients of each sine and cosine on the two sides of this equation. The resulting equations, for the zero-frequency term, for $\cos \omega_f t$, and for $\sin \omega_f t$, respectively, are

$$A_0 = 1$$

$$m\beta A_0 + A_1 + \beta B_1 - \tfrac{1}{2}m\beta A_2 = 0 \quad (9 \cdot 27)$$

$$-\beta A_1 + B_1 - \tfrac{1}{2}m\beta B_2 = 0$$

with similar equations for the higher-frequency sines and cosines. But this set of equations, beyond establishing $A_0 = 1$, is not sufficient to determine the A's and B's. To proceed further, one can assume each A and each B to be a power series in m, and then equate coefficients of like powers of m in the Eqs. 9·27. Using the notation $A_n = \sum_{k=0}^{\infty} A_{nk} m^k$ and $B_n = \sum_{k=0}^{\infty} B_{nk} m^k$, the first (for m^0 and m^1) equations thus obtained are

$$A_{10} + \beta B_{10} = 0$$

$$-\beta A_{10} + B_{10} = 0 \quad (9 \cdot 28)$$

$$A_{11} + \beta B_{11} - \tfrac{1}{2}\beta A_{20} = -\beta$$

$$-\beta A_{11} + B_{11} - \tfrac{1}{2}\beta B_{20} = 0$$

From the first two it is clear that $A_{10} = B_{10} = 0$. Similarly, one finds all the $A_{n0} = B_{n0} = 0$. Knowing this, the last two of Eqs.

9·28 determine $A_{11} = -\beta/(1 + \beta^2)$ and $B_{11} = -\beta^2/(1 + \beta^2)$. Proceeding in this way, one finds for the first few terms

$$A_0 = 1$$

$$A_1 = -m\frac{\beta}{1 + \beta^2} - m^3\frac{\beta^3(5\beta^2 - 1)}{2(1 + \beta^2)^2(1 + 4\beta^2)} + \cdots$$

$$B_1 = -m\frac{\beta^2}{1 + \beta^2} - m^3\frac{\beta^4(\beta^2 - 2)}{(1 + \beta^2)^2(1 + 4\beta^2)} + \cdots$$

$$A_2 = -m^2\frac{\beta^2(2\beta^2 - 1)}{(1 + \beta^2)(1 + 4\beta^2)}$$
$$-m^4\frac{\beta^4(36\beta^6 - 73\beta^4 - 35\beta^2 + 2)}{(1 + \beta^2)^2(1 + 4\beta^2)^2(1 + 9\beta^2)} + \cdots$$

$$\qquad\qquad , \ (9\cdot29)$$

$$B_2 = m^2\frac{3\beta^3}{(1 + \beta^2)(1 + 4\beta^2)}$$
$$+m^4\frac{3\beta^5(32\beta^4 + 3\beta^2 - 5)}{(1 + \beta^2)^2(1 + 4\beta^2)^2(1 + 9\beta^2)} + \cdots$$

If these values are put in Eq. 9·22, the expression for the forced response is obtained. Neglecting terms in m^3 and higher degrees, this becomes

$$\frac{q_r}{Q_f} = \frac{m\beta}{\sqrt{1 + \beta^2}}\sin\left(\omega_f t + \tan^{-1}\frac{1}{\beta}\right)$$

$$+ \frac{m^2\beta^2}{\sqrt{(1 + \beta^2)(1 + 4\beta^2)}}\cos\left(2\omega_f t + \tan^{-1}\frac{1}{\beta} + \tan^{-1}\frac{1}{2\beta}\right) \quad (9\cdot30)$$

This is approximately the result published by Wente.[1]

From Eq. 9·30 it is clear that for the condenser microphone as for the carbon microphone practical design involves a compromise between large signal, obtained by making m large, and low distortion, obtained by making m small. In addition, obtaining a flat frequency characteristic requires that β be large.

These two examples, the carbon microphone and the condenser microphone, serve to indicate the nature of the simpler problems in parametric forcing. The relatively heavy going encountered

---

[1] E. C. Wente, *Physical Review*, **10**, 41, 1917.

in the condenser microphone problem foreshadows the need for relaxing the hope of always obtaining fully detailed solutions and for relying more and more on general arguments which may be made on the basis of such expressions as Eqs. 9·19 and 9·22.

9·4   The nuclear chain reactor.   Several of the physical systems discussed in earlier chapters were actually parametrically forced systems.   But, if in particular the parameters are constant after a certain instant of time, the two problems—direct forcing and parametric forcing—are essentially identical.   The only difference arises in establishing initial conditions.

One of these parametrically forced systems treated in preceding chapters is the nuclear chain reactor (Sections 4·10 and 6·6). This physical system stands in unique relation to the subject matter of this book; for on the one hand it may usefully be discussed as a simple first-order system, whereas on the other hand it furnishes illustrations covering the full scope of this book and, indeed, extending well beyond it.   The reactor will serve here as a good example of parametric forcing.

The discussion will be based on the assumption of a single group of delayed neutrons, giving a second-order system, as in Section 4·10.   The extension to nth-order would involve nothing new in principle, though of course the mathematical complexity increases rapidly with the order.   The differential equation for the neutron density q is therefore taken as in Eq. 4·83, with $\dot{s} = 0$.   That is,

$$\ddot{q} + (\rho_e + \rho_d - \rho_p)\dot{q} - (\rho_e\rho_p + \dot{\rho}_p)q = \rho_e s \qquad (9\cdot31)$$

In this equation the time-dependent parameter is the prompt multiplication parameter ρ_p.   One can consider different forms of time dependence for ρ_p, thus obtaining in Eq. 9·31 various linear differential equations of the second order.

Now a complete discussion of linear differential equations would be far beyond the possible scope of this book.   This would be true even though the discussion were limited to equations of the second order.   The fact is that a substantial portion of mathematical physics is concerned with linear differential equations of the second order and with the functions obtained as solutions of such equations.   So the most that can be done here with Eq. 9·31 is to consider briefly some of the problems associated with it.

Suppose, for example, that ρ_p is a linear function of time,

$$\rho_p = \rho_{p0} + mt \qquad (9\cdot32)$$

This gives a problem with interesting mathematical aspects and one which is also of practical interest, since it represents the effect of constant-velocity motion of a linear control element. One might consider the particular problem of determining q, starting from initial conditions and with numerical values as follows:

$$
\begin{aligned}
q(0) &= Q_1 \\
\dot{q}(0) &= 0 \\
\rho_d &= 100 \text{ (second)}^{-1} \\
\rho_e &= 0.1 \text{ (second)}^{-1} \\
\rho_{p0} &= 0 \\
m &= 10 \text{ (second)}^{-1} \\
s &= 0
\end{aligned}
\tag{9·33}
$$

The homogeneous differential equation obtained by putting Eq. 9·32 along with $s = 0$ into Eq. 9·31 is of a form found listed in tables [1] with its solution given in terms of confluent hypergeometric functions. These functions, moreover, may be found in tables of functions.[2] One might expect, therefore, to be able to proceed smoothly with any given numerical values. It is disconcerting, then, to find that the representative set of numerical values given in Eqs. 9·33 yields numerical data which are quite unmanageable in terms of confluent hypergeometric functions. In fact the problem can be worked out only by starting afresh with the differential equation and finding solutions more tractable for the given numerical values.

In this connection it should be noted that the general solution of a homogeneous linear second-order equation is

$$
q = C_1 f_1(t) + C_2 f_2(t)
\tag{9·34}
$$

where C_1 and C_2 are arbitrary constants, and f_1 and f_2 are any two independent solutions of the equation. *In principle*, for any solutions, f_1 and f_2, it should be possible to determine C_1 and C_2 to satisfy any given initial conditions. *In practice*, however, the feasibility of this determination may be decisively affected by the form of f_1 and f_2. Thus, in the problem of Eqs. 9·32 and 9·33,

[1] E. P. Adams, *Smithsonian Mathematical Formulae and Tables of Elliptic Functions*, Washington, D. C., Smithsonian Institution, 1939. (Cf. item 8.630.)

[2] Jahnke and Emde, *Tables of Functions*, New York, Dover Publications, 1943.

having f_1 and f_2 in terms of confluent hypergeometric functions leads to prohibitive numerical difficulties in evaluating C_1 and C_2, whereas other forms of solutions may be found which make this evaluation possible.

Even then the problem calls for involved and tedious analytical and numerical considerations, which are omitted here.[1] The above discussion has been given to emphasize the fact that, in addition to the difficulty of finding solutions of a differential equation, there may be difficulty in finding solutions of a form suitable for expressing desired numerical results. Questions of convergence of infinite series are especially important, since in many problems the solutions are obtained in the form of such series.

Returning to the reactor as governed by Eq. 9·31, suppose that instead of the linear parametric forcing of Eq. 9·32 one has sinusoidal parametric forcing,

$$\rho_p = \rho_{p0} + m_a \cos \omega_f t \qquad (9\cdot35)$$

Substitution of this into Eq. 9·31 (and assuming $s = 0$) gives a homogeneous second-order differential equation with periodic coefficients. The more general topic of homogeneous linear differential equations (of arbitrary order) with periodic coefficients has received considerable attention, particularly with regard to establishing conditions under which the solutions will be periodic.[2] The condenser microphone as discussed above in connection with Eq. 9·19 gives one example of such a problem. Another particular equation which has received detailed study is the one known as Mathieu's equation.[3]

A detailed study of the response of the reactor to the forcing of Eq. 9·35 would constitute a bigger problem than can be undertaken here. A limited aspect of the problem, however, may be discussed.

---

[1] A more tractable form of equation is given by the substitutions $q = ve^{-\frac{1}{2}\int (A+Bt)\, dt}$ and $t = (z/\sqrt{\pm B}\,) + (2D/B^2) - (A/B)$. These transform the equation $\ddot{q} + (A + Bt)\dot{q} + (C + Dt)q = 0$ into $(d^2v/dz^2) + (n + \frac{1}{2} - \frac{1}{4}z^2)$ $= 0$, which is known as Weber's equation. (For n to have integral values there is, of course, a restriction on the values of A, B, C, and D.) Cf. E. L. Ince, *Ordinary Differential Equations*, New York, Dover Publications, 1944; and Whittaker and Watson, *Modern Analysis*, New York, The Macmillan Company, 1945.

[2] E. L. Ince, *Ordinary Differential Equations*, New York, Dover Publications, 1944, p. 381.

[3] *Ibid.*, p. 175.

This concerns the behavior of the reactor, near an equilibrium condition, in response to small forcing. From Eq. 9·31 it is evident that the reactor is in equilibrium when q has the value $-s/\rho_{p0}$, where ρ_{p0} is a constant value of ρ_p. Calling this equilibrium value q_0, one may put

$$q = q_0 + q_1$$
$$\rho_p = \rho_{p0} + m \tag{9·36}$$

where both q_1 and m are to be treated as small quantities. In particular, m may have the time dependence, $m = m_a \cos \omega_f t$, corresponding to Eq. 9·35.

Putting the values of Eqs. 9·36 into Eq. 9·31, and neglecting products of m and q_1 and their derivatives, the equation obtained for q_1 is

$$\ddot{q}_1 + (\rho_e + \rho_d - \rho_{p0})\dot{q}_1 - \rho_e\rho_{p0}q_1 = q_0(\rho_e m + \dot{m}) \tag{9·37}$$

which is an equation with constant coefficients. Corresponding to this equation for small disturbances, one can write the **parametric transfer impedance** between m and q_1,

$$Z_t(p) = \frac{q_0(\rho_e + p)}{p^2 + (\rho_e + \rho_d - \rho_{p0})p - \rho_e\rho_{p0}} \tag{9·38}$$

and the **parametric impedance**, relevant to Eq. 9·35,

$$Z = \frac{q_{1a}}{m_a} = \frac{q_0(\rho_e + j\omega_f)}{-\rho_e\rho_{p0} - \omega_f{}^2 + j\omega_f(\rho_e + \rho_d - \rho_{p0})} \tag{9·39}$$

Considering that for the reactor to be stable ρ_{p0} must be a negative quantity, it is reasonable to introduce

$$\omega_n = \sqrt{-\rho_e\rho_{p0}}$$
$$\zeta = \frac{\rho_e + \rho_d - \rho_{p0}}{2\sqrt{-\rho_e\rho_{p0}}} \tag{9·40}$$

in terms of which Eq. 9·39 becomes

$$Z = \frac{\dfrac{q_0}{\omega_n}\left(\dfrac{\rho_e}{\omega_n} + j\beta\right)}{1 - \beta^2 + j2\zeta\beta} \tag{9·41}$$

This is seen to be of the same form as for the vibration isolating system discussed in Section 7·10. Thus some idea is obtained of the response of the reactor to small sinusoidal forcing from an equilibrium condition.

Another approach toward an understanding of reactor response is furnished by a consideration of the converse problem, as applied to parametric forcing. Whereas the direct problem of calculating the response to a given time dependence of ρ_p is quite difficult, the converse problem of finding the variation of ρ_p that was responsible for an observed time dependence of q is in principle quite easy, even treating the reactor as an nth-order system, as in Section 6·6. Under the assumption that $s = 0$, the reactor Eqs. 6·68 and 6·69 may be written

$$\dot{q} = (\rho_p - \rho_d)q + \sum_{i=1}^{n-1} \rho_{ei}f_i \qquad (9\cdot42)$$

$$\dot{f}_i + \rho_{ei}f_i = \rho_{di}q \qquad (9\cdot43)$$

Now considering q to be a known function of time, it is clear that each of the simple first-order Eqs. 9·43 may be solved, giving the time dependence of the f_i. Substituting these time functions for the f_i in Eq. 9·42 gives an equation in which ρ_p is the only unknown, and ρ_p is thereby determined.

It is worth noting that this simplicity of the converse problem is achieved here only because of the particular nature of the reactor Eqs. 9·42 and 9·43. Comparable simplicity could not be hoped for in the general nth-order system with parametric forcing. Thus the reactor problem furnishes here, as it did in the matter of solving the auxiliary equation of Section 6·6, an example of the advantage that may be realized by taking account of the mathematical details of a particular problem.

9·5   Feedback through parameters. Discussion of feedback systems in Chapter 8 was based on the idea of direct forcing, rather than parametric forcing. Thus in the scheme of Fig. 8·1 the control action q_c is indicated as a direct forcing of the controlled system. In practice it is convenient or necessary to control some systems by a control action which works through one or more of the parameters of the controlled system. Here again the nuclear chain reactor serves as an example. Automatic control or regulation of the reactor is achieved by having measurements of neutron density exert a controlling action on the value of the multiplication parameter ρ_p.

The mathematical treatment of problems involving feedback through parameters is difficult because the differential equations involve parameters dependent on q and are therefore nonlinear. In the control of the reactor, for example, ρ_p in Eq. 9·31 would be a function of q, making the equation nonlinear. This serves to emphasize the gap between systems with direct forcing and those with parametric forcing—a gap which has perhaps been minimized by the emphasis put on the fact that the differential equations are linear for both. Addition of the feedback concept to the picture breaks this bond, revealing the full measure of the difference between the two types of systems.

In connection with feedback it is appropriate to discuss stability of systems with parametric forcing. In directly forced systems the clear distinction between transient response and forced response makes for easy understanding of the stability concept, both in its physical and in its mathematical aspects. The response to parametric forcing does not in general suggest so obvious a definition of stability. It is possible, however, to give individual discussions of stability for various individual forms of time dependence of the parameters.

For instance, in the simplest case the parameters are constant. The stability problem is then the same as for systems with constant coefficients. This result is not so trivial as it might seem, because of its fundamental role in the response to small disturbance from an equilibrium condition. This method was applied to the example of the nuclear reactor, resulting in Eq. 9·37.

The method of small disturbance may be applied to any form of parametric forcing, including, in particular, sinusoidal parametric forcing. As applied to the nuclear reactor, this resulted in Eq. 9·41. Moreover the problem of large sinusoidal forcing, or the problem of linear differential equations with periodic coefficients, particularly equations of the second order, has received rather intense mathematical study. The results thus obtained, including considerations relating to the stability of such systems, may be found in discussions on Mathieu functions, Mathieu's equation, Hill's equation, and Floquet's theory.[1]

Stability of systems involving feedback through parameters

[1] Whittaker and Watson, *Modern Analysis*, New York, The Macmillan Company, 1945; E. L. Ince, *Ordinary Differential Equations*, New York, Dover Publications, 1944.

concerns the properties of nonlinear systems and might therefore be considered more appropriately in Chapter 11. It may be noted here, however, that the method of small disturbance is again useful, since by this means a nonlinear problem may be "linearized." Although this method does not by any means give a full resolution of nonlinear problems, it frequently yields useful results.

It is perhaps also worth while to note the analogy between nonlinearity due to feedback through parameters and nonlinearity due to other effects. A good illustration of this is the comparison between automatic control of the nuclear reactor and the effect on the reactor of fission products. In both effects the multiplication parameter ρ_p depends on the neutron density q. In the control problem this dependence is *designed* to effect rapid and accurate control of q. In the fission product problem the dependence is *inherent* in the physics of the fission process, since some of the fission fragments have neutron-scattering and neutron-absorbing properties different from those of the materials of which the reactor is built. A similar analogy between designed feedback and inherent feedback was given in Chapter 8 in connection with Figs. $8 \cdot 2$ and $8 \cdot 3$.

9·6 Performance criteria. In this final section of an all-too-brief chapter on parametric forcing, an attempt will be made to review the general situation pertaining to such forcing. A good perspective in which to conduct this review is given by considering possible performance criteria for parametrically forced systems. The microphones discussed in Section $9 \cdot 3$ are examples of duplicators with parametric forcing. That is, the microphones were considered to have the function of producing output voltages which are instantaneously (minimum error) or after a fixed delay (minimum distortion) proportional to the changes in resistance or in capacitance. (Strictly speaking, the practical overall duplicator criterion for the microphones is that the output voltage should duplicate the pressure change responsible for the resistance or capacitance change.) Numerous other examples could be mentioned of parametrically forced systems subject to the criterion of minimum error or to the criterion of minimum distortion.

Parametric forcing is also important with respect to noise. The direct noise forcing represented by the symbol q_n in previous discussions is in many cases a fictitious, equivalent representation of parametric noise forcing. That is, unwanted response is actually due to unwanted variation of parameters, and this response is regarded as due to an equivalent direct forcing q_n. For many purposes this simpler picture is useful and adequate. But sometimes there is a source of parametric noise so important that it is worth the trouble to go into the more exact treatment of this noise as involving parametric forcing. Whether equivalent direct forcing is an adequate representation of a parametric effect is, in general, determined largely by the magnitude of the effect. For, as shown in deriving Eq. 9·37, parametric forcing of small magnitude is mathematically equivalent to direct forcing. Since the usual concept of noise implies a disturbance of relatively small amplitude, the general validity of using an equivalent q_n appears to be well supported. The more exact treatment of parametric noise thus seems to be called for in the more unusual occurrence of a large disturbance, which might be labeled "catastrophic" or "accidental" noise.

A third criterion possibly applicable to parametric forcing is suggested by the concept of parametric impedance developed in Eq. 9·39. One might visualize a problem in parametric forcing in which a system is to be designed for specified parametric impedance. In comparing such a problem with the corresponding problem in direct forcing, however, it is important to bear in mind the fact that both Z_t and Z, as given by Eqs. 9·38 and 9·39, are dimensionally different from the corresponding quantities defined for direct forcing in Eqs. 5·15 and 5·16. In particular, the concept of complementary quantities and their role in defining impedance stand in an entirely different relationship to parametric impedance.

Without going into further detail, it may be said that most of the ideas developed for direct forcing have some more or less clear-cut significance for problems of parametric forcing. The most impressive difference between the two kinds of problems is the increased mathematical difficulty of dealing with parametric forcing. It should be emphasized, however, that only a few scattered references have been given in this chapter to the literature of mathematics and physics which deals with linear differential equations and that this tremendously large literature represents a great reservoir of help for probing further into the problems of parametric forcing.

CHAPTER
10

Distributed Systems

10·1   A reaction trough.   The subject of distributed systems
will be introduced by considering a particular example.   In the
production of continuous rayon thread, chemical treatment of the
thread after spinning may be carried out by pulling it through a
trough of solution.   Suppose this is done at a constant speed of
S centimeters per second.   Suppose further that the function of
the trough is to wash out of the yarn a particular chemical element,
say copper.   Let C denote the concentration of copper in the
yarn, in grams per centimeter.   Let L denote the length of the
trough, and let x measure distance along the trough in the direction
of the thread motion.   That is, the thread enters the trough at
$x = 0$ and leaves it at $x = L$ (see Fig. 10·1).

To maintain the chemical nature of the washing solution, it is
made to flow through the trough in the sense opposite to that of

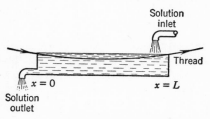

FIG. 10·1.   Reaction trough.

the thread motion.   Let S_s denote the linear speed of this fluid
flow, in centimeters per second.   (The trough is assumed to be
of uniform width.)   Also, let C_s denote concentration, in grams
per centimeter, of the copper in the solution.

It is clear that both C and C_s will depend on x. These quantities will also, in general, depend on time, particularly when one first starts to draw the thread through the trough. But one would expect this transient condition to settle down into a more or less steady state, independent of time. It is this steady condition which is of particular interest here. That is, the problem to be treated here is the investigation of C and C_s as functions of x.

Let $D(x)$ denote the dilution rate, in grams per centimeter per second; that is, D is the mass of copper washed from unit length of the thread in unit time. D is assumed to be independent of S and of S_s. It follows that

$$\frac{dC}{dx} = -\frac{D(x)}{S} \qquad (10·1)$$

By postulating different ways of dependence on x for D, one can get from this equation the corresponding $C(x)$. The simplest postulate is that D is proportional to C, or

$$D = KC \qquad (10·2)$$

where K is a constant. On this assumption, Eq. 10·1 gives

$$C = C_0 e^{-Kx/S} \qquad (10·3)$$

Co is a constant of integration, representing the value of C at the trough entrance, i.e., at $x = 0$.

Similarly, the equation for C_s is

$$\frac{dC_s}{dx} = -\frac{D(x)}{S_s} \qquad (10·4)$$

This equation, taken together with Eqs. 10·2 and 10·3, yields the solution

$$C_s = \frac{C_0 S}{S_s} e^{-Kx/S} + \text{constant} \qquad (10·5)$$

The constant may be evaluated on the basis that the concentration of the incoming flow at $x = L$ is C_{s0}. The equation may then be written

$$C_s - C_{s0} = \frac{C_0 S}{S_s} (e^{-Kx/S} - e^{-KL/S}) \qquad (10·6)$$

A further variation of the problem may be considered. Suppose the copper present in the thread as it enters the trough is only partly in soluble form. Let C refer to the soluble portion, and C_i to the insoluble portion. Assume a reaction rate $R(x)$ converting the copper from an insoluble to a soluble compound. Then

$$\frac{dC_i}{dx} = -\frac{R(x)}{S} \tag{10·7}$$

But the quantity C satisfies the equation

$$\frac{dC}{dx} = \frac{R(x)}{S} - \frac{D(x)}{S} \tag{10·8}$$

And if D is proportional to C, as in Eq. 10·2,

$$\frac{dC}{dx} + \frac{K}{S}C = \frac{R(x)}{S} \tag{10·9}$$

Now this equation is identical in form with the standard first-order equation treated in Chapter 3, the only difference being that x, instead of t, is the independent variable. Hence the solution of this equation for any ordinary functional form of $R(x)$ can be written down at once. Suppose, for example, that $R(x)$ is proportional to C_i; then substitution of

$$R = K_R C_i \tag{10·10}$$

into Eq. 10·7 yields

$$C_i = C_{i0}e^{-K_R x/S} \tag{10·11}$$

or

$$R = K_R C_{i0}e^{-K_R x/S} \tag{10·12}$$

Putting this "forcing" into Eq. 10·9, the methods of Chapter 3 yield

$$C = \left(C_0 - \frac{K_R C_{i0}}{K - K_R}\right)e^{-Kx/S} + \frac{K_R C_{i0}}{K - K_R}e^{-K_R x/S} \tag{10·13}$$

One might go further and suppose that K, instead of being constant, depends on x. The problem of solving Eq. 10·9 then becomes strictly analogous to a problem in parametric forcing, such as the condenser microphone problem of Chapter 9.

Introduction of the concept of C_i has not changed the validity of Eq. 10·4. Thus C_s could be found, for conditions on which the derivation of Eq. 10·13 was based, by integrating $\int - (D/S_s)\, dx$, with $D = KC$, and C given by Eq. 10·13.

The foregoing discussion of the reaction trough has served to illustrate two aspects of the subject of distributed systems. The first aspect concerns the possibility of ignoring time dependence by treating a "steady" condition, which is assumed to obtain after transient response has died out. This gives to the whole picture a certain symmetry. The treatment of *time dependence* of *lumped systems* is balanced by the treatment of *space dependence* of *steady systems*. Each of these is of course only a partial treatment, and the fully rigorous treatment of any system must take cognizance of both time and space dependence.

The second point emphasized by the example of the reaction trough is the fact that differential equations studied with time as the independent variable should be recognized when a space variable replaces time, so that full use may be made of methods presented in earlier chapters. The possibility of substituting x for t, or t for x, may seem obvious enough, but the point is nonetheless worth noting. Whenever a given differential equation is very extensively used in one of these variables, there accumulates a fund of knowledge which one should be alert to use on problems in the other variable.

10·2 Partial differential equations. To deal with the complete problem of distributed systems it is necessary to make use of partial differential equations. Though the full domain of ordinary differential equations is vast indeed, that of partial differential equations is vaster still. How true this is may be felt in the mere realization that in this new domain the number of independent variables may be indefinitely large. It is evident, therefore, that any discussion of this topic which can be given here must be extremely restricted in scope. However, an effort will be made to present a few basic facts about the mathematics of partial differential equations.

Consider first the very simple problem in which q, as a function of x and t, satisfies the linear first-order equation with constant coefficients,

$$\lambda q_x + \tau \dot{q} + q = 0 \qquad (10\cdot14)$$

The symbol q_x is used to denote the partial derivative of q with respect to x; λ is a constant of the dimension of length; and τ is a time constant. Now, without worrying about how it is obtained, the equation

$$q = Q_1 e^{-t/\tau} \left(\frac{x}{\lambda} - \frac{t}{\tau} \right) + Q_2 e^{-t/\tau} \qquad (10 \cdot 15)$$

where Q_1 and Q_2 are arbitrary constants, satisfies Eq. $10 \cdot 14$, as may be verified by differentiating and substituting. Any solution which, like this one, involves two arbitrary constants may be denoted by

$$q = q(x, t; Q_1, Q_2) \qquad (10 \cdot 16)$$

For a first-order differential equation in two independent variables, two arbitrary constants, but no more, may appear in the solution. For Eq. $10 \cdot 16$ and the two equations obtained by differentiating it with respect to x and with respect to t constitute three equations involving Q_1 and Q_2. By eliminating Q_1 and Q_2 from these equations, a single equation is obtained, namely, the partial differential equation, of which Eq. $10 \cdot 16$ may be said to be a "primitive." Correspondingly, if there are n independent variables, one would expect the solution of a first-order equation to involve n arbitrary constants.

Now, since the solution given by Eq. $10 \cdot 15$ contains two—the maximum number—arbitrary constants, one might judge from the corresponding situation in ordinary differential equations that it is a rather general solution, perhaps the most general possible. One is permitted, therefore, some degree of astonishment on realizing that Eq. $10 \cdot 15$ is just one of a whole infinity of more or less similar solutions. If one puts

$$u = e^{t/\tau} q$$
$$v = \frac{x}{\lambda} - \frac{t}{\tau} \qquad (10 \cdot 17)$$

the above solution in Eq. $10 \cdot 15$ corresponds to putting

$$u = Q_1 v + Q_2 \qquad (10 \cdot 18)$$

But the fact is that not only this relation between u and v, but any ordinary functional relation,

$$\phi(u, v) = 0 \qquad (10 \cdot 19)$$

constitutes an integral of Eq. $10 \cdot 14$.

The general treatment of first-order equations which are linear in the derivatives shows that the above situation applies for all such equations. Let the equation be

$$F(x, t, q)q_x + G(x, t, q)\dot{q} = H(x, t, q) \qquad (10 \cdot 20)$$

Form the **subsidiary equations,** which are the ordinary differential equations,

$$\frac{dx}{F} = \frac{dt}{G} = \frac{dq}{H} \qquad (10 \cdot 21)$$

Let

$$\begin{aligned} u(x, t, q) &= A_1 \\ v(x, t, q) &= A_2 \end{aligned} \qquad (10 \cdot 22)$$

where A_1 and A_2 are constants, be any two independent integrals of the system $10 \cdot 21$. Then the **general integral** of Eq. $10 \cdot 20$ is given by putting these functions u and v into Eq. $10 \cdot 19$. Any one integral of the form $10 \cdot 16$ corresponding to the choice of some one functional relation between u and v is called a **complete integral.** The above general method was used to obtain the solution $10 \cdot 15$ to Eq. $10 \cdot 14$.

In a complete integral such as Eq. $10 \cdot 15$, one may inquire into the significance of the constants Q_1 and Q_2. Putting $t = 0$ in Eq. $10 \cdot 15$ gives

$$q(x, 0) = Q_1 \frac{x}{\lambda} + Q_2 \qquad (10 \cdot 23)$$

This indicates that Eq. $10 \cdot 15$ with proper evaluation of Q_1 and Q_2 gives the solution to the problem of finding response starting from an initial straight-line distribution of q versus x, of the form $10 \cdot 23$. But suppose one wishes to solve a problem involving a quite different initial or boundary condition. Clearly, arbitrary assignment of numerical values to Q_1 and Q_2 will in general be totally inadequate. If, for instance, the initial distribution of q with x were sinusoidal, no possible assignment of numerical values to Q_1 and Q_2 in Eq. $10 \cdot 15$ would suffice. What is required is a new *functional* relation between u and v. The problem of determining the functional relation required to satisfy given initial and boundary conditions (or, more briefly, simply boundary conditions) is a very difficult one, vastly more difficult than the simple algebraic evaluation of constants in solutions of ordinary differential equations. Hence the boundary conditions play of necessity a much more fundamental role in partial differential equations than in ordinary equations. In fact, modern research deals with specific problems of satisfying a given partial differential equation and given boundary conditions, rather than with the general problem of finding a solution of the equation with sufficient arbitrary elements in it to permit satisfying any boundary conditions.[1]

The method presented above in Eqs. 10·19 and 10·22 can obviously be generalized to the corresponding case of n independent variables. For some unfortunate reason,[2] equations of the form 10·20 are commonly called linear, even though the functions F, G, and H may involve q. This anomaly in usage of the term "linear" is restricted to first-order partial differential equations. For higher-order equations "linear" means "linear." In partial, as in ordinary, equations, linearity is important mainly because it insures the possibility of superposition, according to which any linear combination of solutions is itself a solution.

The foregoing discussion of first-order equations, linear in the partial derivatives, can serve only as a sort of illustrative introduction to the whole subject. It must be emphasized that, as one goes on to nonlinear first-order equations and then to higher-order equations, it becomes increasingly difficult to establish general results, so that the dominant concept comes to be the individual problem, in which the differential equation and the boundary conditions enter on equal footing. These boundary value problems are of fundamental importance in mathematical physics and have received much study.[3]

10·3 Waves. As emphasized in Chapter 5, sinusoidal forcing is of outstanding importance in the response of lumped systems. A correspondingly important role is played in distributed systems by the phenomena which are called waves. Like all general concepts, the concept of wave is not easily defined. In the broadest

[1] See, for example, J. Hadamard, *Cauchy's Problem in Linear Partial Differential Equations*, New Haven, Yale University Press, 1923.

[2] The apparent reason is that any such equation can be discussed in terms of an associated, truly linear equation. Cf. A. R. Forsyth, *Theory of Differential Equations*, Part IV, Cambridge University Press, 1906, pp. 56–76.

[3] See Chapters 7 and 8, Margenau and Murphy, *Mathematics of Physics and Chemistry*, New York, D. Van Nostrand Company, 1943; Churchill, *Fourier Series and Boundary Value Problems*, New York, McGraw-Hill Book Company, 1941; Courant and Hilbert, *Methoden der Mathematischen Physik*, Berlin, Julius Springer, Vol. 1, 1931; Vol. 2, 1937.

sense, a wave is a response which exists over, or is propagated over, some spatial coordinates. In addition, the wave concept usually implies that the response is finite (that is, does not increase indefinitely with time) and, frequently, that the response is periodic with time. In this latter case, of course, the relation to sinusoidal forcing is especially close.

In the two variables x and t, the equation

$$c^2 q_{xx} = \ddot{q} \tag{10·24}$$

is called the wave equation. The general integral of this equation is

$$q = q_-(x + ct) + q_+(x - ct) \tag{10·25}$$

where q_- and q_+ are arbitrary functions. Since $q_-(x, t + t_1)$ $= q_-(x + ct_1, t)$ and $q_+(x, t + t_1) = q_+(x - ct_1, t)$, the response q_- is propagated with velocity c in the negative x-direction, and the response q_+ is propagated with the same velocity in the positive x-direction. Equation 10·24 deserves its name, not because it governs *all* wave phenomena, but because it governs so *many*. Wave phenomena to which this equation (or its general three-dimensional form) applies include waves on strings, waves in membranes, longitudinal waves in bars, tidal waves (often called shallow-water waves) in liquids, sound waves (of small amplitude), electric waves carried on a cable of negligible resistance and leakage, and light waves and other electromagnetic waves in a continuous, uniform medium. Wave phenomena that cannot be treated on the basis of this wave equation include transverse vibration of bars or rods, surface (or deep-water) waves in liquids, capillary waves in liquids, sound waves of large amplitude, heat flow in continuous media, and flow of electricity over cables having appreciable resistance or leakage.

The various physical problems to which the wave equation may be applied thus have much common mathematical ground. They are not mathematically identical, however, since the boundary conditions are in general different. It is therefore best to illustrate the use of the wave equation by discussing typical particular problems. In the next section a problem of flow of electricity on a cable will be treated in detail. The remainder of this section is devoted to a discussion of a few wave problems, using sound waves for illustration.

Consider first a sound wave which depends only on x and t. This is the so-called plane wave, propagated parallel to the x-axis. It would apply, for instance, to sound waves in a uniform cylindrical tube, provided the sound frequencies were low enough so that the shortest wavelength involved was still large compared to the tube's diameter. At higher frequencies the waves would not necessarily proceed simply down the tube but might also vibrate back and forth across the axis of the tube, so that other space coordinates would be involved in addition to x. This more complicated situation will be discussed later, but the simple plane wave will be treated first.

If the sound is thought of as being in a tube, the question naturally arises as to how long the tube is. If the tube is infinitely long, the most one can say is that any sound q_+ can be propagated in one direction and any sound q_- in the other direction, according to Eq. 10·25. This is not a very interesting situation. Suppose, however, that the tube is of finite length, extending from $x = 0$ to $x = S$. Then one sees the need of specifying *how* the tube ends at these points. Of the many ways in which a tube could be terminated acoustically, the two extremes are most frequently mentioned. These are the closed pipe, meaning a termination at which the sound particle velocity is zero; and the open pipe, meaning a termination at which the sound pressure is zero.[1] That is, the acoustic impedance

$$Z_a = \frac{p}{Au} \qquad (10 \cdot 26)$$

where p is the sound pressure, u the particle velocity, and A the area of the tube, is infinite for a closed end, and zero for an open end.

Suppose the pipe is open at $x = 0$, and closed at $x = S$. These boundary conditions mean that

$$
\begin{aligned}
p_+(0, t) + p_-(0, t) &= 0 \\
u_+(S, t) + u_-(S, t) &= 0
\end{aligned}
\qquad (10 \cdot 27)
$$

As a particular problem to be solved under these conditions, suppose that up to time $t = 0$ the tube is closed at both ends and

---

[1] Strictly speaking, conditions at an open end are not so simple. See P. M. Morse, *Vibration and Sound*, New York, McGraw-Hill Book Company, 1946, p. 198.

is under a constant pressure P units above atmospheric pressure. At $t = 0$, the diaphragm at $x = 0$ suddenly bursts and disappears, so that this end suddenly becomes an open end. What sound waves will be in the tube after $t = 0$?

The conditions in the tube just prior to the bursting of the diaphragm at $t = 0$ are given as

$$p_+(x, 0) + p_-(x, 0) = P$$
$$u_+(x, 0) + u_-(x, 0) = 0 \qquad (10·28)$$

The boundary conditions expressed in Eqs. 10·27 and 10·28 involve the sound pressure p and the particle velocity u. These two quantities satisfy the first-order equations,

$$\frac{\partial p}{\partial x} + \rho_0 \frac{\partial u}{\partial t} = 0$$
$$\frac{\partial u}{\partial x} + \frac{1}{\rho_0 c^2} \frac{\partial p}{\partial t} = 0 \qquad (10·29)$$

in which ρ_0 is the equilibrium density of the medium and c is the velocity of sound. The first of these equations is called the equation of motion and the second the equation of continuity. By differentiating one of these equations with respect to x and the other with respect to t, it is easy to show that both p and u satisfy the wave equation.

Now the problem is to find u and p as functions of x and t which satisfy Eqs. 10·29 and also the boundary conditions of Eqs. 10·27 and 10·28. How can the knowledge expressed in Eq. 10·25 be used in solving this problem? The idea of Fourier series (Section 5·6) leads to a useful suggestion. Suppose one postulates a Fourier series, say, for p:

$$p_- = \sum_{n=-\infty}^{\infty} A_n e^{jn(\omega t + kx)}$$
$$p_+ = \sum_{n=-\infty}^{\infty} B_n e^{jn(\omega t - kx)} \qquad (10·30)$$

where ω is the fundamental angular frequency and k is the wave number. $k = \omega/c$. Then for $p = p_+ + p_-$, one may write

$$p = \sum_{n=-\infty}^{\infty} (A_n e^{jnkx} + B_n e^{-jnkx}) e^{jn\omega t} \qquad (10·31)$$

Each term in the series is in the form of the product of two factors, one of which is a function of x alone and the other a function of t alone. Because of the complex number notation it may not be clear whether the variables x and t are actually separated, but this result at least suggests that one might get solutions in which the variables are separated.

In fact, the method of separation of variables is one of the most useful elementary methods of solving partial differential equations. One assumes a solution to consist of the sum, or the product, of functions, each of which depends on only one variable. If this assumption leads to solvable ordinary differential equations, the partial equation is thereby solved. Here the assumption leads to ordinary equations whose solutions are exponentials, trigonometric functions, and hyperbolic functions. Of these the trigonometric functions are most useful for the problem at hand.

Thus for the general expressions one may take

$$p_n = A_n \cos k_n x \cos \omega_n t + B_n \cos k_n x \sin \omega_n t$$
$$+ C_n \sin k_n x \cos \omega_n t + D_n \sin k_n x \sin \omega_n t \qquad (10 \cdot 32)$$

$$Z_0 u_n = A_n \sin k_n x \sin \omega_n t - B_n \sin k_n x \cos \omega_n t$$
$$- C_n \cos k_n x \sin \omega_n t + D_n \cos k_n x \cos \omega_n t$$

where p_n and u_n are typical terms in series representing p and u. $Z_0 = \rho_0 c$ is the specific acoustic impedance. These terms, p_n and u_n, satisfy not only the wave equation, but also Eqs. $10 \cdot 29$. The four coefficients, A_n, B_n, C_n, and D_n, must now be determined so as to satisfy the four boundary conditions of Eqs. $10 \cdot 27$ and $10 \cdot 28$.

To satisfy the second of Eqs. $10 \cdot 28$, it is clearly necessary and sufficient that B_n and D_n vanish. The first of Eqs. $10 \cdot 27$ requires $A_n = 0$. Thus, with only C_n different from zero, the second of Eqs. $10 \cdot 27$ becomes

$$-C_n \cos k_n S \sin \omega_n t = 0$$

which is satisfied if

$$k_n S = (2n - 1) \frac{\pi}{2} \qquad (10 \cdot 33)$$

This leaves only the "inhomogeneous" condition given by the first of Eqs. $10 \cdot 28$. Clearly, this cannot be satisfied by any one term, p_n.

The problem is how to form a series of such terms to represent P at the initial instant. The terms available are of the form

$$p_n = C_n \sin k_n x \cos \omega_n t \qquad (10\cdot34)$$

with permissible values of ω_n and k_n determined by Eq. $10\cdot33$.

In the problem being discussed, the initial pressure is the same for all values of x, that is, it is a constant, P. The more general problem, in which the initial pressure is some arbitrary function $P(x)$, may be discussed with little additional difficulty. So consider now the problem of determining the coefficients C_n such that $P(x) = p(x, 0) = \Sigma p_n(x, 0) = \Sigma C_n \sin k_n x$, with k_n given by Eq. $10\cdot33$. Before going into the question of *how* to solve this problem, it is important to raise the question of *whether* a solution is to be expected. That is, by what right can one hope to represent an arbitrary function $P(x)$ as the sum of terms, $C_n \sin k_n x$, with k_n values limited to the particular requirements of Eq. $10\cdot33$? This question, of the possibility of representing a given function as the sum of a given set of functions, is one of the fundamental questions of mathematical analysis. It cannot be dealt with here.[1] It is sufficient to warn the reader that this possibility must not be taken for granted, that certain restrictions are imposed on the function $P(x)$, on the set of functions in the series, and on the interval over which the representation is attempted. Fortunately, these conditions are satisfied in typical boundary-value problems, such as the one being treated here.

Evaluation of the coefficients C_n is made, in the usual manner of Fourier series, by integration over the interval $0 \leq x \leq S$. Thus

$$C_n = \frac{\displaystyle\int_0^S P(x) \sin k_n x \, dx}{\displaystyle\int_0^S \sin^2 k_n x \, dx} \qquad (10\cdot35)$$

If $P(x)$ is a constant, P, Eq. $10\cdot35$ with Eq. $10\cdot33$ gives

$$C_n = \frac{2P}{k_n S} = \frac{4P}{(2n - 1)\pi} \qquad (10\cdot36)$$

[1] A concise statement of the principal points is given in E. Madelung, *Die Mathematischen Hilfsmittel des Physikers*, New York, Dover Publications, 1943, pp. 22–26.

The final solution of the problem is therefore contained in Eq. 10·33 together with the equations:

$$p = \sum_{n=1}^{\infty} \frac{4P}{(2n-1)\pi} \sin k_n x \cos \omega_n t$$

$$Z_0 u = \sum_{n=1}^{\infty} \frac{-4P}{(2n-1)\pi} \cos k_n x \sin \omega_n t \qquad (10 \cdot 37)$$

Equations 10·37 represent the pressure and the particle velocity inside the tube from $x = 0$ to $x = S$. The solution, of course, has no physical meaning outside this interval. Note that this solution is periodic in time, so that every $2\pi/\omega_1$ seconds the pressure is uniformly equal to P throughout the tube. In physical reality this does not happen because there is some damping and the sound waves gradually die down. This damping occurs partly at the open end where some of the energy is radiated away as sound, and partly in the medium and on the walls and closed end of the tube where some of the energy is irreversibly converted into heat. All such effects were neglected in the above analysis.

For the sake of emphasis it is advisable to review the considerations involved in the transition from Eq. 10·25 to Eqs. 10·32. That is, knowing that any functions according to Eq. 10·25 would satisfy the wave equation, why did it seem desirable to go to sinusoidal functions in particular? The answer is that by going to sinusoidal functions the solution could be put in a form in which the variables were separated—the solution was the product of a function of x and a function of t. And why is it so desirable to have the variables separated? The answer is that with the variables separated it is much easier to see how the boundary conditions may be satisfied. This, then, is a basic pattern repeated in many boundary-value problems: solve the differential equation in a form with variables separated, thus obtaining **characteristic functions** or **eigenfunctions**—e.g., Eqs. 10·32; use some of the boundary conditions to determine **characteristic values** or **eigenvalues**—e.g., Eq. 10·33; use the eigenvalues and eigenfunctions to satisfy the remaining boundary conditions—e.g., as by Eq. 10·36.

As pointed out in introducing the idea of a plane wave in a tube, the idea must be used cautiously at frequencies high enough to have wavelengths comparable with the tube's diameter. It is *possible* to have a simple plane wave at high frequencies, but it is not very *probable*. At the low frequencies discussed above the tube was treated as a distributed system so far as its x-dimension was concerned, but in the plane normal to the x-axis it was considered as lumped—the cross-section shape of the tube was not specified. Suppose now that it is desired to treat the tube as a distributed system in its transverse y,z-dimensions as well as its axial x-dimension. This means that $p = p(x, y, z, t)$, and the wave equation is

$$c^2(p_{xx} + p_{yy} + p_{zz}) = \ddot{p} \qquad (10\cdot38)$$

Now, if the tube is of rectangular cross section, the boundary conditions on the walls involve particular values of y and of z. One would therefore seek a solution in terms of the separated variables x, y, z, and t. The eigenfunctions would then again be sinusoidal, similar to Eqs. 10·32, except that they would involve y and z in addition to x. The rectangular tube therefore presents nothing essentially new. But suppose the tube is of circular cross section. Then the boundary condition at the circular wall involves a particular value of $r = \sqrt{y^2 + z^2}$. This is not easily expressed in terms of sinusoidal functions of y and z. However, if the wave equation is transformed to cylindrical coordinates x, $r = \sqrt{y^2 + z^2}$, and $\theta = \tan^{-1} y/z$, it becomes

$$c^2 \left(p_{xx} + \frac{p_{\theta\theta}}{r^2} + p_{rr} + \frac{p_r}{r} \right) = \ddot{p} \qquad (10\cdot39)$$

The solution of this equation can be obtained with the variables x, r, and θ separated, so that it is easy to see how to satisfy the boundary conditions. The details of the solution will not be elaborated here.[1]

The above brief reference to the three-dimensional problem serves to lend additional emphasis to the importance of the boundary conditions in determining both the method of obtaining a solution and the nature of the solution itself. The example to be discussed in the next section is also instructive in this respect.

---

[1] For a general discussion of the solution of the wave equation in cylindrical coordinates, see Margenau and Murphy, *The Mathematics of Physics and Chemistry*, New York, D. Van Nostrand Company, 1943, pp. 228–229 and 248–251; also, P. M. Morse, *Vibration and Sound*, New York, McGraw-Hill Book Company, 1946, p. 233.

10·4   A cable problem. Figure 10·2 is a schematic diagram of the cable system to be discussed here. A concentric cable of length S has its outer shield connected to ground and its inner conductor leads through an inductance L to a switch. The far end of the cable, at $x = S$, is open circuit. Up to time $t = 0$, the switch is on position 1, the cable is charged to the voltage E, and no currents are flowing. At $t = 0$, the switch is suddenly moved to position 2, grounding this end of the cable through the inductance L. The problem is to calculate the voltage and the current in the cable after $t = 0$.

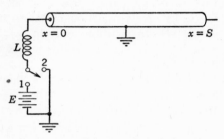

Fig. 10·2.   Diagram of cable system.

It may be noted that this problem is closely analogous to the problem of sound waves in a tube as discussed in the preceding section. In fact, if the inductance L were taken out of the picture, the analogy of the cable problem to the sound problem would be complete; or, if an acoustical inductance (a short length of small-diameter tube) were added at the open end of the sound tube, the sound problem would be completely analogous to Fig. 10·2. The mathematical basis of this analogy may be traced throughout the following treatment. Whether in the electrical or in the acoustical system, the effect of the lumped inductance L at the shorted end of the line furnishes an excellent illustration of the transition between lumped and distributed status of a system. It is principally with this motive in mind, namely, to show in a particular example, over the full range of frequency, the gradual transition from a lumped system to a distributed system, that the cable problem is presented.

The cable is assumed to have no appreciable resistance or leakage. It therefore has but two properties: inductance per unit length, $\mathcal{L}$, and capacitance per unit length, $\mathcal{C}$. Let i denote the current in the cable, and e the voltage across it. The quantities e and i are related by the differential equations

$$\frac{\partial e}{\partial x} + \mathcal{L}\frac{\partial i}{\partial t} = 0$$

$$\frac{\partial i}{\partial x} + \mathcal{C}\frac{\partial e}{\partial t} = 0$$

(10·40)

These equations are completely analogous to Eqs. 10·29, and so it is easy to show that e and i both satisfy the wave Eq. 10·24, with $c^2 = 1/\mathcal{L}\mathcal{C}$. These quantities may therefore be expressed in terms of the characteristic solutions 10·32. The choice of a particular combination of the eigenfunctions must be dictated by the boundary conditions.

Just as with the acoustic system, there are four boundary conditions. Listed in order corresponding to that of Eqs. 10·27 and 10·28 they are:

$$L\frac{\partial i(0, t)}{\partial t} + e(0, t) = 0$$

$$i(S, t) = 0$$

(10·41)

$$e(x, 0) = E$$

$$i(x, 0) = 0$$

The solutions of Eqs. 10·40, with $Z_0 = \sqrt{\mathcal{L}/\mathcal{C}}$, are

$$e_n = A_n \cos k_n x \cos \omega_n t + B_n \cos k_n x \sin \omega_n t$$
$$+ C_n \sin k_n x \cos \omega_n t + D_n \sin k_n x \sin \omega_n t$$

(10·42)

$$Z_0 i_n = A_n \sin k_n x \sin \omega_n t - B_n \sin k_n x \cos \omega_n t$$
$$- C_n \cos k_n x \sin \omega_n t + D_n \cos k_n x \cos \omega_n t$$

The last of the conditions of Eqs. 10·41 requires $B_n = D_n = 0$. Since $(\partial/\partial t)i(0, t) = -(\omega_n C_n/Z_0) \cos \omega_n t$, the first condition requires

$$A_n = \frac{\omega_n L}{Z_0} C_n$$

(10·43)

The second condition requires

$$\cot k_n S = \frac{A_n}{C_n}$$

(10·44)

Combining Eqs. $10 \cdot 43$ and $10 \cdot 44$, since $(\omega_n L/Z_0) = (k_n CLS/Z_0 S)$
$= (L/\mathcal{L}S)k_n S$,

$$\cot k_n S = \frac{L}{\mathcal{L}S} k_n S \qquad (10 \cdot 45)$$

This is the equation, corresponding to Eq. $10 \cdot 33$ in the acoustics problem, which determines the eigenvalues.

The third of the conditions of Eqs. $10 \cdot 41$ is therefore to be met by the series expansion,

$$\sum_{n=1}^{\infty} A_n \left[\cos k_n x + \frac{C_n}{A_n} \sin k_n x \right] = E$$

or by Eq. $10 \cdot 44$,

$$\sum_{n=1}^{\infty} A_n \left[\cos k_n x + \tan k_n S \sin k_n x \right] = E$$

or

$$\sum_{n=1}^{\infty} \frac{A_n}{\cos k_n S} \cos k_n (x - S) = E \qquad (10 \cdot 46)$$

Evaluation by

$$\frac{A_n}{\cos k_n S} = \frac{\displaystyle\int_0^S E \cos k_n (x - S) \, dx}{\displaystyle\int_0^S \cos^2 k_n (x - S) \, dx} \qquad (10 \cdot 47)$$

yields

$$\frac{A_n}{\cos k_n S} = \frac{4E \sin k_n S}{2k_n S + \sin 2k_n S} \qquad (10 \cdot 48)$$

Thus the final solution, corresponding to Eqs. $10 \cdot 33$ and $10 \cdot 37$, is given by Eq. $10 \cdot 45$ and the equations

$$\frac{e}{E} = \sum_{n=1}^{\infty} \frac{4 \sin k_n S}{2k_n S + \sin 2k_n S} \cos k_n (x - S) \cos \omega_n t$$

$$\frac{Z_0 i}{E} = \sum_{n=1}^{\infty} \frac{4 \sin k_n S}{2k_n S + \sin 2k_n S} \sin k_n (x - S) \sin \omega_n t \qquad (10 \cdot 49)$$

It is now possible to show clearly the effect of the inductance L in determining whether the system behaves as lumped or as distributed. Notice first that Eq. $10 \cdot 45$ is of the form $\cot x = \alpha x$, where $\alpha = L/\mathcal{L}S$ is the ratio of the lumped inductance to the total cable inductance. One would expect, therefore, that for large values of this ratio the response would be that of a lumped system; whereas for small values of the ratio the response would be typical

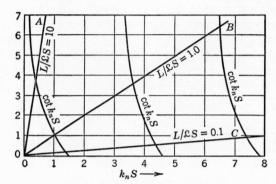

FIG. 10·3.   Eigenvalues of cable problem.

of a distributed system. Figure 10·3 gives a graphical solution of Eq. 10·45, for three different values of $L/\mathcal{L}S$. It is seen that for $L = 0.1\mathcal{L}S$ the values are approaching $(2n - 1)\pi/2$, corresponding to Eq. 10·33. In the other extreme, for large values of $L/\mathcal{L}S$, the values approach $(n - 1)\pi$. The full meaning of these

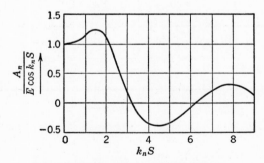

FIG. 10·4.   Amplitude of cable response.

frequencies, however, can be understood only in connection with the amplitude function of Eq. 10·48. This is plotted in Fig. 10·4. The maxima occur at $(2n - 1)\pi/2$, and the amplitude is zero at $(n - 1)\pi$, except for $n = 1$, where it is unity.

The combined significance of these figures is brought out by the three plots of Fig. 10·5, giving the response in the three cases indicated in Fig. 10·3. (The waveforms are only approximate, because only the first few terms in the infinite series of Eqs. 10·49

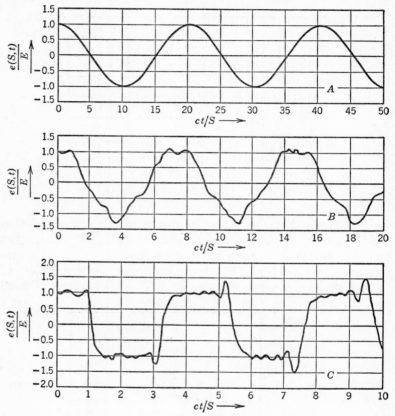

FIG. 10·5.   Approximate waveforms of cable response.

were calculated and plotted.) Thus the total picture includes all the possibilities, depending on the magnitude of L, from the lumped L-C oscillation suggested by curve A of Fig. 10·5 to the square-wave reflections suggested by curve C.

As far as numerical magnitudes are concerned, typical high-voltage cable, for example, might have $\mathcal{L} = 0.06$ microhenry per foot and $\mathcal{C} = 67$ micromicrofarad per foot, so that $Z_0 = 30$ ohms, and $c = 500$ feet per microsecond. For $S = 100$ feet, the inter-mediate case (curve B of Fig. 10·5) would require $L = \mathcal{L}S = 6$ microhenries. For $S = 1000$ feet, the requirement would be $L = 60$ microhenries. An inductance of 6 microhenries is not very much; it is the inductance of a straight wire some 10 or 15 feet long.

In connection with this question of the magnitude of L required to cause an appreciable lumping effect, it is interesting to consider what happens when several identical cables are connected in parallel. The connection is shown for two cables in Fig. 10·6. However,

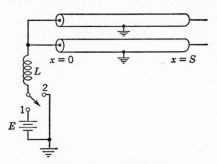

FIG. 10·6.   Cables in parallel.

the discussion will be given for an arbitrary number m. Then, if the inductance and capacitance per unit length are $\mathcal{L}$ and $\mathcal{C}$ for the individual cables, the effective values for the combination are $\mathcal{L}/m$ and $m\mathcal{C}$. Thus the propagation velocity c remains unchanged, equal to $1/\sqrt{\mathcal{L}\mathcal{C}}$; but the impedance of the combination is $(1/m)\sqrt{\mathcal{L}/\mathcal{C}}$. The value of L required to give the inter-mediate case is $\mathcal{L}S/m$. Consider, for example, ten cables with the numerical constants mentioned above. Then the intermediate case is given by $L = 0.6$ microhenry. This small lumped induct-ance, which is that of a straight wire only a foot or two long, might easily be overlooked; yet it has a very marked effect on response, as comparison of curves B and C of Fig. 10·5 emphasizes.

With this discussion of the cable problem the chapter on dis-tributed systems comes to an end. In this brief treatment many interesting topics have of necessity been omitted. By and large, however, the concepts developed in previous chapters can be rather directly applied to distributed systems. There are, of course, features peculiar to the distributed systems. For example, with lumped systems it is difficult to achieve distortionless response over a wide frequency range together with a time delay of considerable magnitude, but with distributed systems this is easy. With the cable discussed above, for instance, it is only necessary to terminate the cable in its characteristic impedance Z_0 to be free of distortion while at the same time achieving a time delay of S/c seconds. Another interesting topic which has been slighted is the application of feedback to distributed systems.

Despite these limitations it is hoped that the material presented in this chapter is sufficient to indicate the nature of distributed systems and to show the direction in which to seek the mathematical techniques applicable to such systems.

Nonlinear Systems

11·1 Mathematical survey. Reference to any textbook on differential equations will show that, of all the possible types of equations, only a very small fraction can be solved. In fact, if one removed from the average textbook all treatment of linear equations, the size of the entire volume would be approximately halved, and that portion dealing with specific solutions would be cut to about one-tenth its original size. This circumstance must be considered in light of the fact that linear equations are an exceedingly special group, constituting a minute fraction of the full range of mathematical possibilities.

At face value this mathematical situation might be taken to mean that the application of differential equations to physics is in its merest infancy, since the great majority of equations are not yet understood in themselves, to say nothing of their application to physics. On the other hand, the application of linear differential equations to physical problems has been an outstandingly successful enterprise. The paradox is resolved by two considerations. First, most physical phenomena involve gradual changes which can therefore be treated to a first approximation on a linear basis. Second, there are many physical phenomena which will be better understood as the mathematics of nonlinear equations is developed. In other words, the success is understandable, but it is not complete; and there is great need for continued development of the nonlinear theory.

Progress in dealing with nonlinear problems was very limited until 1892, when the Russian M.A. Liapounoff published a memoir on *The General Problem of the Stability of Motion.*[1] This work marked the beginning of an impressive development, to which the Frenchman Poincaré made notable contributions, but which has been carried out principally in Russia. The important results of these researches have recently been made available in English.[2]

Thus there now exists considerable literature on the application of nonlinear differential equations to physical systems. It is noteworthy, however, that the development is still quite limited. The number of ordinary differential equations studied is relatively small, the only methods available for such equations are methods of approximation, and practically nothing has been accomplished in the field of partial differential equations. Thus the field is still in the early stages of its growth, and there is much need for further work.

Within the narrow confines of this chapter it is not practicable to summarize the present state of the theory of nonlinear systems. The interested reader is referred to the works just cited. This chapter is devoted rather to a discussion of some of the physical situations in which nonlinearity is important. Some references to mathematical techniques are included, particularly in discussing the specific problem which is the subject of the last section.

11·2 Nonlinear phenomena. Strictly speaking, all physical phenomena are nonlinear. It is just that the approximation of linearity is more or less accurately valid from one situation to another. In graphical terms, any curve is approximated at a given point by the tangent at that point. Depending on the curve, however, the tangent approximation will be more or less accurate over a larger or smaller range. This mode of thinking is useful in proceeding from linearity toward nonlinearity. The phenomenon becomes progressively less linear, or more nonlinear, as the range of variation is increased. In contrast to this **progressive nonlin-**

---

[1] Originally published in Russian by the Mathematical Society of Kharkov, this work was later published in French in the *Annales de la faculté des sciences de Toulouse.* This French version is now available as No. 17 of the *Annals of Mathematics Studies*, Princeton, Princeton University Press.

[2] N. Minorsky, *Introduction to Non-Linear Mechanics*, Ann Arbor, J. W. Edwards, 1947; A. Andronow and S. Chaikin, *Theory of Oscillations*, Princeton, Princeton University Press; N. Kryloff and N. Bogoliuboff, *Introduction to Non-Linear Mechanics*, No. 11, *Annals of Mathematics Studies*, Princeton, Princeton University Press, 1943. See also J. J. Stoker, *Nonlinear Vibrations*, New York, Interscience Press, 1950.

earity, however, there are many instances of **essential nonlinearity,** in which the phenomenon must be understood entirely in nonlinear terms, since there is no meaningful linear approximation for the effect in question. Examples of progressive and essential nonlinearities will be given below.

The subject of friction furnishes a good example. The friction force between moving surfaces is in general a function of the relative velocity between the surfaces. The linear case is the one in which the friction force is simply proportional to the velocity. This may be realized physically by having laminar flow in a fluid layer between the surfaces, or by magnetic damping, in which eddy currents are induced by the motion. Linear fluid damping is frequently called viscous damping because the viscosity of the fluid is the property which keeps the flow laminar. As the relative velocity is increased, however, the laminar nature of the flow is lost and the friction force becomes proportional to a higher power, roughly the square, of the velocity. The friction due to such turbulent flow is commonly called square-law damping. Fluid friction thus provides an example of progressive nonlinearity, as it is characterized by a *gradual* change from the linear to a noticeably nonlinear regime. Dry friction (often called coulomb friction) is, however, essentially nonlinear, since it gives a force which is a *discontinuous* function of velocity.

The nature of viscous damping was illustrated in the hydraulic models discussed in Section 3·6. The effect of square-law damping on such a model may be mentioned here. The differential equation is

$$K^2 \dot{q}^2 + q = q_f \qquad (11 \cdot 1)$$

where K is a constant depending on the various dimensions of the system, on the properties of the liquid used, and to a slight extent (considered negligible here) on the Reynolds number. The solution of this nonlinear equation with constant forcing, $q_f = Q_2$, may be obtained directly by integration. It is

$$\frac{Q_2 - q}{Q_2 - Q_1} = \left(\frac{t}{\tau}\right)^2 - 2\left(\frac{t}{\tau}\right) + 1 \qquad (11 \cdot 2)$$

The quantity τ, introduced here for dimensional simplicity of the equation, is not a constant of the system but depends also on Q_2, according to the relation

$$\tau^2 = 4(Q_2 - Q_1)K^2 \qquad (11 \cdot 3)$$

In Fig. 11·1 the result given in Eq. 11·2 is plotted for comparison with the linear response.

Another example illustrating the difference between progressive and essential nonlinearity is furnished by electron tubes. The typical vacuum triode used as an amplifier has a characteristic which is sensibly linear over an appreciable range and departs more or less gradually from this linearity at the extremes of the range. On the other hand, gas discharge tubes, such for example as are used in cathode-ray sweep circuits, have characteristics which exhibit such a sharp change that it is permissible to describe

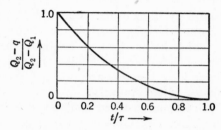

FIG. 11·1.   Response of system with square-law damping.

them as discontinuities. The usefulness of the triode exists *in spite of* its (slight) nonlinearity; that of the discharge tube exists *because* of its (large) nonlinearity.

A third illustration is the shock-mounting of an instrument panel (according to the principle discussed in connection with Eq. 7·13). Suppose the panel is supported by springs that are approximately linear over the range through which the panel is to be permitted to move. Then to restrain the motion at these limits some sort of stops must be provided. Suppose these are pads of hard rubber. Consider now the motion of the panel over its full range. Up to the point at which it makes contact with the stop the panel moves against the spring forces, which, except for small progressive nonlinearity, are linear. In general, contact with the stop would mean an abrupt change in spring rate. Of course, if the stops were initially quite soft and then became rapidly stiffer, the combined effect of spring and stop would not show a marked discontinuity. Ordinarily, however, the spring rate of the stop would be so much higher than that of the suspension springs that, as for the discharge tube, it would be reasonable to speak of a discontinuity. Thus the problem would be essentially nonlinear.

As a final example, one may consider relays and control devices, such as valves. These may be of the continuous type, giving smooth, more or less linear operation; or they may be of the discontinuous, on-off type. The relative merits and disadvantages of the two types constitute material for an involved discussion which will not be entered into here. The point is that the on-off relay is an essentially nonlinear device, which is more or less useful and whose action needs therefore to be understood.

11·3 Oscillators. The technologically important group of devices called oscillators constitutes one of the most significant fields for study of nonlinearity. This is because all oscillators depend for their operation on some nonlinear action. The truth of this may be understood on the basis of material presented in earlier chapters. For a linear system with constant coefficients the only possibility of continuous oscillation arises when one has purely imaginary roots of the auxiliary equation. For a simple second-order system, for instance, this occurs for $\zeta = 0$. Now, why is it not possible to have an oscillator consisting of a second-order system with $\zeta = 0$? The amplitude of oscillation would depend on the initial disturbance which set the system into oscillation. But, although this might be an inconvenient way of establishing amplitude, it would not necessarily rule out such a device. The real difficulty lies in the concept of the zero value of ζ. The actual value of ζ would never remain *identically* equal to zero. Thus the oscillations would either increase or decrease in amplitude. One might control this drift by sensing the amplitude of the oscillation and utilizing feedback to modify the ζ-value in the proper sense. But this modification of ζ would be feedback through a parameter, and, as pointed out in Section 9·5, any such scheme constitutes a nonlinear system.

Feedback is indeed important in oscillators. One may in fact say that there are two principal kinds of oscillators: feedback oscillators and relaxation oscillators. The distinction between the two is similar to the distinction between progressive and essential nonlinearity, in that relaxation oscillators operate by virtue of some discontinuous, or quasi-discontinuous, effect. The bowing of a violin string is an example of relaxation oscillations; here coulomb friction is the discontinuous effect. The cathode-ray sweep circuit is a relaxation oscillator, in which gaseous discharge is the discontinuous effect. The operation of feedback oscillators, on the other hand, may be described as establishing through feedback a zero value of effective damping. It must be emphasized, however, that this zero value is achieved only at a certain amplitude, which is thus the amplitude of the oscillation, independent of initial conditions.

As an example of feedback oscillators, the electronic feedback demonstrator of Section 8·4 may be considered. As discussed there, increased feedback of the term $\dot{q}$ results eventually in negative effective ζ, evidenced by oscillation. The problem now is to consider how nonlinearity establishes the amplitude of this oscillation. In this circuit (Fig. 8·5) there are two sources of nonlinearity. The vacuum tubes themselves do not have perfectly linear characteristics, and the bridge circuits are nonlinear. For present purposes the net effect may be taken as a nonlinear relation between output and input voltages of the first bridge. Calling the output voltage of the first bridge q_1, this means that, instead of $q_1 = q - A_1 C_2 R_2 \dot{q}$, it is necessary here to assume some higher powers of $\dot{q}$. Assume that the gain is of such symmetry that only odd powers are involved, and limit the series to the term in $\dot{q}^3$; thus,

$$q_1 = q - A_1[C_2 R_2 \dot{q} + \epsilon(C_2 R_2 \dot{q})^3] \qquad (11 \cdot 4)$$

where ϵ is small compared to unity.

The control voltage q_c is given by $q_c = -A_2(q_1 - q_d)$, and putting this in as forcing makes the complete equation

$$\frac{\ddot{q}}{(1 + A_2)\omega_n^2} + \frac{(2\zeta/\omega_n) - A_1 A_2 C_2 R_2[1 + \epsilon(C_2 R_2 \dot{q})^2]}{1 + A_2} \dot{q} + q$$
$$= \frac{A_2}{1 + A_2} q_d \qquad (11 \cdot 5)$$

The coefficient of $\dot{q}$ in this equation consists of two terms, one the constant that appeared in Eq. 8·21, and the other the nonlinear term in $\dot{q}^2$. The homogeneous form of this differential equation was discussed by Lord Rayleigh.[1] He showed that, if both terms in the coefficient of $\dot{q}$ are small in magnitude, the approximate solution (of Eq. 11·5 with $q_d = 0$) is (introducing again the symbol $\tau_f = A_1 A_2 C_2 R_2$ used in Chapter 8),

[1] Rayleigh, *The Theory of Sound*, New York, Dover Publications, 1945, p. 81.

$$q = \sqrt{\frac{4(2\zeta - \omega_n\tau_f)}{3\epsilon(1 + A_2)(\omega_n\tau_f)\,(\omega_n C_2 R_2)^2}} \left[\sin \omega_n t\sqrt{1 + A_2} \right.$$

$$\left. - \frac{2\zeta - \omega_n\tau_f}{24\sqrt{1 + A_2}} \cos 3\omega_n t\sqrt{1 + A_2} \right] \quad (11\cdot6)$$

Thus the fundamental oscillation is of angular frequency $\omega_n\sqrt{1 + A_2}$, there is a small amount of third harmonic, and the amplitude depends on the ratio of two small quantities, $2\zeta - \omega_n\tau_f$ and ϵ. For oscillation to occur, as discussed in Chapter 8, the quantity $2\zeta - \omega_n\tau_f$ must be negative. Hence, for a real amplitude factor in Eq. 11·6, ϵ must be negative. Thus, looking back at Eq. 11·5, the coefficient of $\dot{q}$ is negative when $\dot{q}$ is small, but eventually it becomes positive; in other words, at low amplitude the system is unstable and builds up toward larger amplitude, whereas at higher amplitude it has positive damping. In between, the system finds its amplitude of steady oscillation.

Equation 11·5, with $q_d = 0$, is of the form

$$\ddot{q} + \omega_n{}^2 q = \epsilon f(q, \dot{q}, t) \quad (11\cdot7)$$

which is the principal general form of equation studied in the non-linear mechanics of the school of Russian physicists and mathematicians mentioned above. As the above example shows, the fact that ϵ is small and that the equation might therefore be called quasi-linear does not mean that the *effect* of ϵ is small. The limitation of amplitude to the value given in Eq. 11·6 is a phenomenon which has no parallel whatever in linear systems. Thus, although equations of the form 11·7 do indeed show different properties as ϵ becomes larger, the properties of such equations even for small ϵ-values include features which are essentially different from those of linear systems.

11·4   A particle problem. It is fitting that the final section of this book should be devoted to a problem in particle dynamics. The methods and the point of view of this book are based most directly on this branch of physics, as expanded and developed first by Lagrange, later by E. J. Routh and Lord Rayleigh, and more recently by Henri Poincaré and the modern Russian school. It is true that the growth of this science has been greatly aided by many men whose primary interests were in other fields, particularly in communications and other aspects of electrical engineer-

ing. It is also true that the modern concept of "mechanics" is
rapidly becoming completely generalized so as to erase all distinctions as to whether the mathematical results are applied in one domain of physics or another. The facts remain, however, that the
basic advances have been made by men whose interests were
nourished on the problems of classical mechanics, and that the
prototype problem is the dynamical problem, particularly the
dynamical problem of the particle.

The problem to be investigated here concerns the motion of a
particle under the influence of forces such as are exerted on a
charged particle by certain electric and magnetic fields. The equations to be studied apply also to certain motions of a gyroscope.
Motion of charged particles in electric and magnetic fields is of
fundamental interest to designers of mass spectrographs, cathode-
ray tubes, magnetrons, and other electron tubes.

The particular combination of fields to be studied consists of an
electric field, having cylindrical symmetry, and a uniform magnetic field. The electric field may be described in terms of its potential ϕ, the field being taken as the negative of the gradient of ϕ.
Let the magnetic field, represented by the constant B_0, be assumed
parallel to the z-axis and in the same sense. The equations of
motion, for a particle of mass M and charge Q, are

$$M\ddot{x} - QB_0\dot{y} + Q\phi_x = 0$$

$$M\ddot{y} + QB_0\dot{x} + Q\phi_y = 0 \qquad (11\cdot8)$$

$$M\ddot{z} + Q\phi_z = 0$$

Since ϕ is to have cylindrical symmetry, the equations might be
simpler in cylindrical coordinates r, θ, z. Transformed to these
variables, Eqs. $11\cdot8$ may be simplified to

$$M\ddot{r} - Mr\dot{\theta}\left(\dot{\theta} + \frac{QB_0}{M}\right) + Q\phi_r = 0$$

$$Mr\ddot{\theta} + M\dot{r}\left(2\dot{\theta} + \frac{QB_0}{M}\right) + \frac{Q}{r}\phi_\theta = 0 \qquad (11\cdot9)$$

$$M\ddot{z} + Q\phi_z = 0$$

The fact of cylindrical symmetry means that $\phi_\theta = 0$. So the second of Eqs. 11·9 simplifies to a form which may be immediately integrated to

$$r^2(\dot\theta + \omega) = A \qquad (11\cdot10)$$

where

$$\omega = \frac{QB_0}{2M} \qquad (11\cdot11)$$

is the so-called Larmor frequency.

Using Eq. 11·10 to eliminate $\dot\theta$ from Eq. 11·9, these reduce to two in number, which may be written

$$M\ddot r + U_r = 0$$
$$M\ddot z + U_z = 0 \qquad (11\cdot12)$$

where

$$U = \frac{M}{2}\left(\omega^2 r^2 + \frac{A^2}{r^2}\right) + Q\phi \qquad (11\cdot13)$$

and ϕ is any function of r and z.

Multiplying Eqs. 11·12 by $\dot r$ and $\dot z$ respectively, adding, and integrating, one obtains

$$\frac{M}{2}(\dot r^2 + \dot z^2) + U = H + MA\omega \qquad (11\cdot14)$$

where the constant of integration is written $H + MA\omega$, so that H can represent the total energy of the original problem.

It appears impossible to simplify the problem further without making more explicit assumptions about ϕ. So this is a good point at which to pause and take account of the situation. Equations 11·12, 11·13, and 11·14 represent exactly the problem of motion of a particle in a plane, under the forces due to the potential energy function U, and with total energy, $H + MA\omega$. If one can solve the "reduced" problem of Eqs. 11·12 and 11·13, this solution, together with Eq. 11·10, would lead to the solution of the original problem.

To take first the simplest possible form, let $\phi = 0$. Then $U_z = 0$; from this the second of Eqs. 11·12 shows that $\dot z$ is a constant, which may with no essential loss of generality be taken as zero. Then the energy integral Eq. 11·14 becomes

$$\frac{1}{2}M\left(\dot r^2 + \omega^2 r^2 + \frac{A^2}{r^2}\right) = H + MA\omega \qquad (11\cdot15)$$

This may be solved for $\dot{r}$ and then integrated. The result may be put in the form

$$\frac{r^2}{R^2} = 1 + \alpha \pm \sqrt{1 + 2\alpha}\,\sin 2\omega(t + T) \qquad (11 \cdot 16)$$

where T is a constant of integration; and

$$R = \sqrt{\frac{H}{M\omega^2}}$$

$$\alpha = \frac{MA\omega}{H} \qquad (11 \cdot 17)$$

In turn r^2 may be eliminated from Eqs. $11 \cdot 10$ and $11 \cdot 16$, giving (remember that by definition of α and R, $A = \alpha\omega R^2$)

$$\dot{\theta} = -\omega\,\frac{1 \pm \sqrt{1 + 2\alpha}\,\sin 2\omega(t + T)}{1 + \alpha \pm \sqrt{1 + 2\alpha}\,\sin 2\omega(t + T)} \qquad (11 \cdot 18)$$

The integral of this, using θ_0 for the integration constant, is

$$\tan(\theta - \theta_0) = -\,\frac{\sin 2\omega t \pm \sqrt{1 + 2\alpha}\,\cos 2\omega T}{\cos 2\omega t \pm \sqrt{1 + 2\alpha}\,\sin 2\omega T} \qquad (11 \cdot 19)$$

or

$$\tan \theta = -\,\frac{\sin(2\omega t - \theta_0) \pm \sqrt{1 + 2\alpha}\,\cos(2\omega T + \theta_0)}{\cos(2\omega t - \theta_0) \pm \sqrt{1 + 2\alpha}\,\sin(2\omega T + \theta_0)} \qquad (11 \cdot 20)$$

Equations $11 \cdot 16$ and $11 \cdot 20$ are the parametric equations of a circle of radius $R/\sqrt{2}$, with center at x_0, y_0, where

$$x_0 = \pm R\sqrt{\alpha + \tfrac{1}{2}}\,\sin(2\omega T + \theta_0)$$

$$y_0 = \mp R\sqrt{\alpha + \tfrac{1}{2}}\,\cos(2\omega T + \theta_0) \qquad (11 \cdot 21)$$

and with phase angle $-\theta_0$. The (positively charged) particle goes around the circle, with angular velocity 2ω, and in the negative sense. That is, the equations of the circle in Cartesian coordinates are

$$x = x_0 + \frac{R}{\sqrt{2}}\cos(2\omega t - \theta_0)$$

$$y = y_0 - \frac{R}{\sqrt{2}}\sin(2\omega t - \theta_0) \qquad (11 \cdot 22)$$

with x_0, y_0 given by Eqs. 11·21. The four integration constants, α, R, T, and θ_0, could thus all be expressed in terms of the initial position and velocity of the particle.

This case of zero electric force, or $\phi = 0$, can thus be completely integrated. It was explicitly carried out in order to set forth the pattern of a complete solution to this type of problem. The next problem to be considered is the one of logarithmic potential, due to an infinite line of charge along the z-axis. Here the potential is proportional to the natural logarithm of the distance from the z-axis, that is,

$$\phi = -\phi_0 \ln \left(\frac{r}{r_0} \right) \tag{11·23}$$

where r_0 and ϕ_0 are positive constants. Since this is another instance in which U, Eq. 11·13, does not involve z, it is permissible again to assume $\dot{z} = 0$ and consider only motion in the x-y-plane.

The energy integral 11·14, solved for $\dot{r}$, yields

$$\int \frac{r \, dr}{\sqrt{-r^4 + 2R^2 r^2 \left(1 + \alpha + \frac{Q\phi_0}{H} \ln \frac{r}{r_0} \right) - \alpha^2 R^4}} = \pm \int \omega \, dt \tag{11·24}$$

where α and R are again defined by Eqs. 11·17. A problem which has thus been reduced to the evaluation of integrals is said to be "reduced to quadrature" and is considered from an advanced standpoint to be solved, regardless of whether the result of the integration is available in known or tabulated functions. In Eq. 11·24 the integration is not possible in terms of known functions. However, for given values of the constants the orbit may be calculated [1] by numerical integration.

An alternative way of obtaining information about the motion of the particle is to go back to the equation of motion for the coordinate r, Eqs. 11·12, which in this problem is

$$M\ddot{r} + \frac{d}{dr} \left[\frac{M}{2} \left(\omega^2 r^2 + \frac{A^2}{r^2} \right) - Q\phi_0 \ln \frac{r}{r_0} \right] = 0 \tag{11·25}$$

The potential energy function U, whose gradient gives the force in this equation, may be plotted, and the shape of the graph will

[1] Norman D. Coggeshall, "Paths of Ions and Electrons in Non-Uniform Crossed Electric and Magnetic Fields," *Physical Review*, **70**, 270 (1946).

lead to certain conclusions about the motion. For the purpose of plotting it is convenient to write U in the form

$$\frac{U}{H} = \frac{1}{2}\left(\frac{r}{R}\right)^2 + \frac{\alpha^2}{2}\left(\frac{R}{r}\right)^2 - \frac{Q\phi_0}{H}\left(\ln\frac{r}{R} + \ln\frac{R}{r_0}\right) \quad (11\cdot26)$$

Figure $11\cdot2$ shows the shape in curve 1 of the energy function

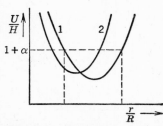

if the charge Q is positive; curve 2 is plotted for the same numerical magnitudes, except that Q is negative. It is seen that the two curves are much the same, which means that the motions will be similar for positive and negative charges. The general nature of the curves is further elucidated by differentiating Eq. $11\cdot26$ and solving for the minimum points. The result is

Fig. $11\cdot2$. Energy curves for logarithmic potential.

$$\left(\frac{r}{R}\right)^2 = \frac{Q\phi_0}{2H}\left[1 \pm \sqrt{1 + \left(\frac{2\alpha H}{Q\phi_0}\right)^2}\right] \quad (11\cdot27)$$

This shows that there will be one and only one real value of r, whether Q is positive or negative.

The curves of Fig. $11\cdot2$, representing the potential energy function for the reduced problem of Eq. $11\cdot25$, determine qualitatively the principal features of the motion, which is somewhat like that of a particle sliding under gravity without friction on the curve. Thus the motion, so far as r is concerned, consists of an oscillation, from the value $U = H + MA\omega$ on one branch of the curve, to the same value on the other branch. These limits of oscillation are indicated, for curve 1, by the dotted lines in Fig. $11\cdot2$. It follows from Eq. $11\cdot10$ that $\dot{\theta}$ will also be an oscillating function of some kind. Thus the general concept for the orbit of the particle is a kind of rosette in which r varies between limits, both positive, while $\dot{\theta}$ in general might change sign. The nature of a typical orbit is roughly sketched in Fig. $11\cdot3$. As suggested by this sketch, the motion is not, in general, periodic—i.e., the rosette does not close.

Thus a considerable amount of information about the motion has been obtained without complete integration of the equations of motion. The same approach, namely, interpretation of the shape of the energy function U of the reduced problem, will now be applied to the more difficult problem of spherical potential,

$$\phi = \frac{B}{\sqrt{r^2 + z^2}} \qquad (11 \cdot 28)$$

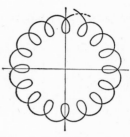

This is the potential, for instance, due to a charge fixed at the origin of coordinates. If this charge is positive, the constant B is positive. (The sign of this charge must not be confused with that of the charge Q on the *moving* particle.)

FIG. 11·3. Nature of orbit under logarithmic potential.

The difference between this problem and the above problem of logarithmic, or cylindrical, potential, is that here ϕ depends on z as well as on r. Hence both of Eqs. 11·12 must be treated. For convenience, U is written in the form,

$$\frac{U}{H} = \frac{1}{2}\left(\frac{r}{R}\right)^2 + \frac{\alpha^2}{2}\left(\frac{R}{r}\right)^2 + \frac{\sigma}{\sqrt{\left(\frac{r}{R}\right)^2 + \left(\frac{z}{R}\right)^2}} \qquad (11 \cdot 29)$$

in which H, α, and R have the same meanings as before, and σ is a new dimensionless quantity, to represent the electric potential, defined by

$$\sigma = \frac{QB}{HR} \qquad (11 \cdot 30)$$

Before considering the two-dimensional dependence on r and z, however, it is interesting to compare the motion, assuming it takes place in the plane $z = 0$, with that under the logarithmic potential discussed above. For this purpose, the curves of Fig. 11·4 show two of the U-curves obtained by plotting Eq. 11·29 with $z = 0$ and with σ having the two negative values shown. The minimum points of these curves (and also of the curves of Fig. 11·2) occur at values of r at which the particle could move in a circle about the origin. That is, they represent the value of r, with corresponding value of $\dot\theta$ given by Eq. 11·10, for which centrifugal force due to rotation, electrostatic force represented by the potential gradient, and magnetic force (so-called Lorentz force) all add up to zero.

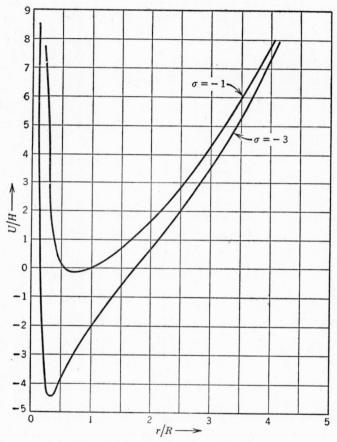

FIG. 11·4. Energy curves for spherical potential *

It is clear from the general similarity of the curves of Figs. 11·2 and 11·4 that the motions, so long as they occur only in the plane $z = 0$, will be much the same for logarithmic and spherical potentials. The main difference in the two problems is involved in the z-dependence, to which attention is now directed.

* For Figs. 11·4 to 11·7, the parameter $\alpha = 1$.

To get some idea of the two-dimensional motion in the r-z-plane, the U-surface represented by Eq. 11·29 may be studied. The surface may be depicted by plotting its contour lines. Figures 11·5 and 11·6 show a few of the contours of two U-surfaces, with the

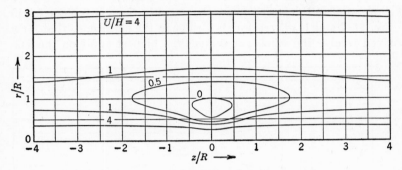

FIG. 11·5.   Contours of U-surface for $\sigma = -1$.

same values for α and σ that were used in Fig. 11·4. For these negative values of σ, the contours are seen to be closed curves for small values of U/H, changing to open lines at the larger values. This means that motion under a value of U corresponding to a closed contour would be bounded in both the r- and z-dimensions

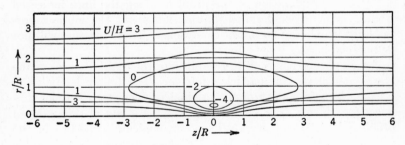

FIG. 11·6.   Contours of U-surface for $\sigma = -3$.

and so would be, in a sense, periodic. Alternatively, one might say that the charged particle is captured by the electric field. On the other hand, for those larger values of U, for which the contours are open, it would be possible for the particle to escape from the influence of the field.

For comparison, Fig. 11·7 shows the contours for a positive value of σ, corresponding to a repelling electrostatic force on the moving particle. It is seen here that any motion near the r-axis is unstable, since there is always a force component away from this axis. Comparison of the contours for positive and negative σ shows that in the positive case the curve in the z = 0 plane (as in Fig. 11·2 and 11·4) represents a ridge in the surface, so that for a given r-value the value z = 0 gives the highest point on the sur-

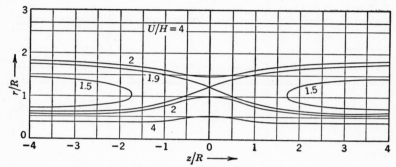

FIG. 11·7.   Contours of U-surface for σ = 1.

face.   For negative σ, the value z = 0 gives the lowest point on the surface.

Further consideration of the problem along the lines indicated would yield further detailed information about the motion, particularly in relation to initial conditions. These matters will not be pursued here.

For emphasis, it is well to recapitulate the main features of the above attack on this particle problem. The first principal step was the **transformation** of the original problem to a simpler "reduced" problem. The second step was the study of this reduced problem in terms of **geometric,** or **topological,** properties of the potential energy function U. By these means a considerable amount of useful information about the solution of the nonlinear Eqs. 11·8 was obtained without complete integration of the equations. These two methods, transformation and topology, are important tools in the general attack on nonlinear problems.

In conclusion, it may be said that response of nonlinear systems is a stimulating and challenging subject for further study, and one that also promises rich rewards in useful practical applications.

Appendix 1

The Laplace Transform in the Study of
Linear Systems

A serious interest in the subject of system response necessarily implies a more or less serious interest in mathematics—in the whole of mathematics as well as in its various parts. Before setting out to achieve a working mastery of any particular mathematical tool, however, the student of system response will naturally want to estimate its potential usefulness to him and to note how its usefulness is related to that of other mathematical techniques. It is in this spirit that consideration is here to be given to the Laplace transformation, which is the modern version of the widely used operational method of treating linear systems.

The main body of this text has been based on the following proposition: *A knowledge of classical methods of solving differential equations, plus a moderate knowledge of the algebra of complex numbers, constitutes necessary and sufficient mathematical equipment for gaining a good insight into the response of physical systems.* As far as sufficiency is concerned, the main text of this book may be offered in proof. The necessity of the classical approach to differential equations can hardly be proved; perhaps it can be justified. The principal justification lies in the author's feeling that, in laying the foundations of as broad a discipline as the subject of system response is believed and intended to be, it is wise to plan for the future, and in the present study this means to plan for nonlinearity. Study of linear systems is almost a closed book; study of nonlinear systems is a book which is just being opened. According to this logic, the necessary introductory point of view is that which, like the classical approach to differential equations, knits together the whole field of linear and nonlinear systems; and any method restricted as is the Laplace transformation to linear equations is automatically relegated to a secondary, incidental role.

Because of the actual practical importance of linear systems, however, one is still wise to examine carefully the Laplace method and to evaluate both its price in mathematical effort and its values in treating linear systems. A summary of these values, which are developed in what follows in connection with a detailed examination of the method, is given at the end of this appendix.

Suppose as a starting point one wishes to treat the simple second-order system by this method. The differential equation for such a system, given as Eq. 4·5, is

$$\frac{\ddot{q}}{\omega_n{}^2} + \frac{2\zeta}{\omega_n}\dot{q} + q = q_f \tag{A·1}$$

The Laplace transform of any nonpathological [1] function, say $q(t)$, is defined as

$$F(s) = \int_0^\infty e^{-st}q(t)\,dt \tag{A·2}$$

where s is a variable never less than zero ($s > \alpha$). This relationship between $F(s)$ and $q(t)$ may be more briefly denoted by writing

$$F(s) = \mathcal{L}\{q(t)\} \tag{A·3}$$

or

$$q(t) = \mathcal{L}^{-1}\{F(s)\} \tag{A·4}$$

Multiplication with the symbol $\mathcal{L}$ may thus be said to indicate the **direct Laplace transformation**; and with the symbol $\mathcal{L}^{-1}$, the **inverse Laplace transformation**.

Applying the transformation to Eq. A·1, one obtains

$$\mathcal{L}\left\{\frac{\ddot{q}}{\omega_n{}^2} + \frac{2\zeta}{\omega_n}\dot{q} + q\right\} = \mathcal{L}\{q_f\} \tag{A·5}$$

Since the transformation is a linear operation, this is the same as

$$\frac{1}{\omega_n{}^2}\mathcal{L}\{\ddot{q}\} + \frac{2\zeta}{\omega_n}\mathcal{L}\{\dot{q}\} + \mathcal{L}\{q\} = \mathcal{L}\{q_f\} \tag{A·6}$$

The transform of the first derivative, using integration by parts, is

---

[1] The function may be discontinuous at an infinite number of points, provided the discontinuities are ordinary ones. Moreover, the magnitude of q must remain such that there exists a number $\alpha \geq 0$ for which the product $e^{-\alpha t}|q|$ remains finite as t approaches infinity.

$$\mathcal{L}\{\dot{q}\} = \int_0^\infty e^{-st}\frac{dq}{dt}\,dt = [e^{-st}q]_0^\infty + s\int_0^\infty qe^{-st}\,dt$$

or

$$\mathcal{L}\{\dot{q}\} = s\mathcal{L}\{q\} - Q_1 \tag{A·7}$$

Similarly it may be shown that

$$\mathcal{L}\{\ddot{q}\} = s^2\mathcal{L}\{q\} - sQ_1 - \dot{Q}_1 \tag{A·8}$$

or, in general,

$$\mathcal{L}\{\overset{n \text{ dots}}{q}\} = s^n\mathcal{L}\{q\} - \sum_{k=1}^{n} s^{n-k}\overset{(k-1)\text{ dots}}{Q_1} \tag{A·9}$$

In these equations the symbols Q_1, $\dot{Q}_1$, $\cdots$, $\overset{n\text{ dots}}{Q_1}$ have the same meaning as in the main text, namely, the initial values of q and its derivatives. In using Eqs. A·7 to A·9 the derivatives must of course satisfy the conditions given in the footnote to Eq. A·2.

Now, using Eqs. A·7 and A·8 in Eq. A·6 and solving for $\mathcal{L}\{q\}$, one gets

$$\mathcal{L}\{q\} = \frac{\mathcal{L}\{q_f\} + Q_1\left(\dfrac{s}{\omega_n^2} + \dfrac{2\zeta}{\omega_n}\right) + \dfrac{\dot{Q}_1}{\omega_n^2}}{\dfrac{s^2}{\omega_n^2} + \dfrac{2\zeta s}{\omega_n} + 1} \tag{A·10}$$

Applying the inverse transformation, so as to obtain $q = \mathcal{L}^{-1}\mathcal{L}\{q\}$, yields

$$q = \mathcal{L}^{-1}\left\{\frac{\mathcal{L}\{q_f\}}{D(s)}\right\} + \mathcal{L}^{-1}\left\{\frac{Q_1\left(\dfrac{s}{\omega_n^2} + \dfrac{2\zeta}{\omega_n}\right) + \dfrac{\dot{Q}_1}{\omega_n^2}}{D(s)}\right\} \tag{A·11}$$

where $D(s)$ is used for $(s^2/\omega_n^2) + (2\zeta s/\omega_n) + 1$. The second of the two indicated inverse transformations may be carried out (by methods to be discussed below), after which Eq. A·11 is

$$q = \mathcal{L}^{-1}\left\{\frac{\mathcal{L}\{q_f\}}{D(s)}\right\} + e^{-\zeta\omega_n t}\left(Q_1\cos\omega t + \frac{\zeta\omega_n Q_1 + \dot{Q}_1}{\omega}\sin\omega t\right) \tag{A·12}$$

Assuming that the remaining indicated direct and inverse transformations can actually be carried out, this equation gives the solution of the second-order direct problem. On comparing this result with that obtained by classical methods, say as given in Eq. 4·20, one is impressed at first glance with the similarity and is inclined to say that the results are identical, the first term on the right of Eq. A·12 representing q_r, the forced response. Closer examination shows that this first impression is wrong. The second term of Eq. A·12 is not the same as the transient response of Eq. 4·20; it differs by having Q_1 and $\dot{Q}_1$ in place of Q_i and $\dot{Q}_i$ (cf. Eqs. 4·18 and 4·19).

The result presented in Eq. A·12 is not peculiar to the second-order problem; a completely analogous equation could be obtained for the general nth-order direct problem. It is therefore evident that the classical method and the Laplace transform method make two quite different divisions of the total response into two parts. It may be assumed, moreover, that these different dichotomies might lead toward two somewhat different points of view regarding response of linear systems. It is important that the degree and nature of this difference be understood.

As for the classical point of view, it has been amply expounded in the main text of this book and needs only to be summarized here. For a given nth-order system there exists for every q_f an n-fold infinity of solutions, each valid over the full range $-\infty < t < +\infty$. By specification of n initial conditions a single one of these solutions is selected. Usually, of course, its validity over the full time range is not of interest, the response being considered over only a finite interval. This total response is given as the sum of two parts: the forced response, representing the permanent accommodation of the system to the forcing; and the transient response, representing the temporary accommodation of the initial conditions to the forcing. Mathematically, the transient response is the complementary function and the forced response is the particular integral of the differential equation.

Now what is the corresponding interpretation to be put on the response in the form of Eq. A·12, given by the Laplace transform method? To answer this question, it is first necessary to understand the nature of the two terms. The term involving Q_1 and $\dot{Q}_1$ might be called "pure transient"; it is the response for $q_f = 0$. The term involving the transform of q_f may be called "normal response"; it is the response to q_f from rest—i.e., assuming $Q_1 = \dot{Q}_1 = 0$. Thus the Laplace method yields the complete response as the sum of the normal response and the pure transient; in mathematical terms, the solution of the unhomogeneous differential equation with zero initial conditions plus the solution of the homogeneous equation with arbitrary (i.e., given) initial conditions.

A deeper significance of the normal response may be seen by writing it in a form obtained by the use of the convolution integral (cf. pp. 155 ff. in Ref. 2, p. 228 in Ref. 3 and p. 54 of Ref. 4 of the references cited at the end of this appendix). In this form the first term of Eq. A·12 is

$$\int_0^t \frac{\omega_n^2}{\omega} e^{-\zeta\omega_n t'} \sin \omega t' q_f(t - t') \, dt' \qquad (A\cdot 13)$$

Now, as may be checked by referring to the discussion given with Eq. 4·39, the entire term, excluding $q_f(t - t') \, dt'$, under the integral sign is the normal response of the second-order system to a unit impulse at $t' = 0$. The corresponding general result is valid, so that the response of any nth-order linear system to a forcing q_f may be written

$$q = \int_0^t W(t') q_f(t - t') \, dt' + \text{(pure transient)} \qquad (A\cdot 14)$$

where $W(t')$ is the normal response of the system to a unit impulse at $t' = 0$.

The function W is called weighting function or memory function of the system. As can be seen in Eq. A·14, the normal response at any time t is made up of values of the forcing at all times $t - t'$ from $t' = 0$ to $t' = t$, with each value weighted according to the value of $W(t')$. It is interesting to note that for an unstable system $W(t')$ is a diverging function and so the most remote values of q_f have the greatest weight in determining the normal response at any instant. It is therefore clear that the concept of normal response is hardly useful in dealing with unstable systems (cf. Chapter 2 of Ref. 4).

Thus both the classical method and the Laplace method lead to rather simple divisions of the response into two parts. It is clear, however, that the Laplace division is of considerably greater mathematical subtlety and is less simply and obviously related to the differential equation itself. It is also apparent that the classical approach leads naturally to putting much emphasis on the forced response q_r and the transient response q_t as separate entities, whereas the transform approach leads naturally to emphasis on the "life history" of the forcing q_f and on the memory function W of the system (cf. Chapter 6 of Ref. 4, in particular pp. 288–290; also Chapter 3 of Ref. 6). These two points of view complement each other. The classical method is of course the more fundamental and therefore the more suitable as basis for a broad perspective which can include stable and unstable systems and inverse and converse, as well as direct, problems, and which can extend these concepts to nonlinear systems.

The foregoing paragraphs constitute a rather general comparison of the Laplace transform and the classical method. It is now appropriate to discuss the Laplace method in further detail. The example given above of the direct problem for a simple second-order system illustrates the method as applied to a single ordinary linear differential equation with constant coefficients. The solution obtained in Eq. A·12 must be completed by carrying out the indicated direct and inverse transformations.

As the names imply, the direct transformation is more easily performed on most functions than the inverse. For present purposes it may be assumed that knowledge of any given inverse transformation has been established by knowledge of the corresponding direct transformation. As an example of the direct transformation, consider $q_f = Q_2 e^{\rho_f t}$. Then

$$\mathcal{L}\{q_f\} = \int_0^\infty e^{-st} Q_2 e^{\rho_f t}\, dt = \frac{Q_2}{\rho_f - s}\, [e^{(\rho_f - s)t}]_0^\infty$$

Now it is clear that if $\rho_f > s$ the integral diverges. But, assuming $s > \rho_f$, the transform is $\mathcal{L}\{q_f\} = Q_2/(s - \rho_f)$. This example illustrates the need, present in all cases, of specifying the range of the variable s over which the transformation is valid.

By applying the direct transformation to various $q(t)$'s a table of transform pairs may be obtained. Table A·1 gives, simply by way of illustration, a few such pairs. Extensive tables of such transforms have been built up (Refs. 1 and 3). Except when in the hands of mathematicians, the Laplace method is most useful when the functions needed are either in the table or may be obtained by linear combination or other simple manipulation of the functions listed.

TABLE A·1

LAPLACE TRANSFORM PAIRS

	$q_f(t)/Q_2$ for $t \geq 0$	$\mathcal{L}\{q_f\}/Q_2$
1	1	$1/s$
2	$t^n(n = 0, 1, 2, 3, \cdots)$	$n!/s^{n+1}$
3	$e^{\rho_f t}$	$1/(s - \rho_f)$
4	$t^n e^{\rho_f t}$	$n!/(s - \rho_f)^{n+1}$
5	$\cos \omega_f t$	$s/(s^2 + \omega_f{}^2)$
6	$\sin \omega_f t$	$\omega_f/(s^2 + \omega_f{}^2)$
7	$\ln t$	$-(1/s)(\ln s + 0.5772)$

With the help of Table A·1 the transformations in Eq. A·12 may be carried out, for example, with $q_f = Q_2$. Then $\mathcal{L}\{q_f\} = Q_2/s$, and the normal response is

$$\mathcal{L}^{-1}\left\{\frac{Q_2}{sD(s)}\right\} = \mathcal{L}^{-1}\left\{\frac{\omega_n{}^2 Q_2}{s(s - r_1)(s - r_2)}\right\} \qquad (A·15)$$

where r_1 and r_2 are, by Eqs. 4·7, $-\zeta\omega_n + j\omega$ and $-\zeta\omega_n - j\omega$, respectively. Now the quantity to be transformed may be written

$$\omega_n{}^2 Q_2 \left(\frac{A}{s} + \frac{B}{s - r_1} + \frac{C}{s - r_2}\right) = \omega_n{}^2 Q_2 \times$$

$$\left(\frac{1}{r_1 r_2 s} + \frac{1}{r_1(r_1 - r_2)(s - r_1)} - \frac{1}{r_2(r_1 - r_2)(s - r_2)}\right) \qquad (A·16)$$

This separation into partial fractions is accomplished simply by determining proper values of A, B, and C, namely, $A = 1/r_1 r_2$, $B = 1/r_1(r_1 - r_2)$, $C = -1/r_2(r_1 - r_2)$, which make the form on the left of Eq. A·16 equal to the form on the right of Eq. A·15. Each of the terms on the right of Eq. A·16 may now be transformed, by items 1 and 3 of Table A·1. The normal response is thus

$$\omega_n{}^2 Q_2 \left[\frac{1}{r_1 r_2} + \frac{1}{r_1 - r_2} \left(\frac{e^{r_1 t}}{r_1} - \frac{e^{r_2 t}}{r_2} \right) \right]$$

$$= Q_2 \left[1 - e^{-\zeta \omega_n t} \left(\frac{\zeta \omega_n}{\omega} \sin \omega t + \cos \omega t \right) \right] \quad (A·17)$$

Combining this normal response with the pure transient in Eq. A·12 gives for the complete response

$$q = Q_2 + e^{-\zeta \omega_n t} \left(Q_i \cos \omega t + \frac{\zeta \omega_n Q_i + \dot{Q}_i}{\omega} \sin \omega t \right) \quad (A·18)$$

in agreement with results obtained in Chapter 4. (Incidentally, the transformation of the pure transient from Eq. A·11 to Eq. A·12 is carried out in exactly analogous fashion.)

As this second-order example suggests, there is no advantage of compactness or brevity in the Laplace method over the classical method in direct problems involving a single forcing function applied to a single nth-order linear differential equation with constant coefficients. In both methods it is necessary to solve an nth-degree algebraic equation, and the total work in carrying out the transformations is generally no less than is required in obtaining the particular integral, especially if one makes it standard practice in working with either method to tabulate for possible future use every newly worked result.

An advantageous feature of the Laplace transform method is the ease with which it accommodates changes in the functional form of $q_f(t)$. Suppose the forcing is one kind of function q_{f1}, say a constant, from $t = 0$ to $t = T_1$; and another function q_{f2}, say a straight line, from $t = T_1$ to $t = T_2$; and a third kind of function q_{f3}, say a sinusoid, from $t = T_2$ to $t = T_3$; and so on. Then so long as the overall combined q_f satisfies the mild conditions given in the footnote to Eq. A·2, the transform of q_f is

$$\mathcal{L}\{q_f\} = \int_0^\infty e^{-st} q_f(t) \, dt = \int_0^{T_1} e^{-st} q_{f1} \, dt$$

$$+ \int_{T_1}^{T_2} e^{-st} q_{f2} \, dt + \int_{T_2}^{T_3} e^{-st} q_{f3} \, dt + \cdots \quad (A·19)$$

This is a simpler situation than with the classical method, where the response at the end of each time interval must first be calculated in order to be able to set up the initial conditions for the next interval.

In problems involving a system of simultaneous differential equations there are certain additional advantages to the Laplace method which become more decisive as the system becomes larger. In order properly to appreciate these advantages, it is well to consider how the initial conditions enter in the two methods. The difference is illustrated in Eqs. A·12 and A·18, the former involving Q_1 and $\dot{Q}_1$, the latter Q_i and $\dot{Q}_i$. The point is that in the Laplace method the effect of the initial conditions is isolated in a separate term, the pure transient. In the classical method the initial conditions are involved with the forced response in the quantities $Q_i = Q_1 - q_r(0)$ and $\dot{Q}_i = \dot{Q}_1 - \dot{q}_r(0)$. This is no appreciable handicap when there is only one response quantity and only one differential equation. But, in seeking m responses simultaneously from a system of m simultaneous equations, as m increases the classical method becomes increasingly awkward, and the systematic orderliness of the Laplace procedure provides a much neater solution.

For a general formulation of this kind of problem, let there be m response quantities involved in m equations,

$$\sum_{j=1}^{m} D_{jk}(p)q_j = q_{fk} \qquad (\text{A}\cdot 20)$$

where k runs from 1 to m, and $D_{jk}(p)$ are linear differential operators. (In most physics problems, the D_{jk} will not be higher than second-order. Thus Eq. A·1 may be considered the same as Eq. A·20 with $m = 1$.)

Transforming both sides of Eq. A·20 (assuming the D_{jk} to be second-order, $D_{jk} = A_{jk}p^2 + B_{jk}p + C_{jk}$), yields the equations

$$\sum_{j=1}^{m} D_{jk}(s)\mathcal{L}\{q_j\} = \mathcal{L}\{q_{fk}\} + \sum_{j=1}^{m} [(A_{jk}s + B_{jk})Q_{1j} + A_{jk}\dot{Q}_{1j}]$$

$$(\text{A}\cdot 21)$$

which constitute a set of m simultaneous algebraic equations in the m unknowns, $\mathcal{L}\{q_j\}$. As for a single q, each of the m responses,

q_j, consists of the sum of a normal response and a pure transient. The normal responses are obtained from the equations

$$\sum_{j=1}^{m} D_{jk}(s)\mathcal{L}\{q_j\} = \mathcal{L}\{q_{fk}\} \qquad (A\cdot 22)$$

and the pure transients from

$$\sum_{j=1}^{m} D_{jk}(s)\mathcal{L}\{q_j\} = \sum_{j=1}^{m} [(A_{jk}s + B_{jk})Q_{1j} + A_{jk}\dot{Q}_{1j}] \qquad (A\cdot 23)$$

Solution of these two sets of simultaneous algebraic equations for the $\mathcal{L}\{q_j\}$'s, followed by inverse Laplace transformations, yields the m normal responses and the m pure transients, which are then added pair-wise to obtain the m complete responses.

The above review has touched on the principal points of the Laplace transform as applied to ordinary differential equations with constant coefficients. There is one further item which may be mentioned, relating to linear equations with variable coefficients (parametric forcing). If the nth-order differential equation has variable coefficients which are polynomials in t, say with highest degree m, the transformed equation in s is a differential equation of order m, with coefficients which are polynomials in s. The transformed equation *may* be simpler, particularly if $m < n$. But the general prospects are not very exciting.

The Laplace transform has also been extensively applied to problems in partial differential equations. It is impossible to give here a satisfactory account of these applications without going much further into the study of partial differential equations than was done in Chapter 10. The general procedure is to transform the equations with respect to time, thus reducing the problem from one involving both time and space coordinates differentially to one involving s algebraically and only the space coordinates differentially. But the method is not always opportune and must generally be used in conjunction with other methods. In short, the Laplace transform is just one of a number of mathematical weapons with which one should be armed who hopes to carry out a broad attack on the domain of partial differential equations. A good discussion of the relation of the Laplace transform to the problems of partial differential equations is given in Chapter 19 of Ref. 2.

The Laplace method is awkward in problems involving multiple-time initial conditions or multiple-point boundary conditions (Lagrange integration problems, cf. Section 2·8). The reason for this, seen in Eq. A·9, is that the transform of a higher-order derivative involves initial conditions, all for the same instant of time, $t = 0$. This feature, from which stems so much of the usefulness of the method in a Cauchy integration problem, in turn causes much of the awkwardness in a Lagrange problem.

It should be noted that the Laplace transformation, to have more than rudimentary usefulness, should be used with complex as well as real values of s. This leads to integration in the complex number plane, for which some theoretical knowledge of functions of complex variables is required. To be sure, complex integration is a mathematical technique which is useful in other ways in addition to its relation to the Laplace transform and which many students of system response will wish to master. But it does represent a mathematical requirement beyond that minimum on which the present book was based.

Finally it should be said that the Laplace transform is useful in solving not only differential equations but also integral equations and difference equations; indeed, it gives a certain desirable unity of viewpoint regarding these three classes of functional equations. Moreover, in the broad field of mathematics the Laplace transform is of use and of interest in many connections (cf. Refs. 2 and 5).

In summary of the usefulness of the Laplace transform to students of system response, the following comments are enumerated:

1. The Laplace transformation, like other mathematical methods, is useful in proportion to the care and thoroughness with which it is studied and practiced. It is not a magic short cut to anything, nor does it, generally speaking, permit the solution of problems which may not also be solved otherwise.

2. Its greatest and most readily available usefulness in problems of system response is in Cauchy integration problems involving a system of simultaneous ordinary linear differential equations with constant coefficients.

3. The Laplace method is advantageous if the functional form of the forcing changes from one time interval to another, especially if one does not need the detailed information furnished by the classical calculation of initial conditions for each interval.

4. Emphasis on normal response, as the more important of the two parts of the complete response, leads naturally to emphasis on the life history of the forcing and on memory of the system—a point of view which is useful, for instance, in considering statistical properties of the forcing-response relationship.

5. To the serious student of the mathematics of system response, the Laplace transformation and its mathematical concomitants will return a good dividend on the effort required to understand and use them.

REFERENCES

1. R. V. Churchill, *Modern Operational Mathematics in Engineering*, New York, McGraw-Hill Book Company, 1944.
2. G. Doetsch, *Theorie und Anwendung der Laplace-Transformation*, New York, Dover Publications, 1943.
3. Gardner and Barnes, *Transients in Linear Systems*, Vol. I, New York, John Wiley and Sons, 1942.
4. James, Nichols and Phillips, *Theory of Servomechanisms*, New York, McGraw-Hill Book Company, 1947.
5. D. V. Widder, *The Laplace Transform*, Princeton, Princeton University Press, 1941.
6. N. Wiener, *Cybernetics*, New York, John Wiley and Sons, 1948.

Appendix 2

Problems and Review Questions

1. A parachute carrying a recording thermometer with a time constant of 4.0 seconds is dropped from a plane at $t = 0$. The recorded temperatures q at 1-second intervals thereafter are:

t	0	1	2	3	4	5	6	7	8	9	10
q	5.0	4.4	4.0	3.9	3.85	3.9	4.1	4.4	4.7	5.0	5.4

Plot these recorded temperatures against time, and on the same graph draw the curve giving the true air temperature. Be explicit about your derivation of the true-temperature curve.

2. As an example of a direct problem for which Table 3·1 does not suffice and for which the method of undetermined coefficients does not yield the particular integral, find the response, for $Q_1 = 0$, according to the equation: $\tau \dot{q} + q = Q_2(\tau/t)$.

3. A capacitor is charged to a high direct-current voltage E. When it is discharged through a certain spark circuit, the voltage across the capacitor, E_c, varies as the step-function response of a second-order system

$$\frac{E_c}{E} = (e^{-\zeta \omega_n t}/\sqrt{1 - \zeta^2}) \cos (\omega t - \sin^{-1} \zeta)$$

In order to measure $\dot{E}_c$ rather than E_c, the voltage E_c is applied to a differentiating circuit consisting of a capacitor C in series with a resistor R, with the output voltage q being taken across R.

(a) Show that q satisfies the differential equation $CR\dot{q} + q = q_f$, where $q_f = CR\dot{E}_c$.

(b) Assuming E_c to have the form given above for the oscillatory discharge, find q, with $Q_1 = 0$.

(c) Given that the value of E is 20,000 volts; the second peak of the discharge voltage E_c (i.e., the fourth extreme value after the spark) is 3000 volts; the natural frequency f_n of the oscillatory discharge is 10 megacycles; the value of R is 72 ohms; and the value of C is 5×10^{-12} farad. Find the dynamic error in q (compared to q_f) exactly $\frac{1}{2}$ microsecond after the spark occurs.

4. The forced sinusoidal response of a second-order system shows a phase lag of 90 degrees at a frequency of 100 cycles per second, and of 120 degrees at 120 cycles per second. What are ζ and ω_n for this system? Considering the system to be a mass on a spring and dashpot suspension, how much would the mass need to be changed to give a system with critical damping? With optimum damping (minimum dynamic error)?

5. Assuming $\zeta = 1.5$ for a second-order system, calculate $\omega_n T_1$ and $\omega_n T_2$ for the times T_1 and T_2 at which the response to a constant (fraction of change remaining to be made) will equal $2e^{-1}$ and $3e^{-2}$. (This amounts to calculating two points for the curves of Fig. 4.10.)

6. A second-order system is subjected to sinusoidal forcing. Careful phase measurements on the forced response give

Forcing Frequency (cycles per second)	Phase Angle (degrees)
18	88.79
19	89.47
21	90.56
22	91.09

Find ζ and ω_n of the system.

7. A second-order system is subjected to sinusoidal forcing; its phase lag is observed to be 110 degrees at 100 cycles per second, and 175 degrees at 1000 cycles per second. Find ζ and ω_n for this system. If at $t = 0$ this system is subjected to a step-up forcing of magnitude Q_2, find the time of steepest slope of the response and determine the value of this maximum slope.

8. An approximation to the saw-tooth voltage wave desired for cathode-ray oscilloscope sweep circuits may be generated by a simple circuit consisting of a battery, a capacitor, a resistor, and a gaseous discharge tube. The capacitor and discharge tube are connected in parallel, and the combination is connected to the battery through the resistor. Assuming that the tube discharges the capacitor instantaneously as soon as the voltage across it reaches a certain critical value, explain how the circuit functions to give the voltage across the capacitor approximately the desired waveform. Discuss the possibility of including some inductance in the circuit to improve the approximation.

9. A mass of 25 pounds is hung on a spring having a rate of 400,000 poundals per foot. A sinusoidal force of amplitude 500 poundals and frequency 32 cycles per second is applied to the mass. Find the amplitude and phase (relative to the force) of the resulting motion. Specify the damping that would have to be applied to reduce the response amplitude to half that of the undamped motion.

10. A U-tube (as discussed in Section 4·12) is forced up to $t = 0$ by a sinusoidal forcing pressure of amplitude 10 centimeters of water and frequency 1.0 cycles per second. At the instant $t = 0$ the forcing pressure is zero and has positive slope. After $t = 0$ the forcing pressure, instead of continuing to vary sinusoidally, rises linearly at the rate of 10 centimeters of water per second. The response of the U-tube up to $t = 0$ may be taken as the forced response alone, which is a sinusoid of amplitude 6.3 centimeters of water and lagging the forcing pressure by 110 degrees. What are the approximate values of ζ and ω_n applicable to the U-tube? Using these values of ζ and ω_n, and the value and slope of the response at $t = 0$, plot the response from $t = 0$ to $t = 3$ seconds.

11. To illustrate the difference between a Cauchy integration problem and a Lagrange integration problem, consider the response of a second-order system with $\zeta = 0.4$. With $q_f = Q_2(\omega_n t + 1)$, plot q_f, q_r, q_t, and q for initial conditions:

(a) Cauchy, $q(0) = 0$ and $\dot{q}(0) = 0$.

(b) Lagrange, $q(0) = 0$ and $q(4/\omega_n) = Q_2$.

What difference in response is seen over the time interval $0 < \omega_n t < 4$ in the two problems? After $\omega_n t = 0$? Explain the relation of these differences to the initial conditions.

12. For the magnet control circuit of Fig. 4·19, plot q/Q_2 versus t for the first 20 milliseconds, using $R = 0$, $L_0 = L = 10$ henries, and $R_0 = R_1 = 2000$ ohms. How would the response differ if R were 2000 ohms instead of zero? Is it better to have large or small R in order to get a quick, large drop in q?

13. A capacitor C_1 is connected in series with the parallel combination of C_2 and resistance R_2. To this series combination an input voltage E_i is applied. Taking as output voltage q the voltage across C_2 and R_2, obtain first the complex amplitude ratio of q/E_i for sinusoidal variation of E_i with angular frequency ω_f. From this (by replacing $j\omega_f$ by d/dt) show that q satisfies the equation: $R_2(C_1 + C_2)\dot{q} + q = q_f$, with $q_f = C_1R_2\dot{E}_i$. Using the numerical values (typical of a voltage divider used for observing spark breakdowns in a cable circuit) $C_1 = 0.0025$ microfarad, $C_2 = 0.25$ microfarad, $R_2 = 72$ ohms, and $\rho_f = 1000$ (second)$^{-1}$, calculate and plot the response for the following time dependence of E_i: up to $t = 0$, E_i has the constant value Q_2; at $t = 0$ it instantaneously drops to zero; and then rises on the exponential $Q_2 e^{\rho_f t}$.

14. A 10-volt alternating-current voltmeter using a copper oxide rectifier is being calibrated and is found to give a deflection $x_d = 0.03q_d^2$, where x_d is in inches and q_d in volts. What is the deflection sensitivity of this instrument? What should be its scale sensitivity? Plot both sensitivities versus q_d on the same graph. Draw a picture (actual size) of the correctly calibrated index scale, laying it out on a circle of 3-inch radius. Assuming a reasonably narrow pointer, what would be the least count in the vicinity of 1 volt? in the vicinity of 9 volts? Considering only the reading error, how accurately (with what probable error) would you write a reading of 1 volt? of 9 volts?

15. State the essential difference between random error and determinate error. What could lead you to suspect appreciable determinate error?

16. Explain the difference between precision and accuracy.

17. Can you distinguish between random error and sampling error? Is sampling error random, determinate, or a mixture of both? Is there any means of deciding that sampling error is chiefly responsible for variation in a series of measurements? How much do the answers to these questions depend on whether the aggregate to be sampled has a symmetric frequency distribution?

18. Given a certain relative frequency distribution, how do you estimate the corresponding collective?

19. A surveyor makes five separate and independent measurements of the distance between two stakes. The results, in feet, are: 522.52, 522.34, 521.59,

523.68, and 522.37.   Express the final result of this series of measurements, using the correct number of significant figures.   Give the reasons justifying your number of significant figures.

20. Suppose you are counting a radioactive sample for which, considering both the sample and the instrument, the true average count is 20 counts per second.   Using the Poisson formula (Eq. 7.28), show what odds you should accept on the following bet: that in the first second of counting after the bet is made, the observed count will be between 19 and 21.   (*Note:* the form, $\log P = -q_d \log e - n \log q_d - \log (n!)$ is convenient for calculating Poisson probability.)

21. A third-order system is governed by the equation: $(p^3 + 13p^2 + 54p + 72)q = q_f$.   If q_f is equal to a constant Q_f up to $t = 0$ and then changes abruptly to zero and remains there, plot q from $t = 0$ to $t = 1$.

22. Consider the stability of the engine with flyball governor, described by Eq. 6.64.   Assuming $M = 4$ pounds, $C = 30$ poundal-seconds per foot, $K = 158$ poundals per foot, and $I = 200$ pound-square feet, determine values of S_e and S_g which will give the system a D-contour indicating a reasonable margin of stability.

23. A certain fourth-order system satisfies the differential equation: $D(p)q = (B_4 p^4 + B_3 p^3 + B_2 p^2 + B_1 p + 1)q = q_d$.   When forced by sinusoidal variation of q_d, the forced response shows the following: at angular frequency of 1.0616 radians per second, a phase shift of -90 degrees, and a gain of 1.263; at angular frequency of 1.225 radians per second, a phase shift of -180 degrees, and a gain of 3.636.   Find the numerical values of B_1, B_2, B_3, and B_4.   Plot the D-contour, and discuss the stability of the system.   Use Newton's method of approximation to get three significant figures on the root of the auxiliary equation near -0.35.

24. What can you say about the response of the condenser microphone, as given in Eqs. 9·22 and 9·29, as m approaches 1?   Is the limiting case, of m actually equal to 1, physically realizable?

25. The displacement y of a laterally vibrating bar satisfies the differential equation: $k^2 V^2 y_{xxxx} = -\ddot{y}$, where k is the radius of gyration of the bar, and V^2 is the Young's modulus divided by the density of the bar material.   By separation of variables find the eigenfunctions and eigenfrequencies for the "free-free" vibration.   At the lowest frequency, to what equivalent mass and spring is the bar analogous?   (For help, consult Rayleigh, *Theory of Sound*, New York, Dover Publications, 1945, Chapter VIII; or Morse, *Vibration and Sound*, New York, McGraw-Hill Book Company, 1948, Chapter IV.)

26. For the response under square-law damping shown in Fig. 11·1, how do you interpret in terms of physical realities the fact that the response is shown as coming to zero in the finite time τ?

27. Consider the nonlinear system with response satisfying the differential equation: $\ddot{q} + \omega_n^2(q + \epsilon q^3) = 0$.   Show that an approximate solution is $q = A \cos \omega t + \frac{1}{4}(\omega_n^2 \epsilon A^3 \cos 3\omega t)/(9\omega^2 - \omega_n^2)$, provided $\omega^2 = \omega_n^2 + (3\omega_n^2 \epsilon A^2)/4$. (Rayleigh, *Theory of Sound*, New York, Dover Publications, 1945, pp. 77–78.)

Appendix 3

Reference List of Symbols and Terms

The use of symbols was guided, to the extent that it did not go against well-established usage, by the attempt to use English capitals for constant quantities, lower-case English for variables, and lower-case Greek letters for dimensionless quantities, angles, and quantities of the dimension of time or its reciprocal. In the following list, symbols are listed alphabetically through English capitals, English lower-case letters, Greek capitals, and Greek lower-case letters. The reference to equations, figures, etc., is in most cases to the point where the symbol was first used; several references indicate (typical) slightly different usages.

Symbols having important basic roles in the generalized theory of the text are marked with arrows in the margin. The notation (s) after a symbol means that the symbol appears with various subscripts at different points of the text.

Symbol	Term or Definition	Reference
A (s)	Area	Eq. 3·22
→ $A_0, A_1, \cdots, A_n$	Constant coefficients in differential equation	Eq. 2·5
B, B_0	Magnetic flux density	Eqs. 4·87, 11·8
→ $B_1, B_2, \cdots, B_n$	Parameters in differential equation	Eq. 2·6
C (s)	Electrical (or analogue) capacitance	Figs. 2·1, 3·10
C (s)	Chemical concentration	Eq. 10·1
C, C_t	Mechanical damping coefficient	Eqs. 6·60, 8·23
C	Control operator expression	Eq. 8·10
→ $C_1, C_2, \cdots, C_n$	Coefficients in transient response	Eq. 2·8
$\mathfrak{c}$	Capacitance per unit length	Eqs. 10·40

257

Symbol	Term or Definition	Reference
D	Density	Eq. 3·21
D	Diameter	With Eq. 3·22
$\rightarrow D$	Differential operator $D(p)$	Eq. 5·3
D	Dilution rate $D(x)$	Eq. 10·1
E (s)	Voltage	Eq. 2·4
F	Neutron flux	Eq. 3·27
F	Force	Eq. 6·60
F	Functional symbol	Eqs. 2·5, 9·19, 10·20
$\rightarrow G,\ \mathbf{G}$	Gain ratio	Eq. 3·11
G	Functional symbol	Eq. 10·20
H	Heat flow	Eq. 3·20
H	Total energy	Eq. 11·14
H	Functional symbol	Eq. 10·20
I (s)	Electrical current	Eq. 7·3
I	Moment of inertia	Eq. 3·26
I	Impulse	Eq. 3·18
K	Various constants	Eqs. 2·1, 6·60
$\rightarrow K_f$	Feedback factor	Eq. 8·2
K_z	Impedance feedback factor	Eq. 8·26
L	Length	With Eq. 3·22
L (s)	Electrical inductance	Eqs. 4·93
$\mathfrak{L}$	Inductance per unit length	Eqs. 10·40
$\rightarrow \mathfrak{L}$	Symbol for direct Laplace transformation	Eq. A·3
$\rightarrow \mathfrak{L}^{-1}$	Symbol for inverse Laplace transformation	Eq. A·4
M	Mass	Eq. 2·1
N	Number of objects	Eq. 7·27
$\rightarrow N$	Differential operator $N(p)$	Eq. 5·6
P	Pressure	Eq. 10·36
P_{m-1}	Polynomial in t	Sec. 2·8
$P(\Delta q_r)$	Probability of random error	Eq. 7·18

Symbol	Term or Definition	Reference
→ Q (s)	Constant of same dimensions as q	Eq. 3·3
Q	Electrical charge	Eq. 11·8
R	Electrical (or analogue) resistance	Fig. 3·10
R	Constant value of coordinate r	Eq. 11·17
R	Reaction rate $R(x)$	Eq. 10·7
S	Specific heat	Eq. 2·1
S (s)	Speed	Eq· 10·1
S (s)	Sensitivity	Eq. 7·5
S	Torsional stiffness	Eq. 4·87
S	System differential operator	Eq. 8·9
S_0	Neutron source	Eq. 4·86
T (s)	Time	Eq. 3·2
T (s)	Temperature	Eq. 2·1
U	Potential energy function	Eq. 11·12
V, V_0	Volume	Eqs. 3·22, 3·23
V	Valve sensitivity	Eq. 4·77
→ W	Weighting function $W(t)$	Eq. A·14
→ Z (s)	Impedance	Eq. 5·15
→ Z_t	Transfer impedance	Eq. 5·16
c	Wave velocity	Eq. 10·24
c	Time-dependent capacitance $c(t)$	Fig. 9·2
e	Base of natural logarithms	Eq. 2·8
f	Density of delayed neutron emitters	Eq. 4·80
f_c, f_i, f_0	Fluid flow rates	Fig. 4·20
f_n	Natural frequency	With Eq. 4·3
g	Gravitational acceleration	Eq. 3·21
g_m	Mutual conductance of vacuum tube	Eq. 7·2

Symbol	Term or Definition	Reference
h	Modulus of precision	Eq. 7·18
i	Electrical current	Eqs. 4·87, 10·41
j	$\sqrt{-1}$	Table 3·1
j	Running index	Table 3·1
k	Boltzmann constant	Eq. 7·1
k	Wave number = $2\pi/$(wavelength)	Eqs. 10·30
k	Running index	Table 3·1
m	Number (e.g., of readings)	Sec. 7·12
m, m_a	Modulation factor	Eqs. 9·15, 9·35
n	Number of objects	Eqs. 3·27, 7·28
$\rightarrow p$	Differential operator	Eq. 5·1
p (s)	Time-dependent pressure	Eq. 3·23
p_+, p_-	Pressure wave components	Eqs. 10·27
$\rightarrow q$	Response quantity	Eq. 2·2
$\rightarrow q_f$	Forcing quantity	Eq. 2·2
$\rightarrow q_d$	Reference quantity	Sec. 2·4
$\rightarrow q_t$	Transient response	Eq. 2·7
$\rightarrow q_r$	Forced response	Eq. 2·7
$\rightarrow q_n$	Noise forcing	Eq. 5·6
$\rightarrow q^*$	Complementary quantity	Sec. 5·4
$\rightarrow q_{aa}$	Arithmetic average of m readings	Eq. 7·15
$\rightarrow \bar{q}$	Limit (for infinite m) of q_{aa}	Eq. 7·15
$\rightarrow q_c$	Control quantity	Fig. 8·1
q (s)	Various values of q or various quantities having dimensions of q	Eq. 4·40
r	Polar or cylindrical coordinate	Eqs. 10·38, 11·9
r	Time-dependent resistance $r(t)$	Fig. 9·1
$r_1, r_2, \cdots, r_n$	Roots of auxiliary equation	Eq. 2·8

Symbol	Term or Definition	Reference
s	Neutron source	Eq. 4·80
s	Variable for cubic transformation	Eqs. 6·17
$\rightarrow s$	Laplace transform variable	Eq. A·2
$\rightarrow t$	Time	Eq. 2·1
u	Torque	Eq. 3·26
u	Time- and space-dependent variable	Eqs. 10·17
u, u_+, u_-	Particle velocity in sound wave	Eqs. 10·26, 10·27
v	Time- and space-dependent variable	Eqs. 10·17
x	Space variable	Fig. 7·3, Eq. 11·8
x_d, x_r	Index displacement and reading	Fig. 7·2
y	Space variable	Fig. 7·3, Eq. 11·8
z	Space variable	Eq. 11·8
Δ	Symbol for determinant	Eq. 6·39
Δf	Frequency interval	Eq. 7·1
ΔQ_m	Estimated maximum error	Sec. 7·6
Δq_m	Estimated maximum error at reading q	Sec. 7·6
$\rightarrow \Delta q_{rj}$	Random error of jth reading	Eq. 7·16
$\rightarrow \Delta q_d$	Determinate error	Eq. 7·17
$\rightarrow \Delta q_{rp}$	Probable error	Eq. 7·19
Δq_{ra}	Average error	Eq. 7·20
Δq_{rm}	Root-mean-square error	Eq. 7·21
$\rightarrow \Delta q_{Rj}$	Residual of jth reading	Eq. 7·23
$\rightarrow \Delta q_{rpa}$	Probable error in q_{aa}	Eq. 7·25
$\Delta^2 q_{rpa}$	Probable error in Δq_{rpa}	Eq. 7·26
Σ	Summation sign	Table 3·1
$\rightarrow \alpha$	Rate-to-frequency ratio	Eqs. 4·23
α	Energy ratio	Eq. 11·17

Symbol	Term or Definition	Reference
α	Limiting value of Laplace variable s	With Eq. A·2
→ β	Frequency ratio	Eqs. 4·23
β_H, β_L	High- and low-frequency limits of amplifier	Eq. 4·70
γ	Ratio of specific heats	Sec. 3·7
ϵ	Parameter of non-linearity	Eq. 11·4
→ ζ (s)	Damping ratio	Eqs. 4·4, 4·94
η	Coefficient of viscosity	Eq. 3·23
θ	Angle	Eqs. 3·10, 4·87, 11·9
λ	Radioactive decay rate	Eq. 7·27
λ	Wavelength	Eq. 10·14
μ	Amplification factor	Fig. 4·14
→ ρ (s)	Rate	Table 3·1
ρ_0	Density of air	Eqs. 10·29
σ	Cross section for neutron capture	Eq. 3·27
σ	Galvanometer sensitivity	Eq. 4·94
σ	Various dimensionless ratios	Eqs. 4·45, 11·30
σ_f	Complex forcing frequency $(\rho_f + j\omega_f)$	Table 3·1
→ τ (s)	Time constant	Eq. 2·2
ϕ	Phase angle	Eq. 3·9
ϕ	Potential function	Eq. 11·8
ϕ	Functional symbol	Eq. 10·19
→ ω	Angular frequency	Eq. 4·8
→ ω_n	Natural angular frequency	Eq. 4·3
ω_f	Forcing angular frequency	Table 3·1
ω_0	Angular frequency constant	Eq. 4·75

INDEX